HISTORICAL

CROPS AND CROPPING

BARE FALLOWING

Frontispiece

CROPS AND CROPPING

by

H. I. MOORE

M.Sc., Ph.D., N.D.A.
Dip.Agric.(Cantab.)

Principal, Seale-Hayne Agricultural College, and
Professor of Agriculture, University College of the South-West, Exeter
Formerly Senior Lecturer in Agriculture and Honorary Reader in Crop
Husbandry, the University of Leeds

Illustrated from photographs taken by the Author

London
GEORGE ALLEN & UNWIN LTD

First published in 1943
Revised Second Edition in 1944
Revised Third Edition in 1946
Revised Fourth Edition in 1949

BOOK
PRODUCTION
WAR ECONOMY
STANDARD

THE PAPER AND BINDING OF THIS BOOK
CONFORM TO THE AUTHORIZED ECONOMY
STANDARD

Printed in Great Britain
by T. and A. CONSTABLE LTD., Hopetoun Street
Printers to the University of Edinburgh

CONTENTS

APPENDICES

LIST OF ILLUSTRATIONS

PREFACE TO THE FIRST EDITION

PROGRESS in farming is traditionally slow but no one can deny the tremendous strides and prodigious efforts made in recent years. Systems have changed with almost revolutionary suddenness, research work has thrown light on vital problems of production, and new machines, seeds and fertilisers offer greater scope for maximum cropping than ever before.

Farmers have little opportunity for reading the technical publications dealing with these advances, and this book has been written in an endeavour to meet the demand for a working guide to modern practice.

Most of the material has been collected in the course of advisory and research work and by reference to the bulletins issued by the Ministry of Agriculture and Fisheries, and the Universities, Research Institutes and Agricultural Colleges throughout the country.

I owe much to scientific friends and especially to Mr. L. R. Johnson for his helpful criticism and advice, and to Mr. R. W. Haddon for his kind permission to quote from articles I have contributed to *The Farmer and Stockbreeder*. My heaviest debt is to countless farmer friends who have described their experiences and enthusiastically co-operated in the conduct of experiments on their farms.

H. IAN MOORE.

May 1942.

PREFACE TO THE SECOND EDITION

To-day there is every stimulus to maximum production from the land. There is an urge to try new methods, an unprecedented call from farmers for information, and the results of scientific research are being incorporated into agricultural practice more rapidly than ever before.

The need for a second edition has provided an opportunity for revising the text to include the results from recent developments in farm practice and the latest information from field trials. Our aim from now on must be to "increase the yield from every field," and I hope that this new edition will be of practical value in attaining this ideal.

The sections on pests and diseases have been revised by my colleagues Mr. L. R. Johnson and Miss D. M. Turner, to whom my best thanks are due. I am also indebted to my publishers for their kindly help and advice in the preparation of this new edition.

H. IAN MOORE.

November 1943.

Chapter One

THE PRINCIPLES OF CROP PRODUCTION

Success in crop production depends upon many factors. A thorough knowledge of the soil and the cultural and manurial requirements of the various crops is of paramount importance. This alone, however, is not enough, for the fertility of the land must be maintained at a high level and it must be kept clean and sweet. Farming tradition enforces the unwritten law that one must "do one's duty by the land," and the aim of every good farmer from earliest times has always been to keep his land in "good heart." Great skill is also necessary in selecting crops and varieties best suited to the conditions of each farm and the multitude of diseases and pests ever present to beset the unwary must be conquered.

Farming requires consummate skill, energy and initiative, and to obtain the utmost possible production from every acre of land demands perfect timing of all operations from seed-time to harvest. Skill in cultivation and generous manurial treatment, however, invariably find a ready response from the crop.

"His fields seemed to know what their master was doing;
And turnips and corn-land and meadow and lea,
All caught the infection—as generous as he."

ROTATIONS

Most of the arable land in Great Britain is farmed according to a recognised rotation of crops which varies according to climate and soil conditions. Thus crops cannot be regarded as separate entities but as part of a system, for obviously the treatment given to any particular field will depend upon what has been done in the past and what is likely to be required in the future.

In recent years rotations have changed considerably, and from time to time it has even been suggested that they were out of date and that the land should be cropped solely with an eye to market probabilities. Many have tried to carry this out in practice but most of these opportunists have had to fall back on

11

established methods, and at the present time the general view is held that whilst there is no necessity for the slavish adherence to rotations as was common with our forebears, it is still necessary to have a clear understanding of the underlying principles oi rotations and to abide by them.

One of the greatest limitations to the growing of similar crops on the same land each year is the problem of weed control. Certain weeds are favoured by carrying out cultivations at specified times of the year. If, therefore, these cultivations are repeated for several years in succession it will enable such plants to become firmly established and in time they may actually dominate the crop, as for instance in the case of continuous wheat growing. In contrast to this, by growing different crops on the same land the cultivations can be carried out at different times of the year, and it is possible to incorporate in the rotation certain "cleaning" crops such as roots or potatoes.

Another factor which militates against too frequent cropping with one particular type of crop is the incidence of insect and fungus attacks which are naturally favoured in this way. Many examples of this come to mind such as finger-and-toe disease in swedes, root eelworm in potatoes, and beet "sickness."

Quite apart from these reasons a well-designed rotation enables the work of the farm to be evenly distributed over the year and levels out the rush periods of seed-time and harvest. Then again, crops differ in their demands upon the chief plant foods. Swedes, for instance, require large supplies of phosphates; clover, potash and lime, whilst wheat requires an adequate supply of nitrogen. Thus, by growing these crops in rotation depletion of the soil in any particular nutrient is avoided. Crops also vary in their rooting habits, some being relatively shallow rooted and capable of taking nutriment from the top layers of soil, whilst others penetrate deeply into the subsoil and are able to feed from a much greater range. By alternating shallow with deep rooting crops, therefore, it is possible to utilise the supplies of plant food in the soil to the best advantage. Another factor of great importance is that not all crops are suitable for the same type of land, and hence a choice must be made from those which are known to succeed best under any particular soil and climatic conditions.

Finally, of course, no one likes to have all his eggs in one basket, least of all the farmer, who knows from bitter experience that in spite of all efforts crop failures sometimes occur, that prices may fall to very low levels when there is a glut of any particular product, and that seasonal variations considerably affect crop yields. Thus in practice a farmer plays for safety, and experience shows that in most seasons the profits from one or more crops are sufficient to carry the losses entailed by others.

Having decided what crops to grow they must next be arranged in orderly sequence and this depends very largely upon the requirements of the different crops. Following sugar beet, for instance, especially when the tops are folded with sheep, it is generally too late in the year to plant wheat. Hence, a spring-sown crop of barley or oats will follow. After a seeds ley wheat may be taken, but, if grazing is required, the ley may be left down over winter and ploughed in spring for a crop of oats, enabling an additional five or six months' keep to be obtained. Some crops such as clover and beans leave the land in good condition, for they are able to utilise the nitrogen of the atmosphere; others are heavily manured and leave adequate reserves in the soil for subsequent crops, whilst the cereals in contrast to this are solely exhaustive. By alternating restorative crops with exhaustive, therefore, the crops are fed on economic lines. Thus it is sound policy to manure for the rotation rather than for a particular crop, for by this means the crop obtained gives the maximum profit and soil nutrients are not unduly depleted.

In practice, the arable acreage is divided into "breaks" or "shifts" of approximately equal area, according to the number of crops to be grown. Alternatives are possible in many cases, as for instance with the "root break" which may be divided between potatoes, swedes, mangolds and sugar beet, according to the acreage of each which is required. In this way the rotation can be lengthened, for the area growing potatoes the first time round will carry beet the next time and so on.

The most widely practised rotation in this country to-day is undoubtedly the four-course or "Norfolk four-course" as it is usually termed. This consists of roots, barley seeds, wheat, and whilst it is more applicable to the medium loams and lighter classes of soil it forms the basis for most of our present-day rotations. A brief description of this rotation will not be out of place at this juncture.

The root crop forms the cleaning crop of the rotation, often receiving dung and artificials, considerable cultivation and, if folded off by sheep, the soil is naturally left in good condition for the following crop of barley.

The fertility is largely in the top soil, and since barley is a shallow-rooted crop it is well adapted to make full use of the nutrients available.

The seeds ley is sown under barley as the cover crop and of all cereals barley is undoubtedly the best "nurse." The seeds enrich the land in nitrogen, give "body" and firmness and thus constitute an excellent preparatory crop for wheat which requires both firmness and nitrogen. Thus the "Norfolk four-course" is a well-balanced rotation though not adapted to all soils or farming conditions. It is easily modified into a five-course by leaving the seeds down for two years or by following the seeds with two cereal crops, wheat and oats, instead of just wheat. Obviously the decision as to the type of rotation practised on any farm must be made by the man on the spot, and no useful purpose will be served by a discussion in these pages of all the types of rotations in use at the present time. In order to give some impression of the diversity of types and the constitution of well-balanced and well-tried rotations, however, the following table is given :—

CROP ROTATIONS

Three-Course	Four-Course		Five-Course		Six-Course			
			High Proportion				High Proportion	
Rich Fens and Silts	Light Land	Heavy Land	Sale Crops	Grass	Heavy Loams	To include Potatoes	High Proportion Sale Crops	General Heavy Land
Wheat	Roots	Bare Fallow	Roots	Roots	Beans	Roots	Roots	Roots
Potatoes	Barley	Wheat	Barley	Barley	Wheat	Barley	Barley	Oats
Sugar Beet	Seeds	Beans	Seeds	Seeds	Oats or Barley	Seeds	Barley	Beans
	Wheat	Wheat	Wheat	Seeds	Seeds	Oats	Seeds	Wheat
			Oats or Barley	Wheat	Wheat	Potatoes	Wheat	Seeds
					Barley or Oats	Wheat	Oats or Barley	Wheat

In recent years there has been a general tendency in England to extend the use of the long ley in rotations as a means of maintaining fertility on economic lines. This practice, which is so common in Scotland, is known as Alternate Husbandry or Ley Farming. It has the advantage over the more usual systems of keeping the arable as arable and the grass strictly as grass, of being more productive, more economic from the manuring point of view, and facilitating the control of both plant and animal diseases.

Ley farming is dependent upon good fencing and an adequate water supply in the fields, and there is no doubt that these considerations have exercised a considerable restricting influence upon the more widespread adoption of the practice. The fencing problem has now been overcome to a great extent by the introduction of the simple system of electric fencing, but the water problem still remains to be solved. It is obvious that ley farming cannot be carried out indiscriminately all over the country, but it is also evident that since the introduction of bail milking, pig and poultry keeping on the fold system, and more especially with the national need for increased food production, this system of farming should receive the most careful consideration from farmers.

MANURING

Plants require food and this they obtain partly from the air and partly from the soil. Most of the plant foods necessary for healthy growth are present in the soil though not always in sufficient quantity, and from the farmer's standpoint manuring concerns the addition to the soil of those substances in which it is so deficient that good crops cannot be obtained. In practice four foods are generally required, namely, nitrogen, phosphates, potash and lime, although very frequently a soil is deficient in the "trace elements" such as boron (a deficiency of which causes heart rot in beet) or manganese (a deficiency causing the disease "grey leaf" of oats).

On the farm, therefore, manuring usually involves the application of these four plant foods. Some may be supplied by the addition of dung, by waste materials such as shoddy or by ploughing in green crops like mustard or lupins, but the great feature of all these manures is their provision of organic matter or humus which is so necessary for the tilth and water-holding capacity of the soil. In contrast to these "organic" manures are the chemical substances which supply one or more plant foods and which are commonly called "fertilisers."

NITROGENOUS FERTILISERS

Nitrogen is by far the most important fertiliser, for not only is it the most expensive to obtain, but is most easily lost from the soil. In spite of these limitations it plays an enormous part in the production of high yields of both arable crops and grass, as shown by the increased yields normally obtained from the use of 1 cwt. per acre sulphate of ammonia which are given in the following table:—

Crop	Increased Yield usually obtained from the use of Sulphate of Ammonia (1 cwt. per acre)
Cereals—Grain . . .	2½ to 3 cwt. per acre.
Straw . . .	5 to 6 ,, ,,
Mangolds	40 ,, ,,
Kale	30 ,, ,,
Potatoes	20 ,, ,,
Swedes	30 ,, ,,
Sugar Beet . . .	14 ,, ,,
Meadow Hay . . .	5 ,, ,,

The following fertilisers are commonly used as a source of nitrogen:—

Sulphate of Ammonia	20·6 per cent. nitrogen.
Nitro-Chalk . .	15½ to 16 ,, ,,
Nitrate of Soda . .	15½ to 16 ,, ,,
Calcium Cyanamide .	20·6 ,, ,,
Nitrate of Lime . .	13 to 15½ ,, ,,
Nitrate of Potash* .	14¾ ,, ,,
Ammonium Phosphate †	11 ,, ,,

* (including also 14¾ per cent. potash)
† (including also 48 per cent. phosphoric acid)

Nitrogen will soon make its presence felt in the soil, and lack of this vital element is invariably indicated by yellow, sickly-looking and stunted foliage. Occasionally an overdose of nitrogen is given and this has the effect of delaying ripening, increasing the tendency of cereals to lodge, and generally producing a rather sappy type of growth which is more susceptible to disease. Many farmers are distrustful of nitrogenous fertilisers on the grounds that they are reputed to "draw" the land or have a "robbing" effect. Nitrogen, in so far as it increases bulk, will naturally require adequate reserves of phosphate and potash in the soil, for when a crop is harvested a certain amount of these elements is removed from the soil, the actual quantity depending upon the yield of crop. Thus it is easy to see that the use of nitrogen demands the judicious use also of phosphates and potash; in other words balanced manuring is necessary.

The plant takes up its nitrogen in the form of nitrate, and consequently nitrogenous fertilisers which are already in nitrate form such as nitro-chalk and nitrate of soda are quicker in action than, say, sulphate of ammonia, which has to be changed into the nitrate form by bacteria in the soil before it can be utilised as plant food. During the summer months when bacterial activity is very considerable this "nitrification" of sulphate only takes some 10 to 14 days.

In practice there is little to choose between sulphate of ammonia and nitro-chalk in so far as the effect on the plant is concerned. The former is preferable for chalks or marls or land where the lime content of the soil need not be carefully watched; the latter should be used on all soils where there is a tendency for lime deficiency, for in a humble way it adds to the lime content of the soil.

On no account should either sulphate of ammonia or nitro-chalk be mixed with lime or slag.

Nitrate of soda is very quick in action and a top dressing given to, say, mangolds takes effect in 7 to 10 days' time under normal weather conditions. It is not to be recommended for frequent application to heavy soils owing to a marked tendency to increase their stickiness. The nitrates of lime and potash are very similar in action to nitrate of soda, but calcium cyanamide should always be applied several weeks before the seed is sown. Sulphate of ammonia which is produced in this country in ever-increasing amounts is our chief source of nitrogen at the present time.

All cereal crops respond to nitrogenous fertilisers, and forage crops such as kale will pay for applications up to 3 or 4 cwt. per acre sulphate of ammonia. In general it is safe to say that there is considerable scope on most farms for a much wider and more generous use of these invaluable fertilisers.

B

PHOSPHATIC FERTILISERS

Phosphates are essential to the growth of all plants, being taken up from the soil in the form of soluble phosphates. Only in recent years has it been fully appreciated how widespread is phosphate deficiency on both arable and grassland.

The chief work of phosphates is in promoting root development, early maturity and uniform ripening. They exert a decided steadying effect upon nitrogenous applications, helping to counteract rankness due to their excessive use, and exert a marked influence in stimulating the development of young seedlings, being especially useful for shallow-rooted crops such as swedes and turnips which have a short growing period.

The following are the normal sources of phosphate:—

Superphosphate . . .	16 to 20 per cent. phosphoric acid.	
Basic Slag	7 to 19 ,, ,, ,,
Steamed Bone Flour . .	27 ,, ,, ,,
Ground Mineral Phosphate .	26 to 38 ,, ,, ,,
Triple Superphosphate .	48 ,, ,, ,,
Metaphos	20 to 21 ,, ,, ,,
Silico Phosphate . . .	33 ,, ,, ,,

Superphosphate is the quickest acting form of phosphate and is made from mineral phosphate. "Triple superphosphate" is now being manufactured and this contains 48 per cent. phosphoric acid, or $2\frac{1}{2}$ to 3 times as much as ordinary superphosphate.

Another recent addition to our phosphatic fertilisers is Metaphos. This is really calcium metaphosphate, the richest source of phosphate at present known, containing as it does some 62 per cent. of phosphoric acid. Such a concentrated fertiliser would be difficult to apply in the requisite small amounts needed for most farm crops, and hence it is mixed with twice its own weight of calcium carbonate and sold as " Metaphos " containing about 20 per cent. phosphoric acid.

Silico phosphate, a fine powder, is produced from rock phosphate by roasting with soda and sand, a treatment which greatly enhances the availability of the phosphoric acid it contains. It must not be mixed with sulphate of ammonia or nitro-chalk, for it contains free lime, which would result in a serious loss of ammonia. It can, however, be mixed with potash fertilisers and with nitrate of soda.

Unlike nitrogen, an excess of phosphate is not harmful to crops nor is it wasted, for what is not used by the crop to which it is applied is held in reserve for the future.

On soils that show a tendency to lime shortage basic slag is generally preferred, for as it contains a small amount of lime, this enhances its value under such conditions. For all practical purposes it can be assumed that 6 cwt. of slag has a lime value equal to 4 cwt. of ground limestone or chalk.

Slag is pre-eminent as a phosphatic fertiliser for grassland, but is also used quite considerably for arable crops. Here, however, it is generally wise to apply it a few weeks before sowing the seed, whereas superphosphate is generally given as a seed bed application.

The phosphoric acid in slag varies in solubility and hence in its availability as plant food. In the "high soluble" slags at least 80 per cent. of the total phosphoric acid content is soluble by the standard citric acid test, whilst in the "low soluble" slags no more than 20 to 30 per cent. may be soluble.

The high soluble slags have a similar action to superphosphate on arable land, though not quite so effective, but the low soluble slags should only be used for acid soils in districts of high rainfall.

The value of slag on acid soils, however, must not be taken as confirmation of the common belief that superphosphate makes a soil acid. This is not the case, but on acid soils superphosphate is unable to exert its full effect until the lime deficiency is rectified.

Steamed bone flour is prepared by grinding bones after first extracting the cartilaginous material. It is an extremely fine powder and forms an excellent drier or conditioner when a number of fertilisers are being mixed together, preventing them from going pasty or setting hard. It has considerable value on light land and is often mixed with an equal amount of super-phosphate for use under such conditions.

Rock phosphates vary considerably in their phosphoric acid contents. They are relatively slow in action compared with superphosphate, and have their greatest use on acid soils and in wet districts, for under these conditions the phosphate is likely to be made more rapidly available to the plant. Not only should they be applied before sowing the seed, but it is important for them to be finely powdered. The best results are obtained when the material is crushed to pass through the standard 120 mesh sieve (a screen with 14,400 holes per square inch).

Rothamsted results indicate that metaphosphate is comparable to superphosphate, and in American trials it has been shown to be equal to superphosphate on neutral and acid soils. On alkaline soils it is less effective, and on a broad basis one can say that where high soluble basic slag gives good results the new product is worth trying. Silico phosphate has proved to be as effective as superphosphate and better than Bessemer slag.

Potassic Fertilisers

Potash is obtained in the form of the various potash manures included in the following list:—

Kainit .	.	.	.	14 per cent. potash.	
Potash Salts .		.	.	20 to 30 ,,	,,
Sulphate of Potash		.		48 ,,	,,
Muriate of Potash		.		50 to 60 ,,	,,

The effect of potash on the plant is to give tone and vigour and help it to resist disease and the effects of adverse weather conditions. In addition, it has a very valuable effect in stiffening the straw of cereals, thus counteracting any tendency to lodging. On light soils it is extremely beneficial, and this is particularly noticeable during spells of dry weather. Under such circumstances crops on potash-starved land will show signs of drying out much sooner than on soils where the potash content is normal.

Any excess of potash in the soil is not lost by leaching, but is firmly held for future use, though when excessive amounts of potash manures are applied to heavy land they tend to increase the stickiness of the soil.

Crops most responsive to applications of potash are potatoes, sugar beet, flax and market-garden crops.

For certain crops, notably sugar beet and mangolds, common salt may be used in place of potash manures. This is only possible, however, on soils where large quantities of potash have been used in the past or on the heavier classes of soil which are naturally fairly rich in potash.

Under normal circumstances the choice of a potash fertiliser will be determined by the price per unit of potash $\left(= \dfrac{\text{price per ton}}{\% \text{ potash}} \right)$, except in the case of potatoes where the higher-grade muriate or sulphate are generally used. The lower-grade potash manures contain a good deal of salt as an impurity and this has a deleterious effect on the cooking quality of potatoes.

From this account of the effects of nitrogen, phosphates and potash on plant growth, it will be very evident that some "balance" is essential between these fertilisers if optimum plant growth is to be obtained. Obviously an overdose of one or the other is wasteful and may actually be harmful in encouraging an unproductive type of growth, as for instance when an overdose of nitrogen increases the growth of potato tops without at the same time increasing the yield of tubers.

In recent years the practice has developed of using concentrated complete fertilisers which are balanced for different crops, being definite chemical compounds and not merely admixtures. The great advantage of these "compounds" lies in the fact that each granule of the material has a definite composition. A further advantage is that they are very soluble and approximately twice as concentrated as a straight mixture. Thus carriage and handling costs are reduced, and being granulated, even distribution by hand or machine is greatly facilitated. The trend in fertilising is towards more frequent small applications of concentrated materials. Trials indicate that when the fertiliser is placed in close proximity to the seed by using a combine seed and fertiliser drill, the amount of fertiliser can be reduced by about 50 per cent. without affecting the yield of crop.

LIME

The value of fertilisers is largely wasted if the soil is short of lime. Although lime is a plant food its chief use is to act as a soil "conditioner." For instance, it is well known how the texture or tilth of a heavy soil is improved by liming. It is also necessary to ensure the free working of bacteria which are essential in the liberation of plant food, and to keep the soil "sweet" and free from injurious fungus diseases such as "finger-and-toe" in swedes.

Unfortunately, lime is not held in the soil, and there is an annual loss of from 1 to 4 cwt. of lime per acre due to its removal by crops and by washing out with rain. In industrial areas this loss is increased by the action of smoke and acid fumes, and even on soils naturally rich in lime such as the Wolds and Downs it is possible to have a shortage in the top layers of soil due to the leaching action of rain.

Unless periodic applications of lime are given to the soil, therefore, it becomes sour and acid, crop yields become more and more unsatisfactory, until finally a state is reached at which lime-loving crops like barley, sugar beet and clover fail.

A lime deficiency is fairly easy to diagnose. First there is usually the presence of such weeds as spurrey (louse-grass, dother, or pickpurse), sheep's sorrel (sour dock) and the yellow corn marigold. The failure or patchy growth of barley, clover, beet, peas or beans in most cases indicates a lime shortage, as does for instance the presence of "finger-and-toe" disease in turnips or cabbages.

These suspicions can be confirmed by a simple colour test in the field using a B.D.H. soil-testing outfit which can be obtained through any chemist.

It is not possible in this way to determine just how much lime is required, and by far the simplest procedure is to consult the Provincial Advisory Chemist who will arrange for the soil to be tested, free of charge. Indeed, if the soil is sampled by the Advisory Chemist it is possible to have a phosphate and potash determination made also.

A deficiency of lime can be rectified by the use of one of the following forms of lime:—

I. Carbonate of Lime . (non-caustic)	. Ground Limestone. Ground Chalk.
II. Oxide of Lime (caustic)	Burnt Lump Lime ("Shell" or "Clot" Lime). Ground Burnt Lime.
III. Slaked Lime . .	. Hydrated Lime.
IV. Waste Limes . .	. Limestone Dust. Beet Factory Lime. "Seconds" or "Small" Lime. Other Waste Limes.

Comparing these different forms of lime:—

   36 cwt. Group I=20 cwt. Group II=27 cwt. Group III=30 to 80 cwt. Group IV.

In the past burnt lime, either lump or ground, has been the favourite liming material amongst farmers. The current production of these forms of lime is quite inadequate to meet the demand following the ploughing up of so much poor grassland that must be limed before it can be cropped successfully.

Alternatives have been found in ground limestone, ground magnesian limestone and various waste limes.

Recent work at Bangor has indicated that ground limestone, even when as coarse as one-eighth of an inch, is useful for correcting soil acidity and the much finer material on the market can thus be used with confidence. It has the advantage of being non-caustic, easier to handle, does not burst the bags on storage and does not cake on the surface after application. Consequently many more farmers are now using it in preference to the burnt forms of lime.

In certain districts there has been considerable prejudice against the use of a magnesian lime on the score that it has a toxic effect on plant growth. There is no evidence to support this idea except when the lime has been used in excessive amounts, and experiments carried out by the University of Leeds have shown in fact that this lime is every bit as efficacious as ordinary lime.

Hitherto there has been little need to use the many waste industrial limes which are available in large quantities. Here again, numerous field trials have shown them to be thoroughly reliable for agricultural use, and indeed on light sandy soils they are superior to the best ground lime.

Most of these limes contain water which in some cases amounts to as much as 50 per cent., and this renders their physical condition unsatisfactory. This is much more apparent than real, and owing to their "dilute" character it is necessary to use them at rates exceeding three tons per acre, which in itself ensures easy and even distribution. If the material is first dumped and allowed to dry out, or after spreading becomes well frosted the clods break down and can be thoroughly incorporated with the soil.

Beet factory lime and the waste from water-softening plants are both excellent liming materials. That obtained from soap works may contain some caustic soda and on this account should be applied during winter, as should the waste limes from tanneries, acetylene works and tar distilleries.

Great care is necessary in the distribution of lime. It should always be applied after the final ploughing and then harrowed into the top soil where it is wanted by the young plant. Even distribution is essential, and as soon after application as possible it is advisable to harrow it in, especially if burnt or slaked lime is used. These quickly go pasty if left on the surface and will set or "cake" into hard insoluble lumps.

It is always well to remember that the lime which disappears is working to advantage. There is no virtue in being able to find lumps of lime in the soil twenty years after application.

For small applications a drill is essential, but when large dressings of waste lime or limestone dust are applied this can usually be done satisfactorily straight from a cart. By far the best method of dealing with quicklime is to slake it in a corner of the field and then spread the hydrated lime by means of a distributor. To put it out in small heaps for slaking is invariably unsatisfactory, for either too much rain falls and the lime goes pasty, or there is not sufficient moisture to ensure complete slaking and lumps remain.

On all soils which are not naturally well supplied with lime, liming should be a routine operation. An application every four or five years will ensure that the soil is maintained in sweet condition and that the full effects of other fertilisers are obtained.

FARMYARD MANURE

Contrary to general belief artificial fertilisers are not substitutes for farmyard manure nor are they ever likely to be. Dung is essential and its use on a generous scale plays a vital part in maintaining soil fertility. A mere chemical analysis can never reveal its true worth, for in the improvement of soil texture and moisture-holding capacity its greatest value lies.

Dung contains the three most important foods of plant life—nitrogen, phosphates and potash, but as a rule it tends to be poor in phosphates. Naturally the composition is determined largely by the class of animal from which it is obtained, and also the type of food fed to the stock. Fattening stock give a richer dung, for instance, than young growing stock, and approximately half the nitrogen and three-quarters of the phosphoric acid and potash which are supplied in the food find their way into the dung.

The composition of dung after a period of storage depends upon the efficiency of the "making," and this unfortunately receives scant attention on many farms.

The losses occurring during making and storage are twofold.

There is firstly the loss of the dark-coloured liquid which oozes from a heap and which contains the quick-acting soluble plant food; and secondly, the loss due to oxidation within the heap. To minimise the loss of soluble material plenty of bedding should be allowed to soak up the urine and some form of protection given to prevent rain from washing through the dung. On many farms dungsheds are provided where the manure can be kept under cover, but on farms not so favourably equipped a rough shelter should be provided. The covering of open fold yards, for instance, not only adds to the comfort of the stock (which means that they thrive better) but the quality of the dung is materially improved.

When oxidation within the heap takes place the nitrogenous plant food is converted into gases which are lost in the atmosphere. This loss is greatest when the heap is loose and allowed to become dry. The remedy, therefore, lies in keeping a heap moist and well consolidated, for this keeps out the air and reduces losses from oxidation to a minimum.

There is no doubt that the ideal way of making dung is to keep it in a covered yard where it can be well trampled by the stock and where the various types of dung can be mixed together.

When indoor accommodation is limited, however, a field heap is necessary, and it is under such circumstances that great care is necessary if losses are to be minimised.

A firm, level site should be chosen for the heap and as it is built up it should be well compacted. A "draw" heap which allows the horses and carts to be taken over the heap each time offers a solution to the difficulty of getting good compaction.

The building of a heap in small sections has also much to commend it, for in this case only a comparatively small surface is exposed to air and rain at one time. Whenever possible an outdoor heap should be given some protection from the rain. Corrugated-iron sheets, or straw from stack bottoms, will turn the rain and prevent leaching. In some districts it is the practice—and a very sound one too—to roughly thatch the dung heap. The means of protection need not be elaborate or expensive, but a little care and thought to the solution of this problem will be well repaid in the improvement in the quality of the dung which will be visible in its increased crop-producing capacity.

In addition to the losses in plant food that can occur during making and storage the value of dung is affected considerably by the method of application. When it is spread on the land and left for some time before ploughing in, a large part of the available nitrogen may be lost by volatilisation as ammonia. This loss will be greatest in dry and windy weather and least in wet weather when the nitrogen is washed into the soil. Extensive trials in America have shown that even when dung is left on the surface for no more than 4 days before ploughing it in, the yield of crop can be reduced by as much as 12 per cent. Frost also appears to have a deleterious effect upon the quality of dung, and exposure to 9 degrees of frost for 48 hours results in half the available nitrogen being lost. The practice of spreading dung on snow also causes serious losses and is not advocated.

Thus, it is evident that every effort should be made to get the dung covered by ploughing as soon after application as possible.

LIQUID MANURE

Liquid manure is a valuable source of nitrogen and potash and 1000 gallons of animal urine supplies approximately the same amount of plant food contained in a mixture of 1 cwt. sulphate of ammonia and 1 cwt. of potash salts. Obviously, therefore, on all farms where supplies are available, efforts should be made to utilise it to best advantage. On many farms this product receives little attention and its utilisation is regarded more in the nature of a nuisance than a benefit. Where proper storage facilities are not available steps should be taken to improvise means of collecting it, and the outfit shown in Fig. 9 gives some idea of how one farmer has tackled the problem. In this instance, the liquid manure from the cow byre is led into a galvanised tank sunk into the ground outside the byre. When filled it is raised by means of a windlass and the liquid run into another tank fixed in a cart used as a distributor.

It is important, of course, to ensure that the washing waters from the cowshed do not pass direct into the collecting tank to dilute the urine. Not that this is harmful but merely necessitates frequent emptying and the unnecessary cartage of large quantities of water.

"Tankage" is eminently suited for application to arable land, being of great benefit for forage crops like kale. Over a period of years the author has found that two applications, each of 1000 gallons per acre, to the kale crop has increased the yield by over 3 tons per acre. When used for a growing crop it should be applied when the foliage is wet if scorching is to be avoided.

POULTRY MANURE

Where supplies of poultry manure are available, this extremely valuable fertiliser is a valuable source of plant food. Fowls produce the following quantity in a year:—

    100 laying birds   .   .   .   80 cwt. fresh manure
    100 chickens (from hatching to
        13 weeks old)   .   .   .   .   9 „   „

and hence where large numbers of birds are maintained on a system which permits the droppings to be collected, considerable quantities will be available. The composition of the manure is very variable and depends upon the type of bird and the ration fed. The percentage of manurial ingredients in an average sample are given below and with it, for purposes of comparison, those of an average sample of farmyard manure:—

	Poultry Manure %	Farmyard Manure %
Nitrogen . .	1·75	·77
Phosphoric Acid .	1·00	·39
Potash . .	·54	·60

It will be seen that an average sample is about twice as rich in nitrogen and phosphoric acid as good fold-yard manure.

The nitrogen is present in a quick-acting form, but because of this there is considerable loss in storage unless precautions are taken to avoid it. The droppings should be stored under a shed to prevent leaching by rain washing through it, and in order to prevent the loss of nitrogen it should be spread out in layers with soil in between each layer, twice as much soil as manure being used. Not only does this minimise the loss of nitrogen but it is also an excellent means of improving the physical condition of the manure. An average dressing of poultry manure for farm crops usually consists of from 8 to 10 cwt. per acre (24 to 30 cwt.

of soil treated manure) and the crops which respond best to an application are sugar beet, potatoes and cabbages.

Town Refuse

Most of the larger towns are now converting the sewage and other waste materials into fertilisers. The actual value of this material is very variable, depending upon its manufacture. In some cases, for instance, shoddy and waste products of like constitution are incorporated together with some quick-acting fertiliser such as sulphate of ammonia. In other cases the crude faecal matter is merely dried and ground into a powder, and as a rule all these products are sold under trade names.

In addition to the actual plant food which these products contain, they have a certain "humus" value for improving the tilth of a soil. No general statement can be made as to the manurial value of town refuse nor as to the price that should be paid, for this will depend upon the chemical analysis—which should always be obtained by the purchaser—and the physical condition of the material.

On farms where the supply of dung is limited, however, these modern prepared wastes are well worth a trial, and it is suggested that each farmer should carry out a simple trial for himself to compare the value of such material with that of, say, dung. It is necessary, of course, that any such trial should be planned on the basis of giving to the crop equal amounts of plant food in the different forms, and the help of the Provincial Advisory Chemist should be sought before deciding what the equivalent quantities of manures are likely to be.

Shoddy

The name "shoddy" is applied to the waste material from woollen, carpet and silk mills. It is valuable as a source of nitrogen, but more especially as a source of organic matter for improving tilth and holding moisture when applied to the soil. For this reason it is used to a considerable extent by light land farmers and in cases where supplies of farmyard manure are not sufficient for the requirements of the farm.

The manurial value of the shoddy varies with the amount of pure wool present, and in practice the price should be regulated according to the amount of nitrogen present (4 to 14 per cent.).

In view of the wide variation that exists between the various grades of shoddy it is important before purchasing to obtain an analysis of the material. As a rule it can be considered good value when the unit price of the nitrogen $\left(= \dfrac{\text{price per ton of shoddy}}{\% \text{ nitrogen}} \right)$ does not exceed about 75 per cent. of that of the nitrogen in sulphate of ammonia $\left(= \dfrac{\text{price per ton}}{20 \cdot 6} \right)$.

For use it is applied at rates varying from $\frac{1}{2}$ to 2 tons per acre, being ploughed in during the winter in the same way as dung. It is important to ascertain that the shoddy is free from oil, for this would prevent rapid decomposition in the soil. Some firms now market a shoddy to which fertilisers such as sulphate of ammonia and superphosphate have been added, the whole being ground into a finely divided condition.

PREPARATION OF SEED BEDS

Crops differ in their requirements of a seed bed; some like potatoes are relatively indifferent to the condition of the tilth provided it is deep, whilst others like barley require a tilth "as light as a feather." Moreover, all soils do not require the same sequence of operations to produce the desired degree of fineness or firmness and cultivation still remains much more of an art than a science.

One of the most important objects of cultivation is the control of weeds, and there is no doubt that the period immediately after harvest is one of the best opportunities for tackling this problem. The fact that so many farms now carry a tractor and cultivating implements means that better use can be made of this opportunity than was possible years ago.

On heavy land autumn cleaning may take the form of killing the rubbish in the clod or, alternatively, it may be worked out and burnt. In the first method the land will be ploughed immediately after harvest and cross-cultivated a few days later to break the furrows into large clods. As soon as the clods are dry on top they should be stirred by a second and perhaps a third cultivating. If during this period the weather is dry and sunny the clods are thoroughly baked and any couch or watergrass which is present is killed. The efficiency of the method is dependent entirely upon suitable weather conditions and if these are favourable the result often compares with a bastard fallow in its effect. During wet weather, on the other hand, no useful purpose is served and in fact it is advisable to give up the project, for under adverse conditions cultivating merely breaks the roots into small pieces which then have the opportunity of becoming established as small plants.

The second method consists of shallow ploughing to such a depth that the plants of couch or twitch are completely inverted. On moist soils the roots of this weed run in a horizontal network about 4 or 5 inches below the surface. Paring or broadshare cultivators are available to loosen the soil to this depth without actually inverting it, and the use of such implements enables the work to be carried out more expeditiously. On heavy land, however, considerable power is necessary to haul these implements and ploughing may be more feasible. Following the loosening of the weeds in this way cultivators and harrows are used to work the couch to the surface, where it can be rolled up with chain harrows, collected into heaps and burnt. A side delivery rake makes an excellent job of collecting the roots once they are on the surface, though it is probable that this task is much too hard on the rake.

The whole secret of successful cleaning by this method depends upon keeping the "wicks" or "twitch" as large as possible to enable a clean job to be made of collection. When they are broken into small pieces it is well-nigh impossible to remove them completely, and every small piece which is left on the land is a potential lusty weed for the following summer.

On light land weeds may be worked out in the manner just described for heavy land. Another method is to stir the surface immediately after harvest to encourage weed seeds to germinate, for then the plants can be killed by the normal winter ploughing.

Broadshare cultivators are ideal for light land cleaning, although even here a good tractor is necessary to pull the implement. Up to 12 or 15 acres a day can be broken in this way and the land should then be left for about a month to allow the weed species to develop, when a light harrowing will expose more weed seeds. Ploughing then follows when convenient.

It is impossible to control all weeds in this way, but in most seasons good results with chickweed, speedwell, cleavers, wild oats, black grass, poppy and charlock is obtained. The seeds of knotgrass, black bindweed, bartsia and fat-hen, however, will not germinate until spring and must be tackled then.

Speedy action is all important for this work, and as soon as the cereal is cut and stooked the cultivator or plough should get busy. When the stubbles are left until spring owing to pressure of work a comparable sequence of operations can be used during favourably dry periods in February or March.

The preparation of the seed bed for any particular crop differs considerably from county to county and even from farm to farm. A broad outline of the procedure is given under the different crops later on, but at this point it might be useful to discuss the general principles.

In producing a seed bed the main object is to thoroughly move the soil to such a depth that the rootlets growing out from the seed or from transplants have such freedom of movement that they can acquire all the nourishment they need. The final tilth should be such that no hard places are left in it and that it will be able to retain moisture for long periods in dry weather.

On heavy land no cultivator can compare with frost and early ploughing is, therefore, advisable. For spring-sown cereals a fine seed bed can then be prepared easily—assuming that the furrows have been weathered by frost and thaw—by cultivating and harrowing.

The best guide as to when sufficient tilth has been obtained is to go into the worst part of the field and drag one's toe along the soil. If there is a good tilthy mould up to the instep all is well, but if hard places and lumps are encountered then in most cases more working would be beneficial.

With autumn-sown crops the ideal seed bed should be somewhat rougher than is favoured for spring sowing, for clods are useful in giving the crop some protection from cutting winter winds and they prevent the surface from running together and caking. This does not imply that less care is required to prepare a tilth in autumn, for the seed must be placed in fine earth to obtain moisture and develop a root system.

One of the greatest dangers to be avoided in spring cultivations is that of over-working the land. Constant stirring may bring about a serious dissipation of soil moisture the loss of which will be seen in the lower yield of crop which results. The danger is greatest when autumn cleaning has not been possible and in consequence the weeds have to be worked out during the early months of the year.

The whole art of preparing a seed bed depends upon the skill of the farmer in choosing the right moment for carrying out the various operations. Although a farmer may appear to get a good crop on land in good heart when "put in badly," experience and experiment prove conclusively that a much better crop is obtained when the seed is sown in a first-class seed bed. There is an old saying, "Better be out of time than out of tune," which implies that it is better to be late in sowing and have the crop put in well than to sacrifice tilth for the sake of sowing the crop in good time. In practice this is generally true, but it is even truer to say that the best results are obtained when one is both " in time" and "in tune."

SELECTION AND TREATMENT OF SEED

The selection of suitable seed is a factor of vital importance in obtaining good yields. It is, of course, the keystone of the crop and a thorough appreciation of the points which should be taken into consideration is of the utmost importance.

Naturally the selection of the variety or strain is the major decision which has to be made, and in this connection it is urged that full use be made of the excellent work being carried out by the National Institute of Agricultural Botany, which carries out annual trials throughout the country of old and new varieties of all crops, the results of which are published periodically and are well worth consideration. In the selection of variety a large number of farmers still stick to an old favourite with something approaching real affection; others must have a new variety regardless of its cost or suitability for their conditions, and there is, unfortunately, a much larger number who choose a variety because of its cheapness or the fact that their neighbours have some to sell.

Each man knows his own land best and experience is a sound pointer as to the suitability of any particular variety. Yet one can be too cautious in this respect, and when a new variety is introduced which has been shown by careful trials to have promise of out-yielding a well-established favourite, it is generally advisable to try a small acreage for comparison. No variety merits a

FIG. 1. SHORTAGE OF LIME—BARLEY HAS FAILED AND SORREL FLOURISHES

FIG. 2. SHORTAGE OF LIME—A PATCHY CROP OF SUGAR BEET

FIG. 3. WASTE—THE DUNG HEAP IS LOOSE, EXPOSED TO THE WEATHER, AND VALUABLE PLANT FOOD IS BEING LOST

FIG. 4. DRESSING SEED GRAIN WITH A MERCURIC DUST—AN ESSENTIAL TASK FOR ALL CEREAL CROPS

FIG. 5. BEFORE SPRAYING : HEAVY INFESTATION CHARLOCK

FIG. 6. AFTER SPRAYING : NOTE SHRIVELLED CHARLOCK PLANTS AND STANDING CEREAL

Fig. 7. Sugar Beet—The Value of Stubble Cleaning in Giving Freedom from Perennial Weeds

Fig. 8. Sugar Beet—Failure to Stubble Clean has Resulted in a Strong Growth of "Twitch" in the Rows and much Hand Hoeing will be Necessary

Cut tuber longitudinally and leave ¼ inch uncut. Note sprouts on each half.

Put cut surfaces together again and leave in cool place.

Setts ready for planting. Note healed surfaces and sturdy sprouts.

FIG. 9. HOW TO CUT A POTATO SETT

FIG. 10. PLOUGHED-OUT GRASSLAND (OLD MEADOW)—FIRST CROP OF OATS
Left : Limed six years previously.   Right : No lime

FIG. 11. INOCULATING LUCERNE SEED BEFORE DRILLING

trial merely because it is new, and not until solid evidence can be given that it is superior to existing varieties is it worthy of a farmer's attention. All too frequently disappointing results follow the sowing of a new and highly-priced "outstanding" introduction. In buying seed, price should never be the first consideration. A high price does not guarantee results nor, for that matter, is the saving of a few shillings per acre justified if the quality of the seed is below standard.

Good plump seed is essential whatever the crop, for big seeds possess good reserves of food and produce, therefore, stronger seedlings than smaller ill-nourished seeds. There is a great feeling of satisfaction when one has bought the best seed on the market, but there can be much greater satisfaction when, after care and attention, one sows home-grown seed of equally high standard. In all cases where home-grown seed is used a farmer should ensure that it is up to scratch. Unfortunately far too often poor yields are the result of a poor, pinched sample of seed, probably badly harvested or of low germination.

During the spring of 1939 the author procured samples of seed grain from twenty farms where home-grown seed was being used. Germination tests were carried out on these samples and the results are tabulated below:—

Number of samples with germination 80 per cent. or over	5
Number of samples with germination 50 per cent. up to 79 per cent.	9
Number of samples with germination below 50 per cent.	6
Total number of samples . .	20

They reveal the striking fact that only 25 per cent. of the farmers were using seed which was up to standard. When it is realised how vital is the part played by the seed in determining the final yield it is hard to comprehend why greater care is not taken. Yet these twenty cases were of good average farms and were not selected because the standard of farming was low. The results at harvest were in conformity with the germination figures, Purchased seed from a seedsman of repute is always up to standard, but there is no reason why home-grown seed should not be of the same high quality.

C

For the small fee of sixpence the National Institute of Agricultural Botany, Cambridge, will carry out a germination test for any farmer, but even this trouble can be avoided by making a rough test at home.

To do this a representative sample of the bulk should be taken and from this a hundred seeds counted at random. These should be placed on a sheet of moist blotting paper in a warm room, one end of the blotting paper dipping into water to keep it damp.

In a few days' time the germinated grain can be counted, and if the percentage is in the region of eighty or more for cereals it is safe to use the bulk. If the germination is less than this a proportionately higher seeding is necessary, but should the figures be less than fifty the bulk is not suitable for seed.

Considerable improvement in the quality of home-grown seed can be obtained by the use of the winnowing machine, and all seed corn should be winnowed until the sample is plump, uniform, and free from weed seeds and broken grains.

The results of an interesting trial will serve to emphasise the essential need for this simple treatment. Once-grown Victory oats were sown in the normal way. A further area was sown with the same home-grown seed, which had been put through the winnowing machine four times and was a really grand sample. The results are tabulated below:—

	Yield per Acre (cwt.)
Victory Oats: Home grown, winnowed four times .	28·5
Victory Oats: Home grown, bulk sample . . .	24·5

Thus, by grading up the sample in this simple way an extra 4 cwt. of grain per acre was obtained.

Many farmers are firm in their belief that a change of seed from one locality to another is essential if the vigour of the crop is to be maintained. There is unfortunately no concrete evidence in support of this theory, and in all probability the explanation can be found in the fact that some districts are naturally well suited for seed production, whilst in others unfavourable harvesting conditions have a tendency to lower the vitality of the seed. No doubt disease also helps to account for the belief, for in some districts the sample of grain may be so badly damaged as to produce only poor yields. Naturally this is likely to show to disadvantage against seed from another district where the crop is free from the particular trouble.

It should be an unalterable law on every farm that all homegrown seed or untreated purchased seed must be suitably dressed against seed-borne diseases. The cost of such treatment in comparison with the beneficial results obtained is so small that the dressing of cereals is an essential routine practice.

The "pickling" of seed wheat with bluestone has for many years been an accepted practice on farms as a means of controlling bunt disease. It is only in recent years that the necessity for dressing seed oats and barley also has been realised and there are still far too many farmers who omit this essential precaution.

Wet treatments have their drawbacks, and dry organic mercurial powders which are much easier to handle have now largely displaced them. Several brands are on the market and the cost per acre is extremely small. The dressing can be carried out conveniently in an old butter churn or any drum, barrel or box that has a tightly fitting lid.

As a rule about 2 oz. of powder per bushel of seed is required, and the only precaution to be taken in using it is to ensure that the operators do not inhale the dust. These mercuric dusts control not only bunt in wheat but also smut and stripe diseases in barley and oats.

Trials in Yorkshire have given increases in yield of the order of 15 per cent. by this simple treatment, and striking differences in the vigour of the seedlings have frequently been noted.

A big advantage of a dry dressing over the older bluestone or formaldehyde treatments is the fact that should bad weather prevent sowing for some considerable time after the seed has been dressed, no loss of germinating power is experienced. Very occasionally complaints have been heard of injury to grain by mercurial dusts. In all cases, however, the trouble has been due to an overdose of the material or to the grain being kept for several weeks in too moist a condition. When the seed is perfectly dry and the instructions issued by the manufacturers are carefully carried out treated seed will store perfectly well for several months.

Occasionally it may have to be stored for another season and then it is a wise precaution to ascertain if the germination has been impaired before sowing it.

Since these mercurial powders are poisonous it is essential to ensure that any surplus dressed grain is not fed to stock until it has been thoroughly washed.

WEED CONTROL IN CEREAL CROPS

In spite of rotational cropping and the periodical use of cleaning crops, weeds still plague the farmer and many call for special treatment. It is not uncommon, for instance, to get a bad infestation of charlock when the normal depth of ploughing is increased. The explanation, of course, is that the seed has been dormant in the land and has been brought to the surface with the deeper cultivations. Quite frequently in the last two years cereal crops on ploughed-out grassland have been smothered by weeds of this type.

Not everyone realises the serious annual loss in yield of crop from weed infestation, and the following examples from Yorkshire farms are typical of a large number of cases throughout the country :—

		Yield per acre	Loss due to Weeds per cent.
Oats .	With charlock . .	15 cwt.	31
	Without charlock .	22 ,,	
Oats .	With poppies . .	12 cwt.	50
	Without poppies .	24 ,,	
Barley	With mayweed . .	6 cwt.	66
	Without mayweed .	18 ,,	

In each case the weed was eradicated by spraying with sulphuric-acid solution.

Not only is the loss in yield of crop serious, but when weeds are allowed to go unchecked they cause indirect damage by harbouring pests and diseases. There is no doubt whatever that if we could only eradicate charlock and runch from our countryside, turnip "fly" would not constitute the menace that it does at the present time.

In cereals mechanical weed control is difficult unless the rows are spaced sufficiently wide to take a steerage type of hoe. The more usual procedure, therefore, is to eradicate the weeds by chemical means.

At first it appears rather remarkable that chemical substances applied to a crop can be sufficiently selective to kill the weeds and only damage the crop to a very slight extent. This is due, however, to the difference in leaf structure between the cereals and the vast majority of the weeds. All the cereals have narrow, upright leaves with tough skins and the growing point is encased in a protective sheath. The most troublesome weeds in spring corn (charlock and runch) on the other hand have flat, hairy leaves, relatively thin skins, and a growing point which is unprotected and hence easily attacked. Thus any chemical substance which is applied tends to settle on the rough spreading leaves of the weed, but slips off the smooth upright leaves of the cereal. In actual practice a certain amount is bound to settle on the cereal, especially when a liquid spray is used, but owing to the toughness of the skin only temporary damage results and the vital point—the growing point—of the plant is untouched. After spraying the corn crop is certainly "browned" slightly, but in the course of a week or two full recovery takes place.

There is a large number of chemicals from which a choice can be made, but the following are most suitable: copper sulphate, kainit, calcium cyanamide, and sulphuric acid.

Copper sulphate has been used for many years now either in the dry form or as a liquid. In cases where the field is a good way from the water supply the powder form is more convenient and 20 lb. per acre should be broadcast on a still, dewy morning when the charlock is in the four-leaf stage. Finely ground copper sulphate should be purchased, and to facilitate even application it can be mixed with 2 cwt. per acre finely ground kainit.

When used as a wet spray a 4 per cent. solution is applied at the rate of 50 gallons per acre. To make up this strength of solution 4 lb. of copper sulphate or "bluestone" are dissolved in water to make up 10 gallons of spray. Copper sulphate is a plant poison and has no fertilising effect on the land.

Kainit, when used as a weed killer, must be in a finely powdered condition. In such a form it can be purchased under the name of "charlock kainit." It is applied at the rate of 5 to 6 cwt. per acre by hand or machine. When it rests on the leaves of the weeds it forms a solution, and as this is denser than the cell sap within, it withdraws the sap and causes the leaf to wilt and die. It has, in addition, a fertilising value which is of most use on the lighter types of soil. In order to keep the kainit dry and in good sowable condition a small quantity of steamed bone flour can be mixed with it.

Calcium cyanamide, a fine black powder, containing in addition to valuable weed-killing properties 20·6 per cent. of nitrogen, should be applied at 1½ cwt. per acre when the leaves are dewy. Care is necessary in its application and the hands and arms of the worker should be well oiled or greased before commencing work.

From 14 to 20 lb. of finely powdered crystalline copper sulphate mixed with 1 cwt. of fine and dry sulphate of ammonia can also be used, being a sufficient dressing for one acre of charlock-infested corn. As with calcium cyanamide the sulphate of ammonia has a valuable stimulating effect on the crop.

In recent years sulphuric acid has taken premier place as a weed killer. The strong acid, known under its trade name of "B.O.V." (Brown Oil of Vitriol), is dangerous and due care must be exercised in its use. The acid arrives on the farm in large, straw-packed, glass carboys each containing about 10 gallons of acid and weighing about 200 lb. Spraying may be carried out under contract, in which case the firm supplies the acid and sprayer, but the farmer undertakes to cart the water. The method is simple, however, and can be carried out by the normal farm staff and equipment.

To carry out the work a large barrel is required for mixing, one or two wooden buckets for measuring out the acid, a wooden pole for stirring, and a spraying machine. The latter need not be elaborate or expensive, and a barrel fixed in a cart and fitted with a pump and sprayer as shown in Fig. 14 is quite satisfactory.

The strength of solution required varies with the type of weed to be eradicated. A 7 per cent. solution is sufficient for charlock, for instance, but for mayweed up to 20 per cent. strength may be required. The rate of application is usually 100 gallons per acre.

Great care is necessary in making up the solution, and *on no account must water be added to the acid but always acid to a large quantity of water.* Great heat is generated during mixing, and thus if water is added to the acid the bulk of the acid comes into contact with a little water and this raises the temperature of the mixture to a dangerous level. What is more, the first few drops of water to be added are heated so violently that steam is generated with explosive force, causing the acid to fly in all directions. It cannot be emphasised too forcibly that the strong acid is extremely dangerous and a drop on the skin causes a serious burn. It will penetrate through clothing and leather and can still cause a burn when it reaches the skin.

With reasonable care there is no reason to be frightened of its use. The workers should be equipped with old clothes and preferably rubber boots, or efficient leggings can be cut from an old motor-tyre inner tube. The spray is not so bodily harmful as the strong acid, but even so it affects the clothes and eyes and any sores about the face or hands. It is a good pre-cautionary measure to wear goggles, and in case of accidents a supply of lime water, washing or baking soda, and some clean water should be kept at hand. A solution of 2 oz. of ordinary washing soda in a gallon of water is as good as anything to have available for the purpose of neutralising the acid.

The mixing of the acid and water is best done actually in the barrel of the machine, if this can be arranged. First the requisite amount of water should be poured in. The strong acid is then poured from a carboy into one of the wooden buckets, and then added slowly to the water in the barrel, stirring carefully. Some prefer to mix the solution in a large barrel on the ground and then transfer the spray by means of a small semi-rotary pump into the barrel of the sprayer.

The barrel should be only partially filled to avoid the solution splashing over, and it should be marked on the inside to indicate the quantity of water to pour in before the acid is added.

Spraying must be carried out when the weeds are small if full benefit is to be obtained. The weather should be calm and dry, for if windy the spray may blow on to the horse's hooves, making him fretful, and if the weeds are damp the strength of the solution will be reduced. When spraying in damp, cloudy weather, the strength of the solution must be increased and the proportion of B.O.V. in the solution increased by about 40 per cent.

A new selective weed killer, Methoxone, is rapidly gaining popularity. This material can act either through the leaves or through the roots, and hence its efficacy is independent of weather conditions. Moreover, the control is independent of the time of application and it may take a month before the weeds die off, the only signs being a yellowing of the leaves and gradual disintegration. The chemical may be applied as a liquid spray or as a powder put on with the ordinary fertiliser drill. Methoxone is not poisonous and is non-corrosive.

Copper chloride, though not so quick-acting as sulphuric acid, can be used with success at a later stage of weed development and is more efficient than copper sulphate. For spring-sown cereals a 3-4 per cent. solution applied at 100 gallons per acre is used.

Di-nitro-ortho-cresol, a yellow dyestuff, in its various compounds has also given good weed control, and under average conditions acts quicker than copper chloride. The warmer the weather the quicker the action, and in May on a hot day, as little as an hour, without rain, is all that is necessary to ensure good control, but in dull cold weather sulphuric acid is the more efficient.

All D.N.O.C. compounds stain the skin, hair and clothing bright yellow and care is necessary in their use. In addition these compounds are corrosive to metals and alloys and when in the dry state are inflammable. The question of the best material to use for weed eradication, strength and rate of application is a matter for expert opinion, and the assistance of the County Advisory Staff should always be sought in the first instance.

Where cereal crops have been undersown with a seeds mixture before spraying, Methoxone or D.N.O.C. must not be used. If the seeds have not germinated, spraying can be carried out with sulphuric acid or copper chloride. When the seedlings are above ground and it is essential to kill the weeds lest they smother the grasses and clovers, copper chloride should be used, but it is essential to wait until the clovers have passed the cotyledon stage. If the weeds are killed first, the seeds mixture can be sown immediately after using sulphuric acid or copper chloride, but ten days should elapse after D.N.O.C., whilst it is advisable not to use Methoxone under these circumstances until more is known of its behaviour. The effectiveness of the various weed killers is given in Appendix VI.

PEST AND DISEASE CONTROL

The old proverb "A stitch in time saves nine" has especial meaning in regard to this problem in farming. Too often when a crop is attacked by insect pest or fungus disease, the farmer waits in the hope that something will happen to stop the trouble or that "all will be well by harvest." Unfortunately, in many such instances all is not well and the crop suffers considerable damage. Frequently advice is sought when it is far too late to apply the necessary control measures. Immediately it is apparent that something is wrong with a crop the trouble should be diagnosed and remedial measures, if such are possible, put into operation. On the other hand, if the cause of the trouble is obscure, or the remedial measures unknown, the County Advisory Officer should be called at once. After all, no "doctor" can give assistance once the patient is dead.

We are prone to place great faith in the weather for pest control. After a severe winter optimism generally runs high amongst farmers, for it is a common belief that a hard winter brings about a reduction of insect pests and kills out fungus spores. Again, during the growing season should some malady beset the crop a change in the weather is looked for as a possible end to the trouble.

In general, little faith can be placed in a hard winter, for though it will certainly harm some species of insects it favours others which are safely sealed up below ground and out of danger from birds, voles, moles, predaceous beetles, and other natural enemies. Then, again, a spring drought which retards crop growth often assists the pests and a bright sunny summer serves to encourage aphides and caterpillars. The summer months of 1942 are likely to be remembered by many farmers for the severe attacks of aphides of all types encouraged by the spell of favourable weather in June and July. Thus on the whole little help must be expected from the weather in this matter.

In most cases prevention is better than cure, for treatment is often costly, whereas evasive methods merely a matter of management. Variations in the rotation, for instance, will serve to control such diseases as "finger-and-toe" in swedes or "clover sickness."

There is no doubt, of course, that healthy growth is always better able to withstand insect attack or disease than weakly and puny crops. This may appear too obvious to be worth mention and yet it is a factor frequently lost sight of. Good seed beds, wise manuring and sowing at the right time are most important in getting strong, vigorous plants. Often a top-dressing of nitrogenous fertiliser can be utilised to good advantage by a strong crop attacked by insects or disease which enables it to grow away from the trouble. A weak plant, on the other hand, is unable to take the stimulant and either succumbs or fails to give the maximum yield.

Of all methods of pest control, however, the one that receives least attention and yet could produce such manifold benefit is that which can be termed "farm hygiene." Many examples of the importance of this aspect of the problem are to be found in the following chapters. There is no doubt, for instance, that charlock forms an excellent breeding ground and shelter for turnip flea beetles, and helps "finger-and-toe" disease to persist; that the black aphis finds a congenial home on docks and other weeds, whilst a common source of potato blight is an old pie bottom where diseased tubers from the previous year are allowed to grow.

It is absolutely essential to destroy by burning all diseased plant material, yet only too frequently one finds diseased roots or rubbish being thrown on to the dung heap. Unfortunately, the results of "cleaning up" are never very apparent, and until that idealistic age is reached when this problem is tackled on every farm much encouragement cannot be expected for the control of pests and diseases in this way. It is already very evident that the cleaning out of dykes and the uprooting of old hedges, which precedes the reclamation of so much derelict land now being brought into cultivation, is likely to have a profound effect in reducing weed infestation. This in its turn will doubtless play a big part in the pest and disease problem which confronts the farmer.

Clean farming, which term implies clean land, seed and methods, is the first step towards healthy plant growth and without this maximum yields can never be obtained.

Chapter Two

GRAIN CROPS

WHEAT

WHEAT is the most important of our grain crops since it is the favourite cereal for the production of bread. The crop does best in fairly dry sunny districts and is grown more or less extensively throughout the eastern and midland counties. Owing to its deep-rooted habit of growth it can withstand long periods of drought and is also very resistant to winter frost provided it is well established by the time severe weather sets in.

Wheat yields well on medium to heavy loam soils which are in a good state of fertility, and it is generally conceded that the more "body" in the soil the more suitable it is for the crop. Wet soils and very light sandy soils are not suitable, nor does the crop grow satisfactorily in sour, acid soils which are short of lime. Provided the land is in good heart quite satisfactory crops can be grown on light land, but as a rule on these soils the yield is only moderate, though the quality of the grain is not inferior. In contrast to this, on peaty soils a large amount of straw is produced with a low yield of inferior quality grain. Wheat is undoubtedly the safest cereal to grow on really rich land, for if a strong-strawed variety is selected there is a reasonably good chance of the crop being harvested without loss from lodging.

VARIETIES

The value of any particular variety of wheat does not depend entirely upon the yield of grain and straw, for such factors as strength of straw, resistance to disease, and earliness or lateness in ripening must also be taken into consideration before making a final selection. What is more, differences in soil play a large part in the success or otherwise of any variety, and one that does well on heavy land in a particular district does not necessarily do equally well on light land. Most wheat growers have found a certain variety to suit their own soil and climatic conditions and this should be grown on the greater part of the acreage devoted to wheat. The remaining acreage might be sown with

43

WHEAT VARIETIES

Name	Suitable Soils	State of Fertility Required	Colour of Chaff	Colour of Grain	Resistance to Lodging	Remarks
Holdfast	Heavy loam	Rich	White	White	Excellent	Finest bread wheat. Very good yield. Can be sown to middle of January.
Bersee	Medium loam	Rich	White	Red	Very good	Very adaptable. Heavy yields, early ripening, 6 days before Holdfast. Can be drilled from October to March.
Pilot	Average	Good	White	Red	Very good	Improved Scandinavian type.
Iron Red	Medium loam	Good	Red	Red	Very good	Improved "Standard Red" type.
Squarehead II	Wide range	Very adaptable	Red	Red	Very good	Improved "Squarehead Master" type.
Defiant	Medium|Heavy	Rich	White	Red	Very good	Heavy yield, average milling quality, ripens early, stands well.
Steadfast	Light	Medium to low	Red	White	Good	Improved "Little Joss" type. Good filling under adverse conditions.
Rampton Rivet	Heavy loam	Low	Grey	Red	Excellent	Very late in ripening; bearded. Greatly improved selection of Rivet.
Als	Medium loam	Medium to rich	White	Red	Very good	Very late in ripening. Very hardy, good quality grain.
Desprez 80	Medium|Heavy	Rich	White	Red	Excellent	Ripens very early, excellent for combining. Should not be cut until fully ripe.

WHEAT VARIETIES—continued

Name	Suitable Soils	State of Fertility Required	Colour of		Resistance to Lodging	Remarks
			Chaff	Grain		
Wilhelmina, Wilma, Victor, Juliana	Heavy loam	Good	White	White	Good	Very reliable varieties.
Yeoman, Yeoman II	Heavy loam	Rich	White	Red	Very good	Excellent bread wheats, cut early for best milling sample.
Scandia, Crown, Steel, Iron III	Average	Good	White	Red	Very good	Late ripening, must be sown in autumn.
Guardsman	Medium loams	Good	Red	Red	Very good	Ripens somewhat later than Squarehead Master.
Jubilégem	Average	Good	White	Red	Very good	Short, erect, stiff straw. Ripens early. Very resistant to Yellow Rust.
Spring Varieties						
A. 1	Average	Average	White	White	Moderate	Ripens late, good yields if sown February.
Atle	Average	Average	White	Red	Good	Superior to the old Red Marvel. Ripens rather late.
Fylgia	Wide range	Wide range	Red	Red	Very good	Can be sown from February to April. Ripens early.
Diamond II	Wide range	Wide range	Red	Red	Good	For drilling end March to April. Ripens early.
Meteor	Wide range	Wide range	White	Red	Good	Ripens fairly early; promising new variety.

one or more of the newer varieties, preferably those showing marked strength of straw, earliness of ripening, and high yields of good quality grain.

The tables on pages 44 and 45 summarise the characteristics of the best-yielding varieties of wheat in cultivation at the present time.

PLACE IN ROTATION

There is, of course, no hard-and-fast rule as to where wheat should be taken in the rotation. When bare fallowing was a common practice wheat was invariably the following crop. Since this practice has declined, however, combined with the fact that the wheat crop was often thin and patchy after a fallow, due in no small measure to attacks of the Wheat Bulb Fly, the crop is more usually taken after seeds. In many districts it follows potatoes, whilst in others, beans, peas, or roots act as the preparatory crop. Quite frequently it may be taken as a second straw crop, in which case care must be taken to clean the stubble after the first crop and a careful watch kept for "Take-all" or "Whiteheads" disease. On many farms wheat is chosen as the first crop on ploughed-up grassland, particularly on the heavier classes of land.

PREPARATION OF SEED BED

The cultivation necessary to prepare a suitable seed bed naturally depends on the preceding crop and type of soil and to some extent upon the district. The aim should be to get a good firm tilth, but one which is not unduly fine, for overworking in autumn is likely to cause the surface to run together and "cap" with the winter rains. This is difficult to break in spring and interferes with the free circulation of air in the soil. Ploughing should, therefore, be shallow (4 to 5 inches) and done as early as possible to give time for the furrows to settle. On light land, in particular, the use of a furrow press is advisable.

When wheat follows seeds or grassland it is important to break the land early, for this is a safeguard against Frit Fly attack of the seedlings. Late ploughing allows the Frit Flies to lay their eggs on the ryegrass in August and September, and the young maggots which hatch out, on finding that the grass which is now ploughed in cannot support them, work their way up out of the sod and into the young wheat plants. Admittedly, this early ploughing involves the sacrifice of some useful keep, but in many districts failure to plough early results in serious damage to the wheat.

The cultivation operations after seeds are simple. The land is ploughed and pressed and the seed sown broadcast and harrowed in or drilled after a rough tilth has been obtained by harrowing. In many instances the seeds drill is attached to the presser, this in turn following the plough with light harrows attached behind. Thus, the operations of preparing a tilth, seeding, and covering are done simultaneously, and in this way large acreages can be covered in a short space of time.

When wheat follows potatoes the soil is already in a friable condition, and in most cases all that is necessary is to broadcast the seed and drag it in. The danger in this connection is that the land may be too friable for wheat, and a common practice in many districts is to broadcast the seed and plough it in with a shallow furrow (2-inch). This is known as "shelling in," and gives not only a firm bottom for the seed but also the roughish tilth on top which is so desirable.

When rough old pasture is ploughed for wheat it is advisable, in order that the seed bed may be firm, to graze any coarse herbage down with stock or, if this cannot be done, to mow it and cart it off before ploughing.

The furrow should be fairly wide, turned well over on to its back to bury all herbage, and a knife or disc coulter and also a skim coulter fitted to facilitate good work.

MANURING

Wheat generally finds adequate nourishment from the residues of previous crops and manurings when the land is in a reasonably good state of fertility. Should the soil, however, be in a low state of fertility it is advisable to give a light dressing of dung (8 to 10 loads per acre) before ploughing with an application of superphosphate at 3 cwt. per acre to the seed bed. When dung is not available the following mixture is recommended as a seed bed application:—

Sulphate of Ammonia .	$\frac{3}{4}$ cwt. per acre,			Ammonium
Superphosphate .	$1\frac{1}{2}$ „ „		or	Phosphate
Steamed Bone Flour .	$\frac{3}{4}$ „ „			1 cwt. per acre.
	$\overline{3}$ „ „			

Before contemplating wheat growing any lime deficiencies in the soil should be made good. It is preferable to lime after ploughing, for this ensures a sweet seed bed.

Wheat seldom responds to applications of potash manures.

In recent years many trials have been carried out to determine whether nitrogen is better applied to wheat in the autumn or spring, and in what quantities it should be used. The evidence, collected from a large number of trials, indicates that spring top-dressings are much more likely to be profitable than autumn applications. Whereas 1 cwt. per acre sulphate of ammonia applied in spring produces an average increase in yield of about $2\frac{1}{2}$ cwt. of grain and 5 cwt. of straw, the same quantity of sulphate of ammonia applied in autumn may give increases of only 1 cwt. of grain and 3 cwt. of straw. There is also evidence that on most farms it is a sound practice to apply up to 2 cwt. of nitrogenous fertiliser in spring rather than the more usual 1 cwt. per acre, the second hundredweight being almost as profitable as the first. It is suggested that in all cases where the average yield of grain falls below 25 cwt. per acre at least 2 cwt. per acre of sulphate of ammonia or its equivalent should be given. Spring-sown wheat should be top-dressed in May in the same way as winter wheat, except when the plant is really strong and rank in growth.

Evidence is available regarding the best time for application. Cambridge results indicate that as the date of application approaches the end of April or the beginning of May the yield of grain as distinct from that of the straw is improved. On the other hand, an early application in February will, by promoting the tillering of the plant, also increase the yield by increasing the number of heads at harvest. Thus, in general, one can say that in all cases where 2 cwt. per acre of a nitrogenous fertiliser is to be applied, this should be divided equally between an early application to promote tillering and a late application in May to increase the size of the heads.

When only 1 cwt. per acre is given this is likely to give the best results from late application. One cannot dogmatise, of course, for much depends upon the type of soil and also the season, but there is no doubt that in many cases where the soil is known to be on a low level of fertility an application of nitrogenous fertiliser to the seed bed in addition helps to get the plant established and bring it through the winter.

Sowing

The amount of seed sown depends upon several factors such as size of grain, district and time of year. Some varieties of wheat have much larger grains than others, and obviously in order to obtain the same number of plants per acre a much heavier seeding will be required than when small-grained varieties are used. Few farmers take cognisance of this fact, and many thin stands of wheat can be attributed to shortage of seed rather than unsuitable soil or weather conditions. When several varieties of wheat are being sown it is necessary to count the seeds in a given weight of each and adjust the drill so that equal numbers of seeds per acre are sown and not, as more frequently happens, equal weights of seed.

In northern and upland districts a heavier seeding is necessary than in the more genial southern districts, and again, more is required for broadcasting than for drilling, because in the former case some seeds may be buried too deeply and fail to germinate.

The time of year also influences the rate of seeding, for with early sowing the plant has plenty of time to become established and tiller out and thus less seed is required. The rate of seeding usually varies from $1\frac{1}{4}$ cwt. per acre in September to $1\frac{3}{4}$ cwt. in November. On ploughed-out grassland these rates should be increased by 30 per cent. to allow for the depredations of wireworms and other pests. For spring seeding the rate should be $2\frac{1}{4}$ cwt. per acre to allow for poor tillering. As a rule spring wheat is most successful when sown during February or March, but earlier seeding may be attempted if soil and weather conditions are favourable and can be delayed until April or even May if necessary.

All seed wheat should be dressed with a suitable preparation for controlling Bunt or Stinking Smut, which is a seed-borne disease. This has been fully discussed in Chapter One.

Local experience will always indicate the best time for sowing wheat in any particular district, but as a rule the third week in October can be taken as a fair guide. September-sown wheat sometimes tends to produce straw at the expense of grain, whilst with November sowings heavy mortality must be expected amongst the seedlings due to adverse conditions. In most districts December and January sowings are attended with great risk, and when the wheat cannot be sown before the end of November the wisest course in most instances is to rely upon a spring-sown variety rather than risk partial failure of the autumn wheat. Under most conditions autumn-sown wheat gives better yields than that sown in spring.

The ordinary depth of drilling is 2 inches, but for sowing late in the season it is seldom advisable to exceed 1 inch in depth. The drill rows should not exceed 6 inches in width.

After Cultivations

In early spring when the frosts are over the land should be rolled to consolidate the soil around the plants. Following a mild winter it is more likely that the surface soil will have "capped," in which case harrowing is much more beneficial than rolling. Although the flat roller is frequently used the ring roller is to be preferred because it crushes the clods better, moves the surface, and leaves it in a looser condition less likely to "cake" or "set" with the spring rains. Rolling and harrowing should be done before the plant is 6 inches high, for when passed this stage the plants receive a severe setback.

Sometimes the growth of the crop in spring is considered excessive and likely to result in lodging of the crop before harvest. The wheat is then said to be "winter proud," and to check the growth grazing, cutting, or spraying with sulphuric acid may be necessary. Great care is necessary to choose the best time for grazing, for should the soil be too wet poaching may result. Grazing usually takes place in April, though if weather conditions are suitable in March the opportunity should not be missed. Occasionally grazing may take place as late as May, whilst in the Fens it is common to run a mower over the crop during the first week in May. The use of sulphuric acid is less drastic and has the advantage that it also kills out many of the weeds growing in the corn. Experience in the last two years seems to indicate that early growth may be utilised for grazing or silage to a much greater extent than has been the former practice. Indeed some farmers have successfully forced early growth by nitrogenous manuring, taken a cut for silage, and still obtained a normal yield of grain.

Hand-hoeing is frequently adopted for the eradication of strong-growing weeds like thistles, and hand-pulling may be resorted to in the case of docks. Where steerage hoes can be used for inter-row hoeing excellent weed control can be obtained. With a careful driver and a steady light-legged horse it is possible to eliminate over 95 per cent. of the weeds in the wheat in this simple way.

HARVESTING

The crop is ready for cutting when the plants have turned yellow below the ear, and on rubbing out a few heads of corn in the palm of the hand the grains are "cheesy." If a milky fluid can be expressed from the seed the crop should be left for a few days longer. Cutting before the cheesy stage results in shrivelled and small grains, poor in quality and a loss in yield up to 20 per cent., whilst later cutting, although giving splendid plump grains, is likely to lead to losses in the field due to shedding.

The crop will further ripen in the field after cutting and whilst it is standing in stooks. The length of time necessary for fielding before the crop can be carted depends upon weather conditions, the ripeness of the straw and the presence or absence of green weeds or grass and clover in the butts of the sheaves.

In most seasons from four to fourteen days are required before it is safe to cart the crop. Once wheat has been thoroughly dry, a small shower does not prevent carting, though to cart oats or barley in the same condition would completely spoil them.

When stacking cannot take place under a Dutch barn the ricks should be thatched as soon as possible. The work of the old-fashioned thatcher who took a real pride in the job is seldom seen to-day. More frequently it is considered sufficient to cover with a layer of straw held in place with nets or ropes. In the Midlands "battens" of straw pegged into position are used, whilst more recently the introduction of a thatch-making machine has made possible the rapid production of thatch "matting," which can be placed in position and tied to the stack with a thatching needle. Even simpler than this is the latest method of covering with Sisalkraft paper held in position with a string net.

YIELD

The average yield of wheat is in the region of 18 cwt. per acre, but on good land yields of 27 to 33 cwt. are fairly common. The weight of straw produced is generally 50 per cent. more than the weight of grain. In other words, the crop is composed of 40 per cent. grain and 60 per cent. straw, this varying within fairly wide limits.

INSECT PESTS

Wireworms.—Wireworms are the grubs of several click beetles and they are among the most serious pests in farming to-day, especially when large tracts of old grassland are coming under the plough. The possibility of large wireworm populations when both permanent and temporary grassland is broken up should always be borne in mind, and this fact alone emphasises the need for proper preparation for and cultural treatment of the crop.

The plants are attacked in the young stage by the wireworms, which eat into the underground portion of the stem below ground level, a succession of dead or dying plants in a row being a characteristic feature of the attack.

Control Measures.—There is no known cure or preventative in the way of insecticidal dressings which can be used on a farm scale. In the event of an attack all that can be done is to encourage the crop to grow away from the pest by cultivation and manuring. The opinion is widely held in farming circles that rolling is beneficial, and while this is true the benefit derived from rolling is largely due to the stimulating effect upon the growth of the crop due to consolidation rather than to any direct effect upon the pest. It has already been pointed out earlier in this chapter that firmness in the seed bed is essential for the successful growing of wheat, and it cannot be too often stressed that bad preparation of the soil militates against the capacity of the crop to withstand the attacks of such pests as wireworms. Similarly, a top-dressing with a nitrogenous fertiliser as a stimulant may be of considerable benefit if the soil is known to be in a state of moderate or low fertility.

Experience during the ploughing-out campaign has shown that given reasonable climatic conditions a crop grown under good soil conditions with adequate manuring is capable of withstanding the effects of even large wireworm populations.

The wireworm feeds mainly in the autumn and again in the spring, and it is for this reason that patching a poor wheat crop with barley, even as late as the end of May, is well worth while.

When the population is known to be dangerously high of course, the judicious selection of resistant crops like peas, beans, flax or forage mixtures overcomes the difficulty, or in very bad cases it may be necessary to re-seed to permanent grassland.

Frit Fly.—As already indicated in this chapter, Frit Fly attack is due to the crop following a seeds ley ploughed almost immediately prior to sowing.

The first sign is a colour change of the central shoot in late autumn to winter, which turns yellow and withers, the rest of the plant remaining green. The yellow leaf can easily be pulled out of the plant, and on splitting open an injured plant one or more yellowish-white maggots may be found. These, however, are small and when fully grown do not measure more than $\frac{1}{4}$ inch long. Affected plants produce secondary shoots, but these may also be attacked and the plants killed.

Control Measures.—The practice of sowing winter wheat after a grass (and particularly rye grass) ley is to be avoided unless the field can be ploughed before harvest. Where oat crops have shown Frit Fly attack there is every chance that rye grass leys still standing in autumn will be infested.

Wheat Bulb Fly.—The first signs of attack are usually in March when the central shoot turns yellow. Examination of affected plants reveals a small white grub feeding within the base of the plants. A rapidly growing crop may escape serious damage, but if the plant is weak and doing badly, the attack may destroy a large part of the crop. The attack occurs in wheat grown after fallow, a fallow crop, or even after, say, early peas, which do not cover the ground during July and August when the eggs are laid. Perhaps the worst injury occurs in wheat after potatoes on light land.

Control Measures.—In districts where this pest is commonest it is inadvisable to sow wheat when the land has been bare in July or August. If the attack is detected at an early stage a top-dressing of nitrogen and a good rolling will often help recovery. Should a seriously damaged crop have to be ploughed out in spring it would be perfectly safe to re-sow with barley.

Slugs.—Slugs can cause severe damage to young wheat in a short space of time, the attacks usually taking place in autumn or spring during spells of damp, muggy weather. The trouble is scarcely noticeable at first, the crop gradually thinning out.

Plants attacked by slugs are "ribboned" or eaten into shreds, and the presence of the pest can usually be confirmed by the slime on the plants or by the slugs themselves which may be found hiding under clods or leaves during the day-time.

Control Measures.—The remedy is simple and cheap and consists of broadcasting a mixture of metaldehyde and bran. The metaldehyde is sold in tablet form under the trade name of Meta (a solid fuel used for camp stoves), ½ lb. of Meta, after crushing, being mixed with 25 lb. of bran. The latter should be moistened with sufficient water to make it crumbly and applied at this rate per acre.

The mixture is broadcast after dusk when the slugs are feeding. The material used at this rate is non-poisonous to plants, farm stock and birds, and will remain active for several days after application. In place of bran, sugar-beet pulp, brewer's grains or wheat chaff may be used.

Another method developed in Yorkshire and used successfully in many parts of the country is to mix 18 lb. of finely ground copper sulphate with 2¾ cwt. of kainit. This should be applied to each acre either broadcast or by means of a manure distributor after dark during mild weather.

Still another method is to broadcast a poison bait made from 1 lb. of Paris green and 28 lb. of bran, these quantities being sufficient to treat an acre. The mixture should be moistened slightly to make the poison adhere to the bran, and care is essential to ensure that poultry or domestic animals do not have access to the bait which is extremely poisonous.

Leatherjackets.—Next to the wireworm this is perhaps the most serious soil pest we have. It is a brown legless grub, tough and leathery, and attains a length of about one inch. The leatherjacket is the grub stage of the Daddy Longlegs fly, which lays its eggs in grass or clover fields in late summer. Unlike the wireworm it lives for only nine months before changing into a chrysalis, and hence an arable field is not infested for more than one season. Owing to the habit of the fly the crop is most likely to be attacked when it follows a late-ploughed seeds ley or permanent grassland.

The grub eats its way through the plant at or slightly below ground level.

Control Measures.—Early breaking of clover leys or grassland in July or early August will largely combat the pest.

The poison bait method of Paris green and bran already described in the case of slug damage can be relied upon to give effective control.

Wheat Shoot Beetle.—Injury to winter wheat by the grub of the beetle known as the Wheat Shoot beetle has been experienced in the Eastern Counties and Yorkshire in wheat after clover. Injury may be noticed as early as January and may continue until the end of March or early April, and the damage may take several forms. Occasionally the stem may be completely severed below soil level as in the case of wireworm attack, or the central shoot may be killed as with the Frit Fly damage, or again, holes may be found in the base of the highest expanded leaf-blade. The grubs are very difficult to find, being only three-tenths of an inch long and of an inconspicuous brown colour.

Control Measures.—Firmness in tilth is a factor of great importance in reducing danger from an attack. Once the beetles become active a top dressing with a nitrogenous fertiliser and a good rolling will serve to stimulate crop growth, and where wheat follows a ley, ploughing should be carried out early.

DISEASES

Bunt or *Stinking Smut.*—Grains of wheat affected with this disease are found to consist of a mass of black spores giving off a fishy odour. During threshing, affected grains burst, discolour and taint the rest of the wheat, and hence not only is the yield reduced but the value of the grain also.

When seed infected with the spores of Bunt is sown both seed and spores germinate together and the fungus, finding its way into the reproductive shoot, destroys every grain.

Control Measures.—Seed wheat should be dressed with a mercuric seed-dressing as outlined in Chapter One.

Smut.—In the case of this disease grains and chaff are destroyed and the whole head of the plant becomes covered with a mass of black spores.

Control Measures.—Seed-dressing does not control this disease as the fungus is actually within the grain and not on the surface as in the case of Bunt. Treatment consists in immersing the seed for ten minutes in water at 128° F., but since this is difficult to carry out in practice the best way is to obtain only clean seed from an uninfected crop.

Yellow Rust.—This is a common disease of wheat, affected plants having bright yellow spots on the leaves. Although the disease has no serious effect upon the growth of the plant it certainly withdraws some food and hence results in a reduction in yield. The annual loss in this country due to Yellow Rust is said to amount to about 5 per cent. of the yield. Some varieties such as Little Joss, Yeoman, and Swedish Iron are highly resistant to the disease, and in districts where it is common these should be grown.

Wheat also suffers from Black Rust and Brown Rust, but these diseases are not so widespread and do not merit attention here.

"Night Ripening," "Whiteheads" or *" Take-All."*—This disease may appear as patches of early-killed plants, though more frequently it occurs as scattered "Whiteheads" as harvest-time approaches. These appear so swiftly that farmers have dubbed the disease "Night Ripening." Confirmation of the cause of the trouble can be obtained by an examination of the base of the stems of diseased plants which, when the leaf sheaths are removed, are seen to be blackened.

The fungus causing the disease remains dormant in the soil inside infected root and stubble residues left after harvest. When the young roots of the wheat plant come into contact with this diseased material they become infected. The rooting system is then seriously reduced, and this generally becomes apparent at a time when the plant is fully grown and is making its largest demand for water and minerals to swell the grain. Lacking these, the grain shrivels and the ears take on a bleached appearance.

Control Measures.—A sound crop rotation is the basic means of control for this disease. Wheat and barley are both attacked, whilst oats suffer from a similar disease in Wales but all non-cereals are safe. The decomposition of the fungus in the infected stubble should be hastened by ploughing as soon after harvest as possible. The preparation of a firm seed bed is essential, and the use of a heavy roller in spring to firm the soil around the roots of the plant is also very desirable.

The roots of perennial and Italian ryegrasses and a number of other pasture grasses may carry the disease. Thus when a ley is broken up for winter wheat it is important to do so in June or July to allow time for a bastard fallow. Couch, slender foxtail, and barley grasses may also serve as weed-carriers of the take-all fungus.

Foot Rot.—This fungus disease attacks wheat, barley and oats but wheat undoubtedly suffers most. The disease may easily be confused with Whiteheads or Night Ripening.

Symptoms of an attack are a "thinning out" and yellowing of the crop with deaf ears at harvest-time. As its name implies the rooting system is seriously affected.

Badly drained soils are more liable to Foot Rot than well-drained soils. Since the organism causing the disease attacks numerous kinds of plants and also exists on soil residues the trouble is more persistent than Night Ripening.

Control Measures.—Seed disinfection with one of the organic mercury dusts is beneficial, since this not only kills any disease on the outside of the grain but gives some protection against organisms present in the soil.

Eyespot.—It has been established recently at Rothamsted that about half the lodging in wheat (and in barley too) is due to a fungus disease called Eyespot. The lodging is characterised by straggling or scrawling of the straw rather than a general leaning in one direction which is more commonly due to rich soil conditions, storms, poor root development or weakness of the straw.

The disease is common in the wheat areas of eastern England, especially where the crop has been grown frequently on the same land or where conditions are favourable for luxuriant growth.

Control Measures.—The adoption of a sound rotation incorporating longish leys is the best means of control known at present. The help of the Provincial Advisory Mycologist should always be sought if this disease is suspected.

BARLEY

Barley is grown chiefly for malting, and for this purpose the grain must be well harvested, carefully threshed, and white and starchy in cross section. Broken or skinned grains, discoloration due to weathering or heating and a flinty kernel are undesirable characteristics and seriously lower the value of the sample.

The most suitable climatic conditions are a moderate temperature with an average, well-distributed rainfall. Hot, forcy weather produces a pinched sample, whilst in districts of high rainfall the husk tends to be thick. Above all, a good dry spring is essential to allow early sowing and plenty of sun during the ripening period, to impart a good colour and hardness to the grain.

Being a shallow-rooted crop it is pre-eminently suited to free-working light loams, and those which are generally recognised as good turnip soils are best for barley. Land of this type is frequently termed "sheep and barley" land. One seldom obtains a good sample of barley from heavy land or soils in a state of high fertility, and peaty soils only produce feeding grain. Fen, heavy clays, and light sandy soils are to be avoided. It is essential, no matter what the class of soil, that it contains an adequate reserve of lime, for on acid soils barley is likely to be a complete failure.

VARIETIES

Barleys grown in this country can be grouped into two classes, winter varieties and spring varieties.

WINTER BARLEYS

Pioneer.—This two-rowed hybrid barley bred at Cambridge is winter hardy and produces grain of good malting quality. It has a short straw, stands well, matures early and is best suited to soils of good or medium fertility.

Prefect.—Is a six-rowed variety also bred at Cambridge. The straw is of moderate strength and the crop ripens about the same time as Pioneer. The plant has a high degree of winter hardiness and the grain is of good malting quality.

SPRING BARLEYS

Plumage-Archer.—This variety has erect, dense and broad ears, a short neck which does not "kink," and short strong straw. On good soils the yield is excellent and the malting quality unsurpassed.

Spratt-Archer.—In contrast to Plumage-Archer this variety has long, drooping and rather lax narrow ears. It tillers well and the straw stands very well. Usually slightly heavier yields of grain are obtained from this variety, the quality being good. Spratt-Archer is the better yielder on light, moderate quality land, and Plumage-Archer on the heavier and richer soils. Both varieties may be sown in the autumn on well-drained soils in sheltered positions in the South without much risk. In dry seasons better malting quality is obtained in this way, although yield may be rather lower.

Abed Kenia and *Abed Maja.*—These are early ripening, resistant to lodging and give heavy yields on very fertile soils.

Camton.—A good standing, stiff-strawed variety giving high yields on rich soils. Very suitable for the combine harvester but essentially a feeding barley.

PLACE IN ROTATION

The crop usually follows swedes or turnips which in the typical sheep and barley districts are consumed on the land. It is generally conceded that the "golden hoof" of the sheep is essential to impart the requisite amount of "body" to these light soils and that the dunging leaves the land in rich condition for the following crop. Very frequently, however, especially on good rich soils, the land is much too fat for the production of a malting sample of barley. Under these conditions it is more likely that the grain will be dark in colour, have a high nitrogen content, and will go down before it can be harvested. To grow a strong-strawed variety such as Abed Kenia may help, but the wisest policy is undoubtedly to take another straw crop before the barley. Then the excessive richness is removed by the first crop and the barley following on will be starchy and of good colour.

Evidence obtained from the Rothamsted Barley Conferences suggests that when barley is grown on rich land after roots, lighter yields of slightly lower quality are obtained than when it follows a corn crop. Should the folding of sheep on roots cause the ploughing to be late and this results in a poor seed bed, it is likely that where barley follows, the quality will be poor and the nitrogen content high. Since the introduction of sugar beet, and especially on farms where it replaces roots, barley has been the following crop.

PREPARATION OF SEED BED

Barley requires a tilth as "light as a feather," and more careful cultivation is required than for any of our other cereal crops. Following a root crop the land should be shallow ploughed

(4 inches deep is adequate) as soon as possible, and when barley follows another straw crop ploughing immediately after harvest is always desirable.

No tilth can compare with a frost mould, and every endeavour should be made to get the land turned over in time to take full advantage of winter frosts. After late-folded roots there is a danger of getting a "leathery" type of furrow which, in spite of subsequent cultivations, only produces a very cloddy seed bed.

As soon as weather conditions permit in February or March the land should be cultivated, keeping the fine mould on the surface. If late ploughing or the absence of frost has resulted in a cloddy tilth, a ring-roller should be used, followed by further cultivations.

When the barley is autumn-sown the cultivations follow the lines already indicated for wheat save that a rather finer tilth is required. It must be remembered, however, that only land which lies dry and warm during the winter is suitable for winter barley.

Manuring

When barley follows roots which have been sheeped off or sugar beet the tops of which are ploughed in, no further manuring need be contemplated. On land which is so rich that the crop is likely to lodge the application of 3 cwt. per acre, superphosphate will be found beneficial and not only hastens the crop to maturity but often helps it to stand up. Should the barley be taken as a second straw crop, however, more generous manuring may be necessary, in which case it is advisable to apply the following mixture as a seed-bed application :—

Sulphate of Ammonia	.	1 cwt. per acre.
Superphosphate .	.	3 ,, ,,
Muriate of Potash .	.	1 ,, ,,
		5 ,, ,,

At one time the use of nitrogenous fertilisers was deprecated on the grounds that they resulted in a grain richer in nitrogen and, therefore, less suitable for malting. Recent extensive experiments have shown, however, that 1 cwt. of sulphate of ammonia can be expected to increase the yield by $2\frac{1}{2}$ to 3 cwt. per acre without lowering the quality.

Frequently the barley crop is used as a "nurse" crop for a grass and clover mixture forming the temporary ley. Wherever this is the case an application of phosphates is well-nigh essential to ensure a good stand of clover. In the North, excellent results have been obtained by the use of 5 to 10 cwt. per acre high grade, high soluble basic slag applied two to three weeks before drilling the seed. Not only has this promoted the even ripening of the barley, but it has resulted in excellent "takes" of seeds where formerly only patchy crops were obtained.

Barley is one of the most sensitive crops to soil acidity, and as already indicated, liming is essential in all cases where a deficiency exists. The prevalence of spurrey (louse grass) or sheep's sorrel (sour dock) or finger-and-toe disease in turnips and swedes would lead one to suspect a shortage of lime and this should be confirmed by actual analysis. The best time to apply the lime is after ploughing and as long before seeding as possible. So sensitive is barley to acidity in the soil that when a crop is seen to be yellowing and "going off" due to this cause, the crop can frequently be saved by the immediate application of from 10 cwt. to 1 ton of ground limestone per acre.

Sowing the Seed

In order to obtain a good malting sample it is essential for the crop to ripen evenly, and for this to happen it is obvious that the seeds must all be sown at the same depth to ensure that they get away together. Thus barley is always drilled and, provided a good seed bed has been prepared, the earlier this can take place the better. Drilling commences in February in the South and extends into March and April in the North. In a late season satisfactory crops can be obtained from seed put in as late as May. Winter varieties are sown from October onwards.

The rate of seeding varies from 1½ cwt. per acre in England to 2 cwt. per acre in Scotland, the drill rows being 6 inches apart or even narrower than this on the lighter soils. After drilling the land should be lightly harrowed and rolled.

After Cultivations

The cultivations carried out between seeding and harvest are usually similar to those given to the other cereals. A light harrowing just before the seedlings come through is frequently beneficial, and a further harrowing later on serves to check weed seedlings. If weeds such as charlock are very prevalent control measures may be necessary to eradicate them, and a certain amount of hand-hoeing must be done when docks and thistles are numerous.

HARVESTING

The crop must be dead ripe before it is cut and at this stage the grain is hard and the skin wrinkled. To cut the crop too soon is fatal when the grain is required for malting, for this results in an uneven sample and the maltster is then unable to obtain that uniformity of germination which is so essential to the production of high-class malt. Thus the old saying, "Wait until you think the barley is dead ripe and then wait another week."

Barley is the most difficult of crops to harvest properly and good judgment and skill are essential qualifications. The best criterion as to when to cut is to examine individual heads when the grain has assumed a uniform "whiteness." A good plan is to bite through several ears at this stage. If they are soft the crop is not ready for cutting and should be left until such time as they bite through firm and clean.

Many well-known barley growers contend that "when you think the crop is ripe, take a fortnight's holiday and begin cutting on your return."

When good weather follows cutting the crop is generally ready for carting about a week afterwards. During the time that it is in stook heavy dews and plenty of sunshine mellow the grain.

Care in stacking is important and only uniformly high-quality grain should be put into each stack. Any portion of the crop which was laid or has been damaged together with the rakings should be stacked and threshed separately. Stacks should also be raked down, for exposed heads deteriorate and spoil the sample if mixed with the bulk grain.

As already indicated great care in threshing is also necessary to ensure that the seed is not injured in any way. In this connection it is far better to sacrifice a few single heads on the straw than set the drum too close and risk "skinning" or breaking the grain. Screening must also be efficient, for lack of attention to this detail can convert an excellent sample into an indifferent one. Conversely, an indifferent quality barley can be made to look very much better by thorough screening. It is essential to feed the sheaves regularly and comparatively slowly, and it is far better to insist on getting a first-class sample of grain from the thresher than to aim at a high output per day.

YIELD

The average yield is about 16 cwt. per acre with approximately the same weight of straw. Under good conditions yields of 30 cwt. per acre or more are common.

INSECT PESTS

Gout Fly.—The commonest type of damage occurs two or three weeks before the ear is shot, the maggot burrowing down one side of the ear. This prevents any further growth in length and causes the plant to become swollen and gouty and prevents the ear from maturing. If the crop is at a rather later stage the ear may manage to emerge showing obvious signs of injury—the grains down one side are eaten—and the development of the uninjured grains is poor. In cases where the crop is very backward the plants are dwarfed and swollen and fail to produce ears.

The maggot pupates in the ear or its surrounding leaves and the mature fly emerges from July onwards. Since young barley is not then available it proceeds to lay eggs on couch grass or early sown winter wheat. The maggots which later hatch out feed on the couch or wheat during the winter and finally produce flies the following spring, and these proceed to attack the barley.

Control Measures.—When the crop is suffering from an attack a top-dressing of nitrogenous fertiliser will frequently stimulate it sufficiently to grow away from the pest although the yield is likely to be affected adversely. Early sowing helps the crop to shoot ear early in the season and at this stage the plant is out of danger. A generous application of phosphates to the seed bed which encourages early maturity is very beneficial.

DISEASES

Leaf Stripe.—This disease is recognised by long brown stripes on the leaves of affected plants and by the "deaf" ears which frequently accompany them. Although it is not so long since this disease was the despair of barley growers, the general use of organic mercury dusts has resulted in it being of little consequence nowadays.

Control Measures.—Dressing the seed with one of the proprietary mercury seed-dressings gives excellent results.

Smut.—Barley may be attacked by Loose Smut or Covered Smut. In the former, which is not so common, the ear is entirely destroyed, becoming a mass of black spores which are gradually blown away. In Covered Smut, on the other hand, the ears of grain are outwardly quite normal but contain a mass of black spores enclosed by thin adherent chaff. When the crop is threshed the diseased grains burst and the spores are liberated to contaminate the healthy seed.

Control Measures.—Loose Smut can be controlled only by using seed saved from a crop free from disease.

Covered Smut is controlled by dressing the seed with an organic mercuric powder.

OATS

The oat is the most versatile of our cereal crops and is grown in every district and under widely differing conditions of soil and climate. Ideally, it grows best in cool, moist districts, and for this reason preponderates over other cereals in the North and West of England, in Wales, Scotland and Ireland. Hot, forcy weather, especially in May before the crop has got well established, is very harmful and frequently results in failures in the south-eastern counties. In districts of high rainfall the yield of straw is very high and of good feeding quality, whilst in districts with a below-average rainfall the quality of the grain is good but the straw suffers in both quality and quantity.

There is no doubt that with oats much depends upon getting early establishment and, good weather in February and March permitting, early sowing is a good foundation for a successful crop.

The crop grows satisfactorily on all classes of soil and, unlike wheat and barley, it can tolerate a considerable degree of sourness due to shortage of lime in the soil. Moisture, however, is all-important, and a clay loam which does not suffer from lack of moisture at the foot is undoubtedly the ideal type of soil. For instance, in fen districts excellent oat crops are grown in spite of the low rainfall, the reason being the abundant supply of subsoil moisture due to the high water-table in these regions. The presence of organic matter in the soil is an added advantage for oats, and for this reason the crop does well on peaty soils and freshly broken turf.

VARIETIES

The oat crop fulfils a dual purpose in that not only is the grain of high feeding value for humans and animals alike, but the straw is also of high feeding value and can replace hay in the winter feeding of stock. High quality grain has a thin husk and a high bushel weight; it is plump and well filled, and the colour is bright, indicating that no heating has taken place in the stack. Nor should there be any smell of mustiness, sprouted or shelled grains. Good feeding straw is fine and grass-like. No one variety combines all the characteristics of high quality grain and excellent feeding straw; in fact, these qualities are largely antagonistic.

The field of choice amongst oats is wide, and it is only possible here to indicate briefly the relative value of the more important varieties which are tabulated on page 66.

PLACE IN ROTATION

In northern and western districts oats generally follow ley, whilst in the South they are frequently taken after roots. In the drier arable districts the crop frequently follows wheat in a five-course rotation of roots, barley, seeds, wheat, oats. The present tendency, however, is to follow even a one-year's ley with spring-sown oats, for this permits the aftermath to be grazed up to ploughing time in January or February. The oat is probably the best crop to take on land ploughed up from permanent grass, except on the heavier classes of land, as the spring sowing allows plenty of time for consolidation and mellowing of the furrows, and the indifference of the crop to a moderate shortage of lime is an added advantage.

PREPARATION OF SEED BED

Yield in oats is very dependent upon early sowing and an adequate supply of moisture. Where winter oats are grown the cultivation of the land follows the lines already discussed for wheat, but for spring oats—which are more commonly grown—every endeavour should be made to get the land ploughed before Christmas. This is especially the case on old pasture and heavy land, for unless in these instances adequate time is allowed for the furrow slices to become well weathered, good seed beds are difficult to obtain. In districts of high spring rainfall, ploughing may be deferred until March, but if the land can be ploughed early in the new year so much the better.

OAT VARIETIES

NAME	GRAIN		STRAW		COMMENTS
	Colour	Yield	Length	Strength	
Spring Oats					
Victory .	White	Very good	Medium	Average	Widely grown ; very reliable : good quality.
Eagle . .	White	Very good	Medium	Good	Slightly resistant to Frit Fly ; slightly better yields than Victory. Where Victory has done well, Eagle deserves a trial.
Star . .	White	Very good	Medium	Good	Excellent general purpose variety ; similar to Victory, but husk is thinner, straw is stiffer.
Crown } King }	Similar	in value to	Star.		
Resistance .	White	Very good	Short	Very good	Resistant to lodging on very fertile soils. Sow in February if possible. Grain rather small.
Onward .	White	Excellent	Medium	Good	One of the most profitable oats to grow. Short, plump grain, thin in the husk, but with a good market value.
Early Miller	White	Excellent	Medium	Very good	Early ripening and very resistant to lodging. Good variety for late districts.
Ayr Bounty .	White	Excellent	Medium	Excellent	Short, plump grain, high bushel weight, early.
Marvellous .	White	Excellent	Medium	Excellent	Grain and straw rather coarse ; should be sown before mid-February.
Black Tartar	Black	Good	Medium	Good	Poor tillering variety and requires heavy seeding. Does well on poor high-lying ground.
Aberystwyth S. 84	White	Very good	Medium	Excellent	Ripens medium late, gives high yields on fertile soils and in districts of good late summer rainfall.
Potato .	White	Good	Long	Average	Grain high milling quality, straw abundant and of good feeding quality. Suited to districts of high rainfall.
Winter Oats					
Grey Winter	Grey	Average	Long	Weak	Hardiest winter variety. Grain and straw good feeding quality.
Unique .	White	Average	Medium	Weak	Exceptional tillering capacity. Sow two-thirds normal rate.
Black Winter	Black	Average	Medium	Weak	Not so hardy as Grey Winter and quality not so good.
	If used as	a winter oat	should be s	own before	end of October.
Bountiful .	Black	Good	Medium	Good	Not definitely winter hardy. Resists lodging better than Grey or Black Winters.
Aberystwyth S. 147	White	Very good	Medium	Very good	Winter hardy, highly resistant to lodging, ripens fairly early.
Aberystwyth S. 81	White	Superior to Grey Winter	Medium	Very good	Resistant to lodging, ripens medium late, winter hardy.
Aberystwyth S. 172	White	Very good	Very short	Very stiff	Winter hardy, suitable for very fertile soils, can be sown early in spring.
Picton . .	White	Very good	Medium	Very good	Winter hardy, resistant to lodging, early ripening.

An exception to the general recommendation to plough early must be made in the case of grassland known to have a fairly high wireworm population. Under these circumstances ploughing just before the seed is sown frequently gives good results, for the wireworms live in the old turf which enables the crop to become established. Early ploughing, on the other hand, would, by allowing time for the turf to decompose, deprive the pest of its natural food and it would therefore turn to the oat crop. Even so, a good tilth is most important, and on heavy land early ploughing may still be justified in order to ensure a good seed bed.

In arable areas the land is worked down in February or March, when soil and weather conditions are favourable, the aim being to get a moderately fine but fairly deep tilth. The seed is then drilled, harrowed in and rolled.

Following seeds or permanent grass oats are frequently broadcast by hand or machine on the furrow slice and merely harrowed in. In this instance it is important to use disc and skim coulters to bury the old vegetation and to plough to a depth of not less than five to six inches. Success on ploughed-out turf depends to a great extent upon getting a firm seed bed. This can be achieved by the use of a furrow press following the plough, or by pressing down each furrow with the wheel of a suitably weighted farm cart. Repeated rollings, if possible with a Cambridge or rib-roller, are also most helpful in getting the desired degree of firmness.

The best implements for breaking down the furrows without disturbing the buried turf are disc harrows, light straight-toothed harrows and heavy rollers. The importance of good consolidation is shown in the results obtained from trials carried out by Leeds University at various centres in Yorkshire in 1939, given below:—

OATS ON PLOUGHED-OUT GRASSLAND, 1939

Treatment of Land	Average Yield of Oats per Acre
Ploughed and tooth-harrowed	20·4
Ploughed and disc-harrowed	23·2
Ploughed, pressed and tooth-harrowed	22·6
Ploughed, pressed and disc-harrowed	24·2

MANURING

Obviously the manurial requirements of the crop will depend on its place in the rotation and the previous treatment of the land. When oats follow roots that have received dung and artificials, or a ley containing plenty of clover, good results can be obtained without manure. Under such conditions of high fertility the danger is more likely to be that the crop becomes badly lodged, and whenever there is a possibility of this it is advantageous to apply 3 cwt. per acre superphosphate prior to drilling, with the object of strengthening the straw and hastening ripening. On light soils 1 cwt. per acre potash salts in addition is also helpful.

When taken as a second straw crop a complete dressing of artificials should be given and the following will be found suitable :—

Sulphate of Ammonia	.	½ to 1 cwt. per acre.
Superphosphate	. .	3 ,, ,,
Muriate of Potash	. .	1 ,, ,,
		5 ,, ,,

The crucial problem in growing good oat crops is to get the young plant over the "speening" or "weaning" stage as rapidly as possible. At this time growth is somewhat laboured and the plants are very susceptible to many diseases and insect pests. Nothing will help them over this difficult period so much as having some quickly available plant food at hand.

Recent work at Rothamsted indicates that a top-dressing of a nitrogenous fertiliser, say 1 cwt. per acre sulphate of ammonia, is a sound proposition. As with wheat, it should be applied late in the season, when heavier yields of grain will be obtained, without unduly promoting the growth of straw which merely increases the danger to lodging. Following a wet winter it is always a good plan to give autumn-sown oats a top-dressing of nitrogen in March.

SOWING THE SEED

The only time to sow oats is when the land is ready and the weather favourable, for the crop suffers badly if the seed bed is unsatisfactory.

In the case of winter oats sowing should be completed by mid-

November, and every possible effort made to get the crop in during October. To sow after mid-November in most seasons is a desperate gamble, and experience is overwhelmingly in favour of waiting until February or early March if seeding is not completed in good time. By sowing winter oats in January or February one often gets better yields and improved quality of grain, and in point of fact, on Down arable land, it is accepted that a mid-January sowing will produce the finest samples. One point must be borne in mind in this connection, namely, that the seed from a crop sown late in this way should not be used for autumn sowing another time round, for some of its vigour will have been lost.

Spring oats are sown in March or early April, and wherever possible it is advantageous to get them in by mid-March at the latest. As soon as Candlemas is past, however, any favourable opportunity for seeding should be taken, for it is far better to risk some slight frost damage than miss getting the seed in on a good seed bed.

The rate of seeding will depend upon the size of seed, its tillering capacity, and whether it is to be broadcast or drilled. Varieties vary considerably in size and yet few farmers adjust the seed drill accordingly. The usual rate of drilling is from $1\frac{1}{2}$ to 2 cwt. per acre, but with some of the large grained varieties such as Marvellous, as much as $2\frac{1}{2}$ cwt. per acre can be justified. On ploughed-out grassland it is necessary to sow about 30 per cent. greater weight of seed than would be used under normal conditions. This allows a good margin for loss of plants through wireworm attack and other troubles peculiar to cereal growing on old turf. When the seed is broadcast, from 3 to 4 stones more per acre is usually required, and with home-grown seed it is important to make sure that it is of high germinating capacity, for a bad harvest or heating in the stack means poor and feeble germination and disappointing results.

All seed oats must be treated with one of the mercurial seed dressings. While most farmers dress their seed wheat with unfailing regularity, it is not generally appreciated how vital is the necessity for dressing seed oats. As will be seen later when discussing the diseases to which the plant is subject, this single precaution can influence the final result enormously.

When broadcast the seed is covered over by a number of

harrowings, the first harrowing always being in the direction of the furrows. Where the crop is drilled, however, the seed should be sown at a depth of from 1 to 2 inches. Drilling in rows 6 inches apart has given better results than wider spacings, and when the rate of seeding exceeds 15 stones per acre the seed should be halved and drilled at twice, the second operation crossing the first. This, incidentally, is an excellent precautionary measure to adopt when wireworm attack is anticipated.

AFTER CULTIVATIONS

Little attention is required after drilling till the crop is ready for harvesting. Rolling, either immediately after seeding or when the plants are a few inches high, may be beneficial especially after ley or old permanent grass. It is much easier to injure oats by working among them than is the case with wheat or barley, and unless the surface has caked or the land is foul with small annual weeds, harrowing should be omitted. Should the crop have been drilled with a steerage-drill then inter-row cultivation can be carried out. The eradication of charlock and other pernicious weeds is best tackled by spraying, and this problem is dealt with in Chapter One. Winter-sown oats can be harrowed in the same manner as wheat.

HARVESTING

The best time to cut oats for general purposes is about a week before the crop is absolutely ripe. If allowed to become dead ripe considerable loss may result through shedding, whereas if the crop is cut too green the development of the grain is retarded and as a result is inferior both in quality and quantity. On some farms, of course, a high value is placed on the straw for feeding purposes, and when this is the case the grain may be sacrificed for the sake of the straw, the crop being cut when it is just turning yellow.

As a rule oats tend to ripen the grain before the straw, and in consequence the crop has to stand longer in stook than is necessary with the other cereals. Seldom is it possible to commence leading in less than a fortnight, and when a start is made it is essential to make sure that the sheaves are thoroughly dry. In wet districts it is usual to "hood" the stooks to keep off the rain and this is done by inverting a sheaf over the top of the stook. Even the lightest of showers is sufficient to stop carting, and in most districts it is common to cart wheat first thing in the morning and last thing at night and reserve the middle part of the day for the oats.

The stacks are frequently built on the small side, and when the crop is not absolutely fit at carting—invariably the case in many of the northern and wetter districts—risk of heating and moulding in the stack is minimised by arranging for some through ventilation. The stacks may be built round wooden tripods, or sheep hurdles arranged to form a triangular ventilating space, or it may even be necessary to pack the sheaves on drying racks of wire and timber built under cover where they can be left to dry out before stacking. Should the season be so unfavourable that the crop has to be carted in a dangerous condition, a sprinkling of common salt over each row of sheaves as they are stacked minimises the danger of fermentation and heating.

YIELD

The average yield of oats is 15 cwt. per acre, but on land of medium quality 20 cwt. per acre can be expected in most seasons. Crops of 35 cwt. and upwards are not uncommon on good land and in good seasons. The weight of straw obtained with the grain-producing varieties is generally about one and a half times that of the grain.

INSECT PESTS

Frit Fly.—Frit Fly is one of the most destructive agricultural pests we have, and a conservative estimate of the annual toll it takes of our oat crops places the loss in yield at 20 per cent.

The small black flies lay their eggs during May on young spring oats and the white maggots, on hatching out, feed in the base of the young shoot, causing it to turn yellow and die. New tillers are produced, but even these will be eaten in a severe attack, in which case the whole plant dies or becomes like a tuft of grass. The maggots turn into brown chrysalides in June, and in July the adult flies emerge. These lay their eggs on the young "bells" in the ear and the maggot feeds on the developing kernel. Thus the grain will be either shrivelled or completely destroyed by harvest. This is one of the causes of the "deaf" or "blind" bells frequently seen on an oat plant at harvest-time. From the oat grains a third brood of flies emerge which lay their eggs on grasses, especially the rye grasses. Here the maggots feed during autumn and winter. Obviously, grasses can withstand such an attack much better than the oats and little material damage results.

Control Measures.—Once the oat plant has passed the four-leaf stage it is not again susceptible until in "ear." Thus, winter oats or early sown and well-established spring oats will not suffer seriously from the first brood of flies. Rapid growth is also very essential, and in this connection the importance of getting a good seed bed, combined with judicious manuring, as a means of encouraging rapid establishment of the young plant must be emphasised. There is evidence that the variety "Eagle" has some resistance to Frit Fly attack, and the production of resistant varieties seems to offer the greatest chance of success in controlling the pest. A recent introduction, "Sandford," is reputed to combine resistance with good standing and yielding properties.

Stem Eelworm.—The condition in oats known as "Segging," or "Tulip-root," though common is not nearly so prevalent as Frit Fly. The first obvious signs of trouble in oats is a swelling of the base of the plant which, when in the seedling stage, may be a darker colour. Later the leaves may be yellowish and they become thick, stiff and sedge-like, and it is from this condition that the term "segging" has arisen. Affected plants are stunted in growth, the side shoots are twisted, and ripening is delayed. Many plants succumb and patchy crops result.

Control Measures.—Slight attacks can be minimised by encouraging vigorous growth with a top-dressing of nitrogenous fertiliser. Over-cropping with oats must be avoided, and since the oat strain of eelworm also attacks beans, this crop must not be sown. Certain weeds, e.g. cleavers, are attacked, which is another reason why clean farming is so important.

Root Eelworm.—Recent work has shown that a totally different eelworm can cause root injury in young oat plants and that this species is similar to the one which causes "Potato Sickness." The roots of attacked plants are short and very branched. In a severe attack, the plants will die, whilst those which survive are short and thin in the straw and grain production is poor. The tips of the leaves are frequently purplish in colour.

Control Measures.—There are no remedies for an attack, but by taking precautions such as avoiding continuous cereal cropping on infested land, increasing the seed rate and lengthening the rotation, the danger of serious injury can be lessened. The sowing of winter instead of spring varieties is also an advantage, for, sown in autumn, the plants are in a more advanced stage by the time the eelworm attack develops, and will, therefore, be better able to withstand it.

When a field is known to be highly infested it may be desirable to sow it down for a number of years and thus give it a complete rest from cereal crops.

Other Pests.—Leatherjackets, wireworms and slugs can also cause serious damage to oat crops, the first two being especially liable to occur when old grass is ploughed out. Control measures for these pests are discussed on pages 52-54 in connection with the wheat crop.

DISEASES

Smut.—When plants are attacked by this disease the productive shoots are covered with a mass of black fungus spores as they emerge from their sheaths. These spores are carried by the wind to healthy grain and remain dormant until the seed is sown the following year. Then they become active again, and entering the young plant the fungus finds its way to the ear where a fresh crop of spores is produced. Thus the ear is entirely destroyed and becomes a mass of black spores which, when they are blown away, leave the naked stalks.

Control Measures.—Dressing the seed grain with one of the mercurial powders is the simplest means of control.

Leaf Spot or Stripe.—Up to ten years ago this disease was the bane of farmers in the North of England. Long brown spots can be seen on the leaves of affected plants but the fungus may also kill them outright. The disease is especially troublesome in cold springs when, owing to delayed growth of the germinating seed, the fungus can gain the upper hand. Investigations carried out by the West of Scotland Agricultural College and the University of Leeds have shown that whilst the disease cannot be killed by seed treatment it is so inactivated that the plants grow away from it.

Control Measures.—All seed oats should be dressed with a mercurial seed dressing.

Grey Leaf.—This disease is somewhat troublesome in certain areas, more especially following a dry spring. Grey blotches are produced on the leaves which gradually wither, with the result that few or no ears are formed. With good growing weather, however, the crop will frequently grow away from the disease.

It is now known that this condition in oats is due to a lack of available manganese salts in the soil and may be induced on light land by heavy liming, since this tends to convert the soluble manganese salts into insoluble forms incapable of being utilised by the plant.

Control Measures.—Applications of manganese sulphate to the soil immediately before sowing at rates varying from ½ to 1 cwt. per acre have given good results. The addition of 2 cwt. per acre superphosphate at the same time is helpful and enables the manganese sulphate to be evenly distributed.

An alternative treatment, and one which sometimes does good, is the application of 1 cwt. per acre sulphate of ammonia. Nitrates should never be used on land liable to this disease, since for some unknown reason they aggravate it.

RYE

Rye has always been regarded as the Cinderella of cereal crops in this country, although in recent years it has received some encouragement from the fact that there is an increasing demand for rye "crisp bread." In the reclamation of poor light land, rye can be used to good advantage as a pioneer crop. In this way it is possible to obtain a cash return during the period when the soil is being restored to fertility by the addition of lime and other plant foods.

Rye is essentially a crop for poor land under hot, dry climatic conditions and where more remunerative crops would fail. On the sands and gravels of the Eastern Counties it is the only cereal which can be relied upon to produce a crop, particularly as most of these soils are devoid of lime. This does not imply that rye will not grow under more congenial conditions of soil and climate, and when grown on better-class land, especially if it has received some fertilisers in addition, yields of grain up to 30 cwt. per acre have been obtained. As a general rule, however, the other cereals leave a greater margin of profit than rye on good land.

VARIETIES

Because rye readily cross-fertilises new varieties or selections quickly become crossed and revert to the original type. Thus few varieties are in cultivation.

Winter or Common Rye.—This is the chief variety. It is extremely hardy, well suited for poor land, and ripens early.

Giant Rye produces more grain and straw than the common variety but requires rather better soil conditions. This variety is suitable for soiling purposes and usually ripens a week earlier than common rye.

Star.—This is a Swedish variety with larger grain and stronger straw than common rye. On poor light land it has not proved superior to the native strains, though it might yield better on more fertile soils.

A number of improved strains are being introduced which are shorter in the straw and give a higher yield than the common variety.

PLACE IN ROTATION

As rye is less liable to damage by wireworms than other cereals, it is frequently grown after permanent grass or a long ley. In other cases it follows potatoes or oats. On really poor light land rye frequently follows lupins which are ploughed in as green manure. A rotation of lupins and rye can be followed for several years until such time as the land is in better heart and can carry oats and potatoes. When grown as a catch crop it follows another cereal and is sown in autumn for folding off in spring. A mixture of rye and rape is useful for early grazing by sheep or cattle, and a mixture of rye and vetches makes very good silage provided it is cut before the rye shoots.

PREPARATION OF SEED BED

The crop is not fastidious in its requirements of a seed bed, and the preparation of the land follows similar lines to that required for wheat. Like wheat, rye prefers a firm seed bed. If the crop is taken after ley the land should be ploughed and pressed and the seed broadcast on the furrow and harrowed in. Following another straw crop the seed can be drilled after ploughing and harrowed in, whilst after potatoes the normal procedure is to broadcast the seed and simply plough it in with a shallow furrow 2 to 3 inches deep. In some instances the seed may be merely dragged in with heavy cultivators.

MANURING

Rye seldom receives special manuring, but on all the poorer classes of soil moderate dressings of fertilisers are well repaid by the increased yields obtained. Taken after roots or seeds the crop requires no manuring other than a top-dressing in spring of sulphate of ammonia at the rate of 1 cwt. per acre.

When farmyard manure is available it may be applied to rye with advantage, 10 to 12 tons per acre being ploughed in before seeding in autumn. Especially in cases where attempts are being made to build up fertility, this light dressing of dung is an advantage. As a substitute for dung, lupins are frequently grown, either ploughing these in green, folding with sheep, or harvesting for seed. Even in the latter case some root and leaf residue still remains to add to the humus content of the soil. Failing the use of dung or green manure it is always wise to give a moderate application of a balanced fertiliser, and the following mixture is suggested :—

| Superphosphate | . | . | 2 cwt. per acre. |
| Muriate of Potash | . | . | 1 ,, ,, |

$$\frac{}{3}$$

This should be applied prior to sowing the seed and should be followed up by a nitrogenous top-dressing in February or March, say, 1 cwt. per acre sulphate of ammonia. In place of the superphosphate an application of 3 to 4 cwt. per acre of basic slag can be given, especially if the land is known to be deficient in lime.

Sowing the Seed

The seed should be sown as early as possible, certainly two to three weeks before the normal time for sowing autumn wheat in the district. Sown in good time the plant will be well established before frost sets in. On sandy soils the early establishment of the plant is important, for it minimises the risk of the soil "blowing" in the strong winds of spring time. Though the writer prefers early sowing—not later than the second week in October—sowing can take place when soil and weather conditions permit up to about the beginning of March.

The rate of seeding varies from 1 cwt. per acre in early autumn to 1½ cwt. per acre for the later sowings.

After Cultivations

When the crop is sown in early autumn on land in fairly good heart it can be grazed down by sheep in early spring, and then allowed to ripen for grain. This is not advisable on poor land, however, for by grazing off such cover as there might be merely allows drought to burn the soil to the great detriment of the crop. Late grazing in all cases is inadvisable.

Whether the crop is grazed or not it should be harrowed and given a heavy rolling in spring. Little weeding is necessary as a rule as, owing to the earliness of the crop, it tends to keep weeds in check.

Harvesting

Rye is the first of the cereals to ripen and is generally ready for cutting at least a fortnight before wheat. The straw is always dead ripe by the time the grain is fit for cutting, and hence the crop can usually be carted after fielding for about a week. When high quality rye straw is required for thatching or special purposes, it is usual to cut the crop before the ear has filled and not to thresh it, which would, of course, damage the straw.

Yield

The average yield of grain varies from 12 to 16 cwt. per acre, whilst the straw is considerably more—30 cwt. to 2 tons per acre being obtained. In many instances the straw is more valuable than the grain, though not in war-time.

RYE AS A GREEN CROP

Early sown rye provides excellent sheep meat in spring as growth is early, and after the crop has been folded there is ample time to get the land in with roots. For this purpose the seed is sown in August at the rate of 1 cwt. per acre. A mixture of 1 cwt. of Giant Rye and ½ cwt. of vetches per acre is an excellent crop for soiling (cutting green) and has been used extensively at Harper Adams College Farm. This mixture, sown about the third week in September, can be cut the following May whilst, when sown in February, it is ready for use the following June.

Rye is also used to some extent in silage mixtures in which, owing to its earliness, it is useful for supporting the straggling weak-stemmed tares. When used in this way, however, early cutting is essential before the rye becomes tough and fibrous.

In some districts it is a common practice to sow about 2 stones of vetches per acre along with the rye. The mixed crop is then harvested in the normal way and the two classes of seed separated when the crop is threshed. Since vetches usually command a high price and grown in this way are obtained in addition to the normal crop of rye, the practice is decidedly attractive. The vetch straw is, of course, of high feeding value and should be combed out from the rye or the mixed straw thrown to stock to do their own selecting.

MIXED CORN

Mixed corn crops are more certain than straight cereals, are easy to grow, adaptable to a wide range of soil conditions and have the great advantage that they will yield heavy crops of either corn or fodder.

"*Dredge*" *corn* is the term usually applied to a crop which consists of a mixture of cereal grains, barley and oats being most commonly used.

"*Mashlum*" consists of one or more cereals (usually oats) with one or more leguminous crops (usually beans or peas).

The growing of dredge corn has largely been confined to Cornwall and the South-west, where in many cases the whole of the grain was consumed on the farm by cows and pigs. The proportion of oats to barley is generally two of the former to one of the latter, and quite frequently a small proportion of spring wheat is included in the mixture, the total seeding being at the rate of 15 to 16 stone per acre.

It may be asked why dredge corn is sown in preference to single cereals when the former can only be used for feeding purposes and in normal times commands a much lower price. The answer is that by sowing a mixture of cereals one plays for safety. The Frit Fly of oats or the Gout Fly of barley may cause serious damage in certain districts, but by sowing a mixture of oats and barley it is reasonable to expect that one or other will succeed. A further reason is that in some districts owing to soil and climate being unsuitable for the production of first quality grain it is necessary to concentrate on the production of feeding grain, in which case yield per acre is the all-important factor. A mixture of cereals is likely to yield better than a single crop.

The mashlum crop is most popular in the dairying districts of Ayrshire and Lanarkshire where the bean is a speculative crop, but when grown in mixture with oats seldom fails.

The customary rate of seeding per acre is about 14 stone of beans and 9 stone of oats, and since beans require a longer growing season than oats it is usual to plant the beans two or three weeks before the oats and so allow the two components to reach maturity at or about the same time.

On ploughed-out grass "mixed corn" is likely to be grown on a much wider scale, particularly on dairy and stock-rearing farms, for a cereal-legume mixture is a valuable feed for grinding in winter, and used in conjunction with hay and roots will provide a well-balanced diet for milk production. Moreover, these mixtures have the advantage that should summer grazing be scarce they can be cut and fed green in July or August, or they will make good hay if fodder is likely to be scarce, and if the weather is bad can be converted into useful silage. Thus mixed corn can be regarded as a sound insurance to take out and the almost complete absence of risk, combined with the many ways in which the crop can be utilised, should make a wide appeal at a time when great efforts are necessary and risks are dangerous.

Very naturally a crop of this type can be grown over a wide range of climatic conditions. On the stiffer soils beans will form an important part of the mixture, whilst on the lighter classes of soil barley and peas naturally contribute largely to the crop.

VARIETIES

For mashlum crops, Potato and Sandy oats are commonly used with Carse or Kilbride beans. A very common "dredge" mixture includes black Tartarian and white Marvellous oats with some Spratt-Archer barley and a small proportion of April-Bearded wheat. There are few fixed ideas on the problem of varieties, and in most cases the safe rule to follow is to sow only those varieties which have proved their worth under the conditions prevailing on the farm where they are to be grown.

PLACE IN ROTATION

Mixed corn naturally takes the place of either oats or barley in the rotation. For instance, in the seven-course rotation common in Cornwall, of (1) wheat, (2) oats, (3) roots, (4) barley, (5) seeds hay, (6) seeds pasture, (7) seeds pasture, dredge corn replaces oats and barley on soils or under climatic conditions unfavourable to the growing of good straight crops of either oats or barley.

On newly ploughed land where the ravages of wireworms and the possibility of soil poverty are inimicable to the growth of good cereal crops, a "mixed corn" crop is frequently a much safer choice.

PREPARATION OF SEED BED

This will very naturally follow the lines already outlined for cereal crops except that a greater margin of safety exists in that a really good seed bed is not so vitally important. The land should be ploughed in autumn or early winter and allowed to lie until spring. Nothing further need be done until the sowing of the crop, when a good discing or the use of cultivators will prepare the necessary amount of tilth for a seed bed. Good results can be obtained by sowing on the furrow and harrowing in the seed, finishing off with a heavy rolling. Obviously, where this is practised the ploughing must be good to prevent any "puffiness."

MANURING

The manuring naturally depends upon the condition of the soil and its previous treatment. Barley and legumes require a sweet soil, and when these crops are included in the mixture lime must be applied after ploughing, working it into the seed bed, unless the soil is already well supplied.

Where dung is available a light dressing applied in autumn and ploughed in proves very beneficial. In addition an adequate supply of readily available plant food is essential in order to ensure a good crop, and the following suggestions will be found suitable for the majority of cases:—

Fertiliser (Cwt. per Acre)	Condition of Soil		
	Poor	Average	Rich
Sulphate of Ammonia . . .	I	I	
Superphosphate . . .	3	3	3
Muriate of Potash . .	I		
Total . .	5	4	3

The object of the phosphate on land in good heart is to make the crop yield more grain and improve the standing power of the straw.

Basic slag may be used to replace the superphosphate, in which case the quantities recommended should be increased by 50 per cent. It is preferable to apply the slag some few weeks before sowing the seed, and in any case it must on no account be mixed with sulphate of ammonia.

Sowing the Seed

Seeding may take place from March to May, depending upon soil and weather conditions and the type of mixture used. For instance, in a late season a barley-pea mixture may be sown as late as May and still do well. This is particularly useful on land known to have a high wireworm population, for when it is sown late the chances are that by that time the wireworms will have finished the spring feeding period, and the crop is left unharmed.

The following well-tried mixtures will be found useful as a basis on which to compile others adapted to any set of conditions:—

> Barley or Oats . . 10 stone per acre.
> Grey Peas . . . 4 ,, ,,
> ———
> 14 ,, ,,

F

Barley	.	.	.	.	4 stone per acre.
Oats	.	.	.	.	3 ,, ,,
Tick Beans	.	.	.	3 ,, ,,
Vetches	.	.	.	2 ,, ,,
Grey Peas	.	.	.	2 ,, ,,
				14 ,, ,,

In all cases where beans form a large part of the mixture and it is intended to ripen the crop of grain—as, for instance, the mashlum crop of:—

Beans	.	.	.	.	14 stone per acre.
Oats	.	.	.	.	9 ,, ,,
				23 ,, ,,

it is customary, and advisable, to sow the beans two to three weeks before the oats. The beans are then ploughed in with a shallow furrow, the oats being broadcast on top and harrowed in about a fortnight later. The variety S. 84 is very suitable for this purpose.

AFTER CULTIVATIONS

Any crusting of the surface before the crop is well through should be broken by light harrowing, but this should only be done when the surface is dry. A light rolling is beneficial in most seasons and particularly on the lighter types of soil.

As a rule the only treatment which follows during the summer is the spudding of thistles or the hand-pulling of docks. The smothering effect of the crop is relied upon for weed eradication or suppression.

HARVESTING

No hard-and-fast rules can be laid down as to the best time to cut, for much depends upon the season and the type of mixture sown. In the case of a simple oat-legume mixture the crop may be cut when the oats are ripe and the beans in the pods are black at the point where they are attached to the pods, or when the peas are brown and dry but before the pods start to split. It is a mistake to defer cutting too long in the hope that the pods will be better filled, for shedding may sacrifice a good deal of the crop. Although too early cutting is also inadvisable this is preferable to cutting too late, because in the former case although a lower yield of grain must be expected the feeding quality of the straw is considerably higher.

YIELD

A good crop yields 18 to 24 cwt. of mixed grain and 25 to 30 cwt. of straw.

PESTS AND DISEASES

The pests and diseases attacking this mixed crop are the same as those common to individual crops. When two or more crops are sown together it is unlikely that they will all be attacked in the same season. Hence the margin of safety is such that one can anticipate with a reasonable degree of assurance that an average yield of crop will be obtained. Pests or diseases may, however, affect the relative proportions of the ingredients obtained at harvest.

BEANS

The bean crop has a twofold value in farming, for being a leguminous plant it enriches the soil in nitrogen and at the same time it forms the most valuable source of protein that we have. Until war broke out much of the land formerly devoted to beans was under grass owing to the high cost of working heavy clay, but now that the need for replacing imported protein-rich cakes has arisen the crop is likely to be grown on an ever-increasing scale.

Beans grow satisfactorily under a fairly wide variety of climatic conditions, but they do best in mild sunny districts where the annual rainfall is not high. It is not wise to sow them on land more than about 600 feet above sea-level nor in districts where the rainfall is heavy and seasons are late. Severe frost may seriously damage autumn-sown beans unless they are covered with snow, but they do so much better than spring-sown varieties that the risk is often justified.

As a crop beans are noted for their suitability to heavy land conditions, though they will grow satisfactorily on most types of soil excepting those which are light and sandy. They do best, however, on medium to heavy loams provided these soils are adequately drained and well supplied with lime, for like most legumes, beans will not grow in sour, acid soils which are short of lime.

VARIETIES

Beans are divided into two main classes, winter beans and spring beans. In the South the "winter bean" which is fairly hardy, with a good tillering capacity, is grown extensively, whilst in the North it is more common to grow the "spring bean" which resembles the winter bean except that it does not tiller so well, ripens two to three weeks later, and is more likely to be damaged by black fly or aphis. There is some evidence that the frost resistance of winter beans is connected with the depth and earliness of sowing, and a good deal of research work remains to be done on these points. Trials in Yorkshire point to the fact that when sown early the seed should be at least 4 inches below the surface. November sowings may need to be no more than 2 to 3 inches deep, whilst in the spring 2 inches would appear to be ample.

Other spring varieties are:—

Scotch Horse, Kilbride, or Carse bean : hardy and commonly grown in Scotland and the North of England.

Tick or English Horse bean: grown to a considerable extent in the Eastern Counties. It has a large number of pods and crops well.

Heligoland bean: is hardy and early, well suited for late districts and crops well.

Mazagan bean: large, flat, white-seeded bean which seldom grows more than 2 feet in height.

Plant breeders, notably at the National Institute of Agricultural Botany, are devoting considerable attention to beans, and new and improved varieties are likely to be available soon. Better podding varieties are urgently needed and more uniformity of type. In addition, if varieties resistant to Chocolate Spot disease can be evolved, greater interest will be taken in the cultivation of this crop.

PLACE IN ROTATION

In the normal four-course rotation of roots, barley, seeds, wheat, beans will replace part of the area under clover. This is especially useful on land subject to the diseases of these crops, for it enables an eight-year interval to elapse between the growing of either clover or beans on the same ground. The crop may, however, be grown between two corn crops and then it is sown in rows to permit of cleaning operations. Beans are probably more resistant to wireworm and leatherjacket attacks than any other farm crop, and hence do well on freshly broken grassland. Many cases have been recorded in the last two years of exceptionally good crops following ploughed-up permanent grassland in which the wireworm population was known to be considerably higher than was considered safe for cereals.

PREPARATION OF SEED BED

There are three methods of sowing beans which are in common usage:—

1. Drilling with a cup-feed drill;
2. Drilling on ridged land with a 3-row drill;
3. Ploughing in;

and the cultivation varies with the method adopted.

In general practice it is usual to plough beans in if sown in autumn but to drill them when a spring variety is used.

1. *Drilling.*—If the stubble is filthy it should be worked to kill the wicks which are then collected and burnt. Weed seeds also germinate and are killed at the same time. When dung is to be given it should be spread on the surface after cleaning and the land ploughed to a depth of 6 or 7 inches. Heavy land especially should be ploughed early and left in the furrow over winter to become well weathered. Prior to drilling in spring the artificial manures should be applied, the soil cultivated and harrowed to give the necessary amount of tilth, and the crop can then be drilled either with a special bean drill or with a cup-feed corn drill in which alternate coulters are stopped up.

2. *Drilling on Ridge.*—The land is ploughed in autumn and left to weather over winter. In early spring a tilth is prepared by cultivating and the soil is drawn up into 26 to 27-inch drills by means of a double mould-board plough. Dung is then spread in the bottom of the drills, and the seed dropped on top with a special three-row bean drill or by hand-sowing. The ridges are then split to cover the seed, followed by harrowing and rolling before the seedlings come through.

3. *Ploughing in.*—The beans are either broadcast by hand or sown with a drop drill on the surface and then ploughed in. They may, however, be sown in every second or third furrow

by means of a small drill fixed on the plough. They are usually placed 3 to 4 inches deep, and the advantage of sowing in the furrow is that the beans are in rows and weeds can, therefore, be controlled by horse-hoeing during spring and early summer. The method of ploughing in avoids the risk of being held up with drilling on heavy land in wet weather, and further, the beans are well covered and out of the way of birds.

In the West of Scotland beans are often broadcast on the furrow in February and harrowed in. About three weeks later, a late variety of oats is broadcast and harrowed in. The interval between sowing the two crops enables them to ripen for cutting at the same time, and the beans are separated by screening when the crop is threshed out.

Manuring

It is generally considered by farmers that dung is essential for good crops of beans and experimental results confirm this view. The dung should be applied on top of the land and ploughed in unless the crop is sown on the ridge. As already mentioned, soils must not be sour but must contain a reserve of lime. The best procedure is to apply the lime after ploughing so that it can be worked into the surface soil. Phosphates are also necessary, and the crop appears to respond particularly well to applications of basic slag. In the absence of farmyard manure, potash manures are beneficial.

The following dressings are recommended:—

> Superphosphate . . 4 cwt. per acre⎫ applied after
> or ⎬
> Basic Slag (high grade) . 5 cwt. per acre⎭ ploughing.

If dung is not available muriate of potash at 1 cwt. per acre should be added to the above phosphatic dressings and applied at the same time.

Sowing the Seed

Winter beans should be sown early and whenever possible sowing should be completed by the middle of October. Sowing before October often means that the crop becomes too forward for winter conditions and will then be more subject to frost damage, whereas if sown late in November the seedlings may be caught by an early frost as they come through.

Whenever, therefore, sowing is delayed beyond the end of October it is much safer to wait and put in a spring variety. In the case of spring beans, sowing should take place on the first favourable opportunity in February. If they are late sown in, say March or even April, they may be a complete failure due to attack of black fly, although if the season is wet and favourable for growth late sowings may sometimes do quite well. The usual rate of sowing is $1\frac{1}{2}$ cwt. per acre, when sown in autumn, and $1\frac{3}{4}$ cwt. for spring-sown varieties.

AFTER CULTIVATIONS

It is better not to reduce the surface to too fine a tilth in autumn, for this may cause the land to "cap" or cake badly, which is difficult to break in spring. Quite frequently when beans are ploughed in the land is left unharrowed, the roughness of the ground apparently being of no detriment to the crop. In point of fact some cloddiness is an advantage in that it shelters the young plants from keen, cold winds, and the clods break down to give a nice mould in spring.

As soon as soil conditions permit in spring the land should be harrowed, and a week or two afterwards the beans can be horse-hoed for the first time. This should be continued throughout the season as often as practicable. Occasionally hand-hoeing is resorted to when horse-hoeing is no longer possible, but owing to the high cost of labour this is not common.

HARVESTING

Beans are usually one of the first crops to ripen. The crop should be cut before it is dead ripe, for if allowed to become really mature considerable loss from shedding results, especially if the ground is hard and rough and the binder liable to bump a lot. Time of cutting also influences the feeding value of the straw, and if the crop is left until it is dead ripe the straw will be fibrous and unpalatable, whereas when cut on the green side it may be little inferior to good hay. A safe rule to follow is to cut when the eye or point of attachment of the bean to the pod is black but before the leaves and stem have turned completely black. The binder should be set low in order not to miss the pods near the ground, and it is advisable to use an old knife and canvases, for these are likely to undergo hard wear.

Once stooked, the crop will take little harm from showers, but it should not be carted until the sheaves are thoroughly dry. The time necessary for them to reach this condition naturally depends upon prevailing weather conditions and the greenness of the straw when cut. Carting should not commence, however, until the straw in the centre of the sheaves is really dry, for if carted when damp, the beans will mould in the stack. The stack should be thatched or otherwise protected from rain as soon as possible, for, being very open in character, it is easily penetrated by rain. Many farmers carry the thatch down to the ground to protect the large numbers of pods which are invariably exposed on the outside of the stack, and this is a wise precaution.

New beans are not suitable for feeding to stock and the crop is often left unthreshed until spring, for this allows the beans to dry thoroughly and obviates the risk of colic when fed to farm stock.

YIELD

Although the average yield per acre for the country is no more than 16 cwt. per acre, crops of 30 cwt. per acre are not uncommon. On good bean land over a number of years one can expect an average yield of 20 cwt. of grain and 25 cwt. of straw per acre.

The practice of sowing a new beans with a cereal crop is becoming increasingly popular. No reduction in the yield of cereal is experienced as a rule and the beans, which are easily separated at threshing time, are obtained as an additional crop.

INSECT PESTS

Weevils.—As soon as the crop comes through the ground the leaves are notched by the weevils. This in itself is not serious, but when growth is slow the weevils may gain the upper hand, and should the young terminal shoot be eaten the plant will be of little further use.

Control Measures.—The severity of attack is largely governed by climatic conditions and rate of growth. Under good growing conditions beans are not likely to suffer much from weevils. In a severe attack dusting the crop with lime or slag will act as a deterrent. Horse-hoeing to assist growth is helpful, but the best means of control is to ensure fertile conditions in the soil by wise manuring before sowing takes place.

Black Fly or Aphis.—About June the Black Aphis collects on the top of the young bean shoots. If the weather is hot and dry the insects rapidly multiply, and in the short space of a few weeks the plants become filthy with honey dew and weak from the loss of sap sucked from them by the flies. The whole crop may then be a failure.

A cold spell of weather or heavy rain may reduce the number of "flies" sufficiently to enable the crop to grow away, and hence whether an attack is likely to develop to serious proportions or not is largely a matter of speculation.

Control Measures.—The pest at first is usually confined to one or two small patches in the field. Much can be done to minimise its spread at this stage if the tops of infested plants are pinched out and burnt, or if a nicotine dust is used with a small hand-sprayer. In either case the amount of labour involved is small.

Later, when the attack becomes general, little can be done unless a power sprayer is available and the crop can be dusted with a nicotine powder. Usually winter-sown beans suffer less from black fly than spring beans.

Diseases

Chocolate Spot.—This is the most dreaded disease of beans and is due to a fungus belonging to the well-known parasitic genus "Botrytis." There appear to be two more or less distinct types according to the severity of the outbreak or to the age of the crop when the disease appears. In the less serious and most characteristic stage the leaves and shoots become covered with chocolate-brown spots, and affected plants though not killed are retarded in growth and the yield is greatly reduced. In its worst form, the stems and leaves of the plants turn black and the crop is practically killed.

Control Measures.—Absolute control of the disease is not yet possible. Attacks occur generally on soils lacking in phosphates, lime or potash. An application of potash to the crop appears to make the plant so resistant to the disease that it can withstand the second stage of the attack although the chocolate spots may be present.

PEAS

Peas can be grown with several purposes in view. The ripe grain may be harvested and threshed for stock feeding or for packeting for use in winter as a table vegetable, or the crop is picked green for use as a fresh vegetable. Whatever the purpose for which it is grown the crop is of great importance in war-time. As a source of protein it is extremely valuable for blending with starchy foods like oats in the preparation of balanced rations for meat or milk production, whilst as a table vegetable it can play a large part in war-time human dietary. It is becoming increasingly common to grow peas in conjunction with a cereal crop, by which means one can get a balanced ration direct instead of growing separate crops to be mixed when required. When harvested for grain the straw, after threshing, forms good fodder for all classes of stock.

The methods of cultivation are much the same in all cases, the varieties grown determining the purpose to which the crop is likely to be put.

Open, well-drained soils adequately supplied with lime are ideal for peas, and whilst the lighter loams are generally regarded as best the crop grows well on heavier loams provided the soil is well drained and the district one of low rainfall.

A sufficient supply of lime is vital and where any doubt exists as to the lime content of a soil, as indicated by the presence of such weeds as spurrey or louse grass, and sour-dock or sorrel, it is advisable either to apply lime and make sure, or have the soil tested. The crop is also very susceptible to weather conditions and once well established prefers a reasonably dry season. Excessive moisture results in the production of too much haulm or straw, delays ripening, and low yields of grain are obtained. On heavy soils in a wet year the crop may turn yellow and be a complete failure; on the other hand, hot dry weather favours insect attacks and the yield will then suffer accordingly. Thus, on the whole, the ideal season can be regarded as one of moderate temperature and rainfall and with no extremes of heat or cold.

VARIETIES

For Stock Feeding :

Grey or Dun Peas.—Within this group there is considerable variation as to length of straw, size of pod, earliness, and so on. The Warwick or Early Warwick, the Minter or Early Minter, and the Norfolk Dun are names frequently applied to varieties within this group. In general they are early in ripening with an average length of straw, and in the majority of seasons it is possible to harvest them and get the land ploughed before the wheat is ready for cutting. The grain is a pure dun colour and the flower purple.

Maple Peas.—This variety is characterised by the speckled or blotched markings of the seed, the grain being light brown and the blotches whitish yellow. The flower is purple. It is a long-strawed pea with numerous rather small pods which ripen late. In a wet season maples are apt to grow too much straw and too little corn, and the class is best suited to dry conditions. The peas find a ready demand for pigeon food and hence usually command a higher price than the other groups.

Partridge Peas.—The earliest ripening varieties of Maple peas generally go under this name.

Black-eyed Susan, Sweet Jessie or Jessie's.—This variety is common to the Eastern Counties, where it is regarded as a heavy cropper well suited to the lighter and poorer classes of soil. It is a mid-season variety with long straw and grain varying in colour from dun to brick-red with a black eye.

Prussian Blue, Small Blue, Lincoln or Louth Blue.—This is a small-grained, blue-green pea which bears numerous small pods on long slender straw. The flowers are white and the variety is easy to grow and harvest and gives as good yields as the larger grained purple-flowered varieties. It is commonly grown in the Louth district of Lincolnshire.

For Packing :

Harrison's Glory, Large Blue, Marrowfat, Koopman's Glory (selection from Harrison's Glory).—This is a large blue-green pea, fairly robust and a good cropper. It is a comparatively dwarf variety with white flowers, and when garden peas are scarce may be used for picking green.

Both the Prussian Blue and Harrison's Glory are used for canning, for which purpose they are first dried in the normal way. In a badly selected stock of either variety some purple-flowered varieties may appear. These produce dark-coloured seeds which turn almost black on cooking and this necessitates hand-picking in the factory. Thus, in order to get a good market for the seed it is essential to use a guaranteed stock of seed.

Blue peas are frequently grown on contract, the common procedure being for the merchant to supply the seed and the grower to receive a fixed price according to the excellence of the sample.

For Picking Green.—For picking green there is a wide choice of varieties, and it is not within the scope of this book to give a detailed description of each. The following short list, however, includes the most popular and well-tried ones.

Varieties are classified into three main groups: "early," "second early and main crop," "late main crop and late," according to their normal season of cropping.

Name	Height (feet)	Length of Pod (inches)	Number of Peas in Pod	Cropping Capacity
Early				
British Lion . .	3-4	3-4	5-7	Good.
Thomas Laxton .	3	2½-3½	6-8	Good—favourite variety.
Superb . . .	2½-3	3½-4	8-10	Very good.
2nd Early and Main Crop				
Stratagem . .	2½-3	4-4½	7-9	Good.
Onward . .	2½	3½-4½	6-8	Good — strong haulm.
Lincoln . . .	2½	3-4	6-7	Very good.
Alderman . .	5-6	4-4½	8-10	Good.
Standard and Prince Edward are strains of Alderman.				
Late Main Crop and Late				
The Gladstone .	4-5	4½-5	7-9	Good.
Autocrat . .	4	4	7	Very good—one of best late peas —resistant to mildew.

As time goes on new varieties are introduced and old ones are dropped, but it is never wise to grow a large acreage of a new variety until it has been tried on a small scale for a number of years under the special conditions of individual farms.

In selecting any variety the following points should be taken into consideration. Dark pods retain their fresh appearance and are preferred in the market, whilst pickers very naturally favour large-podded varieties. The flavour is of importance and must be sweet with no trace of mealiness, whilst a good market variety should yield 30 per cent. or more of saleable peas. Ease of shelling is also a market point of some importance, and pods with depressed sutures are difficult to shell and are not favoured. Finally, any variety, and particularly a late one, should be resistant to mildew.

Place in Rotation

On most farms peas follow a cereal crop. Being a soil improver the crop frequently alternates with beans or clover in a four-course rotation and this has the advantage of extending the period of rest between like crops, for peas, beans and clover often do not succeed well when grown too frequently on the same land. Peas do quite well after other crops such as roots and potatoes, for weeds are then less likely to be troublesome. It is necessary, however, to avoid fat land or there is a danger that the crop will run to straw and will not pod well. The crop may follow cabbages or similar vegetables where market gardening is practised, and in the Cambridgeshire fens the rotation followed is celery, potatoes, wheat, peas.

The crop does well on ploughed-up grassland as it is practically immune from attack by wireworms. It has been a common experience, for instance, since the war, that a mixed crop of oats and peas on ploughed-out grassland frequently results in a good average crop of peas with practically no oats present since these are taken by wireworms.

Preparation of Seed Bed

The crop is regarded as one of the worst land-foulers we have, and hence every effort should be made to sow it on clean land. Peas thrive best on a stale furrow which has been worked down to a fine surface mould, and therefore it is important to get the land ploughed before Christmas.

Directly the soil is dry enough in January or February it should be dragged and harrowed to a fine tilthy condition. As the seed is large it can be sown in a tilth that would be considered too cloddy for spring cereals, and in point of fact it is better to have the seed bed too cloddy than too fine, for care must be taken to keep the surface from crusting over.

MANURING

It is seldom that farmyard manure is applied direct to the crop, most growers contending that direct application leaves the soil too loose and puffy for peas. Moreover, there is the danger that over-generous use of dung may encourage an undue proportion of straw and delay ripening.

On land in average condition good results can be obtained from an application of phosphates, whilst on light soils potash may well be given in addition. As already mentioned peas have a rooted objection to acidity, and in all cases where there is a shortage of lime this must be rectified.

For average soils and conditions 4 cwt. per acre super-phosphate applied to the seed bed or 6 to 8 cwt. basic slag applied during the winter will be found of great benefit. On light loams 3 cwt. of superphosphate and 1 cwt. of muriate of potash will provide a suitable dressing.

Nitrogenous fertilisers must at all times be used sparingly, for there is a danger that growth of haulm will be excessive and that maturity will be delayed. When, however, a plant is weak and does not appear to progress as it should, or when the soil is known to be rather poor, the application of 1 cwt. per acre of sulphate of ammonia or nitro-chalk as a side dressing is of real benefit to the crop.

SOWING THE SEED

Early sowing is desirable, and in favourable districts and seasons drilling can take place in January or February. In backward seasons, especially on the heavier classes of land, drilling may not be possible, however, until March or even April. It is always well to remember in this connection that sowing late on a good seed bed is to be preferred to an early start when soil conditions are unfavourable. The advantage of early sowing is that when the crop is well established it is better able to withstand insect attack in May and June. On this account in recent years, November sowing has been frequently practised in East Anglia with good results, for although an autumn-sown crop is more susceptible to risk of frost damage this is more than counter-balanced by its resistance to insect attack. Thus, whilst January and February sowings are common in the earlier districts of the East, sowing in March and April is usual in the North and Midlands.

The actual quantity of seed used varies with the district and the variety of pea, the range of seed rate being from $1\frac{1}{2}$ to $2\frac{1}{4}$ cwt. per acre, with an average of about $1\frac{3}{4}$ cwt. The seed is almost invariably drilled in rows 9 to 12 inches apart and about $2\frac{1}{2}$ inches deep. It should be dusted with an organic mercurial seed dressing. After drilling, or when the plants are about an inch or so high, the land is rolled with an ordinary flat roller, especially when it is inclined to be puffy.

AFTER CULTIVATIONS

A few light harrowings may be given when the soil is dry to check the development of weeds, and inter-row cultivations will continue as long as it is possible to do so without risk of damaging the crop. Occasionally one or more hand-hoeings may be given, but this is soon prevented by the plants straggling across the rows.

HARVESTING

To avoid confusion it may be helpful to deal with the harvesting operations for corn and for green peas separately, as these differ in essential details.

For Corn.—Careful harvesting is absolutely essential, for the quality of the crop (and hence the price obtained) depends upon the attention it receives at this stage. Shrivelled peas of poor colour can never command a good price and may, in fact, be unsaleable.

Cutting should begin as soon as the majority of the pods are brown but not sufficiently hard and dry to split open when handled. If the crop is cut too soon the peas shrivel and may be fit only for feeding, whilst if cut when overripe many of the pods split in the field and a lot of the peas are lost.

For small acreages the crop may be cut with a sickle or a scythe or even pulled up, but more commonly the mowing machine is used, pea lifters or guards being attached to the fingers of the cutter bar to lift the haulms off the ground and assist the cutting. A pea-harvesting attachment is used by some growers which consists of thin steel bars attached to the cutter bar of the mowing-machine. This arrangement causes the peas to slide out of the way of the machine on its next round.

About two days after cutting the peas require turning and this is usually done by hand. If good weather prevails the crop is merely turned every second day or so until both straw and corn are dry and the crop fit for carting. Turning is still necessary when the weather is wet, for if the pods are allowed to lie too long on wet ground they split and this results in serious losses by the shedding of the peas. Even and good drying can always be obtained irrespective of weather conditions by placing the crop on tripods as soon as possible after cutting.

Carting must not take place before the crop is fit or moulding in the stack will follow. Threshing can be carried out within a month or so of stacking, care being taken to adjust the concave to avoid splitting the grain.

For Green Peas.—When green peas are to be marketed, gangs of casual workers are employed to strip off the pods and place them in bags or hampers on the basis of a fixed charge per bag or hamper. Occasionally the crop may be sold as it stands ("on the ground") to the merchant who arranges to carry out the picking. The package most commonly used is known as the "half-bag" which holds 40 lb.

A good woman picker will average 8 bags per day, whilst, if the crop is good and a large-podded variety has been grown, 10 bags can be reached. As a general rule pickers pull the haulm as they go and strip off all the pods, and hence great care is necessary in choosing the time at which pulling commences to avoid a large proportion of "flat pods" in the crop, which would, of course, reduce the value of the sample and the price paid. Pulling when the crop is over-mature and the pods are dis-coloured is equally disastrous from the sale point of view. The haulm is left in the field to be dried or it may be carted fresh for silage.

YIELD

When harvested for corn a good average yield is 17 cwt. per acre with a straw yield of 20 to 25 cwt. When the crop is picked green the yield varies very considerably from season to season, and depends also upon whether the variety is a first early or main crop. The following can be taken as fair average returns :— "first early," 70 bags; "second early," 120 bags; "main crop," 150 bags. A good crop of main crops, however, might run to 250 bags in a favourable season.

INSECT PESTS

Weevils.—The damage to the young plants from weevils is closely akin to that done to beans and is characterised by the notching or scalloping of the leaf edges. A severe attack can destroy the crop.

Control Measures.—A mixture of equal parts of calcium arsenate dust and finely powdered calcium carbonate applied at the rate of 40 lb. per acre when a bad attack is first noticed gives useful control. The dust should preferably be applied when the plants are wet with dew. Calcium arsenate can be used alone at the rate of 20 lb. per acre.

Slugs may attack the seedlings, but good results can be obtained by the use of the poison bait already outlined on page 54.

DISEASES

Peas are subject to a number of diseases, but the best means of keeping them in check is to sow only sound seed from a firm of repute, prepare a good seed bed, and by judicious manuring and sound cultivation induce strong healthy growth in the early part of the season.

In wet, cold springs the seed is prone to rot in the ground before germination takes place. The exact reason for this is not yet known, but it has been established that treatment of the seed prior to sowing with one of the recognised mercurial treatments reduces the risk of losses from this cause very considerably.

G

Chapter Three

FORAGE CROPS

MAIZE

MAIZE is regularly grown in certain districts of England for use as green fodder or for ensilage. Where the crop succeeds it is invaluable in dry summers when pastures are badly burnt and a succulent food is required for cows to keep up their yields. In all districts where summer droughts are experienced a small area of maize should be grown as an insurance against shortage of keep.

Maize is a sun lover and once it is well established can withstand and indeed flourishes during long periods of drought. Unfortunately it is very susceptible to frost, and hence the area in which it can be grown successfully is restricted to the southern and eastern districts of England. Good crops are occasionally obtained as far north as Yorkshire, but its cultivation in these parts of the country is attended with a considerable amount of risk.

Deep, rich, free-working loams are ideal for maize, but nevertheless it can be grown satisfactorily under a wide range of soil conditions from clay to sand and fen. Tremendous crops are obtained on warm, light soils in fairly moist seasons.

VARIETIES

Commercial or Plate feeding maize is not suitable for seed purposes, for, owing to heating, many samples will be found to have a very low germination. It is always wise, therefore, to purchase seed maize from a reliable seedsman, though this may be a good deal more expensive.

White Horse Tooth.—This variety yields immense crops and is of very rapid growth. It should be used for feeding green.

Jaune Gros du Domaine is an early maturing French variety and, having a higher dry matter content than White Horse Tooth, is better suited for ensilage. The yield is good.

Compton's Early.—A comparatively new variety which matures earlier than the other varieties and hence is well adapted for later districts. The yield per acre is lower than that of White Horse Tooth, but it is suitable for fodder or for ensilage.

Early Leaming and *Eureka* are early maturing varieties of recent introduction and well worth a trial.

PLACE IN ROTATION

Maize usually occupies a portion of the root break. In many instances it will be grown on the same land each year, thus enabling a convenient piece of ground to be selected near to the feeding yards or to a pasture to which the green crop can be carted in September or October. The crop may also follow an early catch crop of rye and vetches, or crimson clover which has been folded off with sheep. Late ploughing, however, is always attended with some risk in the case of maize, for if the seed bed dries out germination may suffer.

PREPARATION OF SEED BED

When the crop is grown as part of the root break stubble cleaning will be necessary (see page 29). A liberal dressing of dung should then be applied and ploughed in. On the heavier types of soil, especially if the furrows have been well frosted, a tilth should be obtained in spring by cultivating alone. If weeds have grown during the winter, however, it may be necessary to shallow-plough, taking care not to bury the frost mould too deeply or to dissipate the surface moisture.

On light land no difficulty will be experienced in getting the requisite amount of tilth for seeding. On weedy land repeated cultivating and harrowing may be necessary to bring the weeds to the surface, where they can be collected and burnt. Afterwards the dung can be spread and ploughed in.

A fine tilth must not be produced at the expense of moisture and undue working of the seed bed in spring should be avoided. It is far better to sow in a rough but moist seed bed than in a very fine but dry one.

MANURING

Maize, as might be expected from the rapidity of growth and capacity for giving heavy crops, requires very generous manuring. As already indicated a dressing of dung should be given wherever practicable, and this is best applied in autumn to allow time for it to become well incorporated with the soil before sowing. In this way it will materially improve the water-holding capacity of the soil.

Where liquid manure is also available an application at the rate of 1000 gallons per acre can be given prior to sowing the seed.

This should be followed up by one or two top-dressings of nitrate of soda or nitro-chalk, each 1 cwt. per acre, as soon as the crop is up.

When dung is not available some artificial manures will be required as a substitute, and in this case the following mixture should be applied during the operations necessary to prepare a seed bed:—

Sulphate of Ammonia	.	1 cwt. per acre.
Superphosphate .	.	3 ,, ,,
Muriate of Potash .	.	1 ,, ,,
		5 ,, ,,

On the heavier classes of soil the potash can be omitted.

The crop should later be top-dressed, as indicated already, with 1 to 2 cwt. per acre of a quick-acting nitrogenous fertiliser.

SOWING THE SEED

Sowing must not take place until all danger of late frosts is over, and hence in most districts the period of mid-May to mid-June can be regarded as suitable for seeding. Late-sown crops often give a lower yield and for silage purposes are rather watery. Thus every endeavour should be made to get the crop in as early as possible, consistent with safety.

The seed may be drilled with a hand drill of the Planet Junior type, with an ordinary cup-feed drill, or it can be ploughed in every second furrow. In the latter case it may be sown by hand or by means of a small bean drill attached to the plough. Some growers sow maize in an open furrow, then split the ridges and roll as is the common practice with potatoes. Whatever method is adopted, however, the seed should be deposited 2 to 3 inches deep to protect it from rooks. The rows should be 20 inches apart to allow horse-hoeing during the early part of the growing season, and the seed rate will vary with the variety, 84 lb. per acre being required in the case of White Horse Tooth and Jaune

Gros, whilst 56 lb. per acre is sufficient for Compton's Early and the other early maturing varieties.

Immediately after drilling the land should be well rolled and harrowed to conserve moisture.

AFTER CULTIVATIONS

Careful watch must be maintained for rooks which, having once found the crop, will take every grain unless it is protected.

High stringing is often practised, but the best method by far is to secure oneor two rooks, and after tearing them to pieces deposit the remnants in various parts of the field where they can be seen. Tarring the seed to prevent it being taken by birds is not advocated, for this may adversely affect germination.

As soon as the rows are clearly visible horse-hoeing should commence, and this operation can be repeated so long as it is possible without damaging the crop. Occasionally the plants are rough-thinned to about 8 inches apart and may be earthed up as a means of checking weed growth.

HARVESTING

Cutting commences in August and continues until the frost becomes keen. The crop is usually cut by hand as required and fed to stock on pasture, being mainly used for dairy cows, young stock and horses. It is certainly wasteful to commence cutting too soon, for in mid-season the crop makes rapid growth. On the other hand, the temptation to cut early can be very great if, during August, the pastures begin to dry up and the milk yield to tail off. To all intents and purposes maize can be regarded as roughly equivalent in feeding value to cabbages and kale. To avoid damage by frost, and to ensure that the crop is utilised before the stems become woody in October, it is frequently cut and stooked in the field until required. In this way it will keep for some time. A better way, however, to utilise that portion which is surplus to the needs of the moment is to ensile it, for which purpose a chopper and blower, though not essential, is advantageous.

YIELD

An average crop yields 20 to 25 tons per acre of green-stuff, but on good soils in a favourable season and with generous manuring 35 tons per acre is not uncommon.

LUCERNE

Lucerne is one of the most valuable leguminous crops we have either for cutting green or making into hay, and few can compare with it for growing so much in return for so little attention. It is a crop which can remain down for from five to seven years, it is unsurpassed for producing growth in a period of drought, it can be fed green, made into hay or silage, or dried artificially and ground into a meal. The produce is rich in protein and minerals, and when the period of utility of the crop is over the land is left in a rich condition for succeeding crops.

In spite of these outstanding merits the crop is not widely grown, which is due, no doubt, to a lack of appreciation of its value on the part of farmers. Many believe that it is a difficult crop to grow, and this has arisen in all probability from the failure of many farmers to secure a "plant." The idea is generally prevalent also that the crop is only suitable for the warmer and drier districts of southern and south-eastern England. There is no doubt, however, that when the merits of the plant and its cultivation are better understood many more farmers will grow it.

The crop can stand hard weather and high rainfall. It is the most certain of crops in a period of drought, and although it revels in the warm, dry weather of the South, it can do extremely well in the colder, less congenial conditions of the North.

Lucerne grows on a wide variety of soils provided they are well drained, have an adequate supply of lime and are in reasonably good heart. The ideal soil is a chalky loam overlying a free-draining subsoil, for under such conditions the crop can obtain complete freedom from acidity and has plenty of scope for the development of its extensive root system. To attempt its cultivation on an acid soil, on the other hand, is to court failure, and there is no doubt that many disappointing results can be accounted for in this way.

VARIETIES

Most varieties of lucerne are named after their country of origin, but plant breeders are working hard to develop strains which are more suited to our own conditions, and there is evidence that they are meeting with considerable success.

Provence.—This is perhaps the most widely grown variety and has shown itself reliable under very varied conditions. As the seed is always harvested under ideal conditions the germination and establishment of the plant can be relied upon. Only English strains are obtainable at the present time.

English-grown Provence.—Good English strains are frequently superior to Provence in that they are acclimatised to our conditions. The difficulty, however, is that so frequently harvest conditions in this country are not ideal and the germination of the seed is then comparatively low. Heavier seed rates are therefore necessary. In the future, however, we shall have to rely more on our own stocks, and greater care and attention to harvesting may follow.

Grimm has been found to be very hardy in North America and has proved satisfactory in this country during the last ten years. It is early, dense and leafy and at the moment constitutes our main supply of seed.

Ontario Variegated.—Trials now in progress indicate that this variety is very similar to Grimm.

Rainy River.—A Canadian variety similar in yield and persistence to Grimm.

Marlborough.—A New Zealand variety which has shown promise in trials in Norfolk and Essex.

In purchasing lucerne seed it is essential to obtain it from a seedsman of repute, for inferior seed of low germinating capacity can only give very disappointing results. New strains are being developed which set seed readily in this climate, a feature which is not common to existing English strains.

PLACE IN ROTATION

Lucerne should preferably follow a cleaning and deep rooting crop such as potatoes or roots. Owing to the number of years that it holds the land it cannot be regarded as a normal rotation crop, though quite frequently a portion of the land due for seeds ley will be sown to lucerne. More often a suitable acreage near the homestead is chosen where the crop is handy for cutting and carting during the summer months, or it may be grown as a substitute for meadow hay in mixture with cocksfoot, ryegrass and red clover.

PREPARATION OF SEED BED

Before sowing, the land must be as clean as a new pin, for more failures result from attempting to grow lucerne on filthy or, at any rate, only partially clean land than from any other cause except that of lime shortage. The crop should hold the land ιor five to seven years, but this cannot be so if twitch, watergrass or other perennial weeds are present in large quantities.

Under such circumstances the weeds will smother the lucerne by the second or third season and the land has then to be broken up. Thus, the full usefulness of the crop cannot be obtained. As already indicated, if lucerne follows potatoes or roots it is an advantage, in fact the necessity for thorough cleaning of the land is so important that it would be worth while in many cases to grow two successive root crops, or to give the land a bare fallow to get it really clean before attempting the cultivation of this crop.

MANURING

Any lime requirement must be fully met, for lucerne will not grow satisfactorily where there is even the suspicion of a shortage.

If farmyard manure has been applied to the previous crop as it would be in all probability if this were potatoes or roots, well and good. Phosphates are then essential in order to get a good "plant" and the crop responds well to basic slag. Half a ton per acre of high grade, high soluble basic slag is not too generous, and this should be applied a few weeks before sowing. In place of the basic slag 4 to 5 cwt. of superphosphate per acre can be used, being applied just prior to sowing the seed, and on the lighter types of soil the addition of 1 cwt. muriate of potash per acre is an advantage. If the soil is known to be in poor condition an application of 1 cwt. per acre sulphate of ammonia or nitro-chalk helps to stimulate the plants in the early stages of growth.

SOWING THE SEED

In order to grow well lucerne requires on its roots certain bacteria which are not present in all soils. Hence, to ensure their presence it is advisable to sow them with the seed—in other words the seed is inoculated.

This is not a snag, and the process is both simple and cheap—about 3s. per acre—to carry out. The necessary substances—they are called cultures—can be purchased with the seed from most seed merchants or from such well-known manufacturing chemists as Allen & Hanbury or Boots. Two cultures are sufficient to inoculate 28 lb. of seed, and require to be diluted with one pint of skimmed milk to effect a thorough distribution of the bacteria over the seed. With the cultures a whitish powder (di-acid calcium phosphate) is sent, and this is dissolved in the skimmed milk. Then the bacteria, which appear as a whitish scum on the inclined surface of a jelly in the test tubes, is scraped out with a clean stick and thoroughly mixed with the milk. The culture tubes should be rinsed out several times, and the seeds are then thoroughly wetted with the treated milk.

The seed should be sown as soon after inoculation as possible, but it must be dried in a shady place before drilling or it may stick in the cups of the drill. Inoculated seeds must not be exposed to sunlight which destroys the bacteria, and hence if the seed is broadcast it should be harrowed in at once.

The seed may be sown in spring or late summer with or without a nurse crop. There is no doubt, however, that by far the best plan is to drill it in rows 10 to 12 inches apart without a nurse crop. It is then possible to hoe between the rows and keep weeds in check. Moreover, one can run down the rows with a plough in late autumn and turn a shallow furrow (2 to 3 inches deep) over the crowns. This performs the dual purpose of keeping weeds in check and protecting the plants in winter. All that is necessary in spring is to harrow the ground to expose the lucerne plants once more, when they soon start vigorous growth.

For drilling, a turnip or corn drill can be used, the coulters being adjusted to the required width. It is also possible to use a turnip drill adjusted for, say, 20 to 24-inch rows by traversing the ground twice, to make the drills half this distance. A very steady horse is required and accurate steering is necessary.

It is preferable to sow the crop alone and not under a nurse crop of corn. The latter fosters weeds and keeps the lucerne in check, thereby preventing it from getting a good start in life. Provided the seed is good and the land clean, a heavier seeding than 20 lb. per acre is seldom necessary. The best time for seeding is in April or May, although if the land is not thoroughly clean at this time it is far better to partially fallow and sow the seed in July or August not deeper than ½ inch on a fine firm seed bed.

Good results may be obtained by sowing the lucerne in mixture instead of as a pure seeding, and on light land subject to annual weed infestation or on very heavy land which is difficult to work in summer this method is to be preferred. Good results have been obtained from the following mixtures:—

	lb. per acre.			lb. per acre.
Perennial Ryegrass .	10	Lucerne . .		20
Lucerne . . .	14	Cocksfoot . .		5
Broad Red Clover .	3			25
Late-flowering Red Clover	3			
	30			

After sowing, the land should be lightly harrowed to cover the seed and then given a good rib rolling.

AFTER CULTIVATIONS

Germination of the seed is rapid, and as soon as the rows appear weeding must begin and continue until the crop is really well established. A good deal of patience is required to get the fullest benefit from lucerne, but care and attention to the problem of weed eradication is a factor of great importance.

A light cut may be obtained in the first season of sowing, but this must not be taken too close to the ground. Subsequently three to four cuts per season can be obtained, cutting taking place before the flower opens. Many growers cut or graze the plant about October to prevent the formation of winter buds, asserting that when winter buds form, the first severe frost not only kills them but often injures the plant to such an extent that it may never wholly recover or it may even be killed outright.

A number of growers, however, hold the opinion that the last growth of the season should be left standing to accumulate a food reserve, then to wither down and provide protection for the crowns over winter. Much more evidence is needed before one can say with confidence what the autumn treatment of lucerne should be.

When lucerne has been sown in a corn crop it is important to set the knives of the binder high. It is also necessary to remove the stooks about every ten days, for lucerne is much easier to kill in this way than red clover. If, owing to wet weather, the corn has to remain out for a considerable time it is well worth considering the removal of the sheaves to some near-by grassland where they can be dried without risk to the lucerne.

HARVESTING

Lucerne is the most certain of all green fodder crops in a dry season, and by cutting the crop in stages it is possible to arrange for a supply of green-stuff through the entire summer. For this reason all milk-producers should endeavour to have a certain acreage of lucerne each year.

The making of good lucerne hay is an art. Lack of care results in the valuable leaf, which is very brittle, being left in the field. To prevent undue loss, the crop should be cut in the afternoon and always turned whilst the dew is still on it. It should not dry out in the swath, but, when still half-fit, be made into small cocks. These can be increased in size as the hay dries by putting two into one. The hay must be stacked very dry to avoid heating.

Lucerne makes excellent silage, but it is best to mix it with some grass whenever this is available. Molasses should be sprayed on to the crop during the filling process.

When grazed, care must be taken that the stock do not become "blown," especially if they are turned on to it from old and rather poor pasture. It is also advisable to avoid close grazing, confining the grazing to the spring and reserving the summer and autumn growth for mowing.

YIELD

Under average conditions where three cuts per season are obtained the total weight of green fodder per acre is in the region of 15 to 20 tons. This, on most farms, will be grown at considerably less expense than any other forage crop.

It need hardly be mentioned, perhaps, that when heavy crops are removed each year it is essential to keep up the fertility of the soil by an occasional application of phosphate, plus some potash for the lighter soils, and an occasional dressing of dung in autumn is beneficial.

SAINFOIN

Sainfoin is an extremely valuable leguminous plant in the sheep districts of southern England. Like lucerne it can be utilised in many ways; for cutting and feeding green in summer, for grazing, or for hay. Where clover-sickness disease is prevalent it is frequently grown as a substitute for red clover. It has an excellent reputation as a healthful food for sick or weakly animals and the hay is much sought after ₁or blood stock.

As a drought resister sainfoin is second only to lucerne and for this reason is grown extensively on the dry, chalky soils in the neighbourhood of the Downs. A warm and dry climate is essential. Although it seems to prefer the lighter types of soils containing a good deal of lime it grows satisfactorily on many other soils, provided they are well drained, well supplied with lime, and the climate is suitable. The crop ₁ails utterly on wet land. On the poorer and lighter classes of soils sainfoin, by reason of its deep rooting habit and the enrichment of the soil in nitrogen, forms an excellent preparatory crop for wheat or sugar beet.

VARIETIES

There are two main types, namely, Common and Giant.

Common Sainfoin is a perennial which is usually left down for three or four years. It attains a height of about 2 feet and flowers in late May or June, and is best used for grazing as it produces very little aftermath when mown. Four regional types are known, Cotswold, Hampshire, Vale of Glamorgan and Eastern Counties. Cotswold is very persistent, prostrate in habit and moderately vigorous. Hampshire is coarser and more vigorous than Cotswold and equally persistent, whilst Vale of Glamorgan resembles Hampshire but is more prostrate and more persistent. The Eastern Counties type is more vigorous than Hampshire but less persistent, and is really intermediate between Common and Giant sainfoin. Several local stocks within these regional types have a good reputation.

Giant Sainfoin gives much more bulk than Common, but only lasts for two or three years. It establishes itself quickly, gives two crops of hay in a season and is well suited for rotation cropping.

PLACE IN ROTATION

Sainfoin usually replaces the clover ley in the rotation and is commonly sown with barley as a nurse crop. Frequently a few pounds of Giant sainfoin will be sown in mixtures for 2 or 3 years' ley to be followed by wheat. Some lands cannot grow sainfoin more than once in eight years, and in Hampshire it is considered that once in fifteen years is quite frequent enough.

When the crop is intended to hold the land for several years it is important, of course, to see that it is sown on clean land. Thus it is preferable to sow after roots or even after a bastard fallow, and under these circumstances it is not uncommon to dispense with a nurse crop.

Preparation of Seed Bed

Very little seed bed preparation is necessary as the crop is usually drilled under oats or barley as a nurse crop. It is important to secure a good, firm seed bed, and hence it is advisable to ring-roll prior to sowing the seed. In order to ensure a good "plant" it is advisable to sow the sainfoin at the same time as the corn crop, giving only a light seeding of the latter. The nurse crop should be drilled and harrowed in and this can be followed by a good ring-rolling. The sainfoin can then be sown with the same corn drill immediately afterwards, and at right angles to the corn. It is then lightly harrowed in and rolled again.

The crop can be sown under wheat, but here early drilling, as soon as soil and weather conditions are suitable, is necessary, for the wheat plant must not be so far advanced that it suppresses the sainfoin seedlings.

Manuring

Being a leguminous plant, an adequate supply of lime in the soil is essential. On many of the soils where sainfoin is commonly grown this is ensured, for they are chiefly chalky loams. Elsewhere, if a shortage of lime is suspected, it must be rectified before sowing takes place.

Prior to sowing, a phosphatic dressing should be applied. On the medium to heavy classes of land an application of high soluble, high grade basic slag, at the rate of 10 cwt. per acre, will give good results. On the lighter classes of soil the slag can be replaced by 4 to 5 cwt. per acre of superphosphate with 2 cwt. potash salts in addition.

When it is available, a dressing of well-rotted dung should be applied in the first autumn. This not only serves to nourish the plant in the early stages of growth but affords a measure of protection from frost.

In all cases where sainfoin is to be left down for a number of years, it is advisable to give a further application of dung in three years' time, together with a moderate dressing of some phosphatic fertiliser.

Sowing the Seed

The seed is usually drilled in rows about 7 inches apart and about 1 inch deep, from February to May. If drilled deeper than this, though it germinates the shoots may fail to reach the surface and die underground.

Seed may be obtained in the husk (unmilled) or with the husk removed (milled), the advantage of milled seed being that it has a higher germination. Unmilled seed always contains some husks that are either empty or only partially developed, and a further disadvantage is that it is difficult to eliminate large weed seeds such as brome grass, or burnet, unless the seed is first milled. It is essential to use only fresh-coloured seed which is plump and light brown in colour, for when the seed is black or shrivelled it denotes that it is either old or has been harvested badly.

The seed rate is 56 lb. per acre for milled seed or 100 lb. per acre if the unmilled seed is used, but recent work has shown that when the seed bed is carefully prepared these quantities can be reduced.

The usual practice in the Eastern Counties is to grow sainfoin as a pure crop, but in the south and west of England it is a common constituent of temporary or permanent ley mixtures. The following mixtures have given good results:—

Two Years' Ley:

Perennial Ryegrass	6 lb. per acre.
Cocksfoot	12 ,, ,,
Giant Sainfoin	10 ,, ,,
Dorset Marl Red Clover . . .	4 ,, ,,
Alsike Clover	2 ,, ,,
White Clover	2 ,, ,,
	36 ,, ,,

Cotswold Mixture:

Perennial Ryegrass	14 lb. per acre.
Cocksfoot	7 ,, ,,
Rough-stalked Meadow Grass . .	3 ,, ,,
Timothy	3 ,, ,,
Common Sainfoin	4 ,, ,,
Cotswold Late-flowering Red Clover .	4 ,, ,,
Wild White Clover	1 ,, ,,
	36 ,, ,,

When sowing the sainfoin as a pure crop a little trefoil or red clover—2 to 3 lb. per acre is sufficient—may be mixed with it to occupy the land whilst the sainfoin develops and to assist in smothering the weeds.

AFTER CULTIVATIONS

When grown alone the crop should be kept clean until it is established.

HARVESTING

For hay the crop must be cut as soon as flowering begins, for delay at this time not only results in a lower quality hay, but also impairs the future cropping capacity of the plant. Like lucerne it requires very careful handling in the field to avoid loss of leaf, and turning can be most safely carried out in early morning when the dew is on the leaves. Fortunately, the crop is not readily spoiled if left in the swath, even by wet weather.

Usually a crop of seed is taken from the sainfoin before it is broken up. In the case of the giant type two crops of hay are taken in the first year and seed from the second crop in the second year. Common sainfoin is cut for seed in its last year, as the saving of seed is apt to impair the vitality of the crop. As soon as the lower seeds are fully ripe, these being most valuable, the crop is cut, and this operation is best carried out early in the morning or in the evening when the plants are damp, for by so doing loss of seed is avoided.

The crop must not be carted before it is thoroughly dry, and the waggons used in carting should have sheets spread in the bottom to collect any seed which is shelled out. In addition it is advisable to stack on sheets laid over the ground.

YIELD

The average yield of hay is about 30 cwt. per acre, which is equal in feeding value for all practical purposes to good clover hay.

The yield of seed in the husk is about 5 to 6 cwt. per acre.

GRASS AND CLOVER MIXTURES

Grass and clover mixtures, or as they are more commonly called, "seeds mixtures" or merely "seeds," occupy a vital place in arable farming. The fertility of mixed farms can best be maintained by resting fields for one or more years under a seeds crop and, indeed, on many farms the ley is the pivot of the rotation.

A good ley can far outyield permanent pasture or meadow, giving both earlier and later keep in any season. Moreover, the quality of the hay is excellent, the grazing clean and healthful, and all the time the crop occupies the land the clovers are building up reserves of nitrogen in the soil. This, together with the valuable humus which is added to the soil when the ley is finally ploughed under, ensures excellent arable crops with little additional manuring.

Satisfactory "takes" can be obtained on almost any type of soil and under widely differing climatic conditions. The lightness or heaviness of a soil is of much less importance than the presence or absence in a soil of sufficient quantities of phosphate, potash and lime. As might be expected under conditions of moderate or high rainfall the best results are to be looked for, but it is amazing how well these seeds leys stand up to dry conditions when permanent grassland is at a very low level of productivity.

VARIETIES

A "seeds mixture" consists of a number of different grasses and clovers chosen to supply the particular needs of the farm and most suited to soil and climatic conditions. Years ago it was the common practice to include small quantities of a large number of species in a mixture, presumably on the assumption that if conditions were not right for one grass or clover they would surely be right for another. Frequently, in a three-year ley fifteen to twenty grasses, clovers, and so-called "herbs" were included. In practice this resulted in much wastage of seed, especially of the less important ingredients of the seeds mixture. We have come to realise by now, however, that instead of making the mixture suit adverse soil conditions we should so cultivate and fertilise the land that conditions are made suitable for the growth of the desirable plants, thereby enabling much simpler mixtures to be used.

Of the grasses, Perennial ryegrass, Italian ryegrass, Cocksfoot and Timothy, and of the clovers, Late-flowering Red Clover, Broad Red Clover, White Clover, Wild White Clover and Alsike are by far the most valuable. All these plants grow well on a great variety of soils and under widely different climatic conditions. Mixtures for almost any purpose can be made from this selection, and the problem is really one of balancing them in suitable proportions to meet the particular needs for which the mixture is required.

New and valuable strains of most of these grasses and clovers are now available. They are generally called "indigenous" strains to distinguish them from the ordinary "commercial" strains.

These new strains are mostly leafier and more persistent than the commercial strains, although as one might expect they are a good deal more expensive and do not as a rule give such early growth in spring.

The following brief description of the grasses and clovers mentioned above is given because a thorough understanding of these individual characteristics is essential if a wise selection of plants for any particular purpose is to be made.

Perennial Ryegrass.—This is probably our most valuable grass. It thrives well on the richer types of soil, but on poor sandy land tends to die out after three or four years. Even so, it is worth including in mixtures for this type of land, for it gives good herbage in the first few years and prevents the growth of weeds. Provided it is well manured, however, it can be made to thrive even on poor land, and few grasses are superior in its ability to withstand bad management, though this, if persisted in, will cause it to die out. When grown alone it is not such a good yielder as Italian ryegrass, but when sown in conjunction with clovers it has been found to give heavier yields than when Italian ryegrass is used. This is due to its kindlier nature with the clovers, for the Italian ryegrass with its tall-growing, tufted habit of growth tends to smother the low-growing clovers. Perennial ryegrass is the first of the perennial grasses to commence growth in spring and the last to stop growth in autumn. It does not, however, produce much leafage in July and early August, especially if the weather is dry at the time.

Commercial Strains.—Ayrshire and Irish.

There is no essential difference between these two strains. Both are early in spring, rather stemmy, and give rather poor mid-season grazing.

H

Indigenous Strains.

Aberystwyth S. 24.—Quite an early type and maintains good mid-season grazing, being more persistent than commercial strains.

Aberystwyth S. 23.—This is essentially a pasture strain. It is very leafy, very persistent, and late flowering. In addition it is winter-green and grows well in late autumn and winter, but is later than the commercial strains in spring.

Aberystwyth S. 101.—Very similar to S. 23 though not quite so late in spring. It requires rather better soil conditions than S. 23.

New Zealand Certified.—A more leafy and persistent strain than "commercial" seed and gives good mid-season grazing, but it is not so persistent as the Aberystwyth strains.

Kentish has all the features of leafiness, lateness and persistency, but it is not so uniform a type as the above strains.

Italian Ryegrass.—This is almost an annual grass and usually does not survive in any quantity for more than two seasons. It is excellent for stubble grazing and an early spring bite and is often included in long duration mixtures, for it gives grazing soon after seeding down and whilst the more permanent constituents in the mixture are becoming established. It is useful for growing under irrigation conditions or for catch cropping, and for this purpose is sown at the rate of 40 to 50 lb. per acre.

Its easy establishment, rapid recovery from cutting or grazing, and winter greenness make it one of the most valuable short-term ley grasses we have.

Commercial Strains Only.—Chiefly Irish.

Short Rotation Ryegrass H. 1.—This is a cross between perennial and Italian ryegrasses having something of the qualities of both parents. It provides more bulk than perennial ryegrass yet persists for 2 to 3 years.

Cocksfoot.—An excellent yielder, producing herbage of high feeding quality. It starts growth about a fortnight later than perennial ryegrass and should always be grazed when young, for with increasing age it loses its palatability. It is subject to winter burning and may become the aggressive plant in the mixture unless kept in check. Hard grazing from mid-April to mid-

September will reduce the amount of cocksfoot in the sward. It grows under a variety of soil conditions and is especially valuable on light dry soils where perennial ryegrass does not do well.

Commercial Strains.—Danish and American.

At least a fortnight earlier in spring than the indigenous strains, these are rather stemmy and less persistent but are succulent and palatable in spring. The Danish type in particular has for long been a most valuable constituent of long leys.

Indigenous Strains.

New Zealand Akaroa.—More leafy and persistent than Danish; it is also later to start growth in spring. On the other hand, it is more winter-green which is a valuable characteristic.

Aberystwyth S. 26.—This is a very persistent strain and with suitable management will give heavy and leafy crops of hay. Where perennial ryegrass tends to die out on rather poor soils and under heavy grazing this cocksfoot should be tried in its place. It produces growth late in the season and is much more winter-green than Danish.

Aberystwyth S. 143.—A strain which withstands sustained sheep grazing and produces under such conditions continuous growth. Plenty of leaf and good hay crops are obtained when the land is in good heart. It is late in the season like S. 26 but gives more autumn grazing than Danish.

Timothy.—One of our most valuable hay grasses which thrives especially well on the heavier and peaty types of soil. It is frequently sown alone to form timothy meadows and under suitable conditions will give as much as 4 tons of hay per acre. It commences growth late and hence gives only a poor aftermath but is winter-green. Being extremely palatable it is liable to be punished by stock especially in the early part of the season, and for this reason it does best when the dominant member of a mixture.

Commercial Strains.—American and Scotch.

Indigenous Strains.—These strains are more leafy and persistent, and under suitable conditions will withstand heavy grazing owing to their great tillering capacity.

Aberystwyth S. 51.—Is an improvement on the commercial type, producing a more leafy hay and the plant is more persistent. In addition it is better able to withstand grazing.

Aberystwyth S. 48.—This is essentially a pasture strain and stands up well to heavy grazing. A further advantage is that it is adaptable to a wider range of soil conditions than the commercial type.

Aberystwyth S. 50.—This is a small, prostrate and spreading plant and is valuable for grazing purposes on peaty marginal land.

Late-flowering Red Clover.—(Single cut cow grass.)

This type of clover persists for 2 to 4 years and gives a heavy cut of hay but little aftermath.

Three strains of the clover are of especial merit, namely, Montgomery Red, which is very persistent and gives a heavy cut of hay; Cornish Marl, which is extra late and of great tillering capacity; and Aberystwyth S. 123, which is more persistent than either Montgomery or Cornish and is more productive in the second and third years. This strain is admirably suited for sowing with timothy in mixtures for three-year hay leys.

Broad Red Clover.—This type of clover is only of use in one-year mixtures, as it does not make any contribution to the hay or the grazing in the second year. It is 7 to 10 days earlier than the late-flowering type, gives considerable grazing in the first autumn after sowing and good aftermath after cutting and grazing. English strains are superior to those of foreign origin, and Dorset Marl in particular is an extremely valuable type. This is the earliest of the broad-leaved clovers, and produces not only a heavy first cut of hay but also an excellent second crop for hay or grazing.

White Clover.—The type of clover which is sometimes termed "Dutch White" is a somewhat larger plant than the wild white clover, and is not so long-lived. The seed is a good deal cheaper than that of wild white and hence is of use for one-year leys. The following strains are of particular merit: New Zealand white has a greater yielding capacity than the common Dutch and is more persistent, whilst Aberystwyth S. 100 is capable of lasting for four years, and on good land is not only very productive but has a longer growing season than other types of white clover.

Wild White Clover.—This plant is essential in all long duration swards. Hard grazing favours its development, since the plant is susceptible to the competition of tall-growing grasses. It is much more drought-resisting than the grasses and has tremendous value as an improver of poor pasture. Too much wild white, however, is undesirable because the stock-carrying capacity is low, it being of such close growth with a very short season of productivity. Both Kentish wild white and New Zealand certified strains are noted for their vigour and persistence.

Alsike clover is not a heavy cropper but is often included in seeds mixtures in small quantities as a safeguard, being hardier and less susceptible to lime shortage than the red clovers.

Trefoil.—An annual plant which is frequently included in seeds mixtures, particularly where early spring grazing is required for sheep. In conjunction with Italian ryegrass it gives an excellent early bite, and is especially valuable on thin dry or sandy soils where the better clovers do not succeed.

For normal purposes not more than one or two pounds of seed should be included in a mixture, for the plant takes up a good deal of space in comparison to the amount of keep provided. Moreover, it is a ready self-seeder and must not be given too much scope.

No mention has been made of rough and smooth-stalked meadow grasses which are included in so many long-term leys and permanent mixtures. Many farmers are staunch advocates of the inclusion of one or other of these grasses in all mixtures which are to remain down for more than three years. Some, in fact, go so far as to sow only perennial ryegrass, rough-stalked meadow grass and wild white clover. Mixtures of this type generally produce a fine, close-knit sward which always gives the impression of being a really good pasture. From observation and careful records, however, it is the author's experience that many of these "good looking" pastures have not the same stock-carrying capacity as the somewhat coarser and more open swards which contain a high percentage of cocksfoot. Rough-stalked meadow grass, for example, produces little or no growth during drought, whereas cocksfoot survives dry weather remarkably well.

It is always possible to include one of these grasses in mixtures, and 1 to 2 lb. per acre in mixture 7 would give a denser sward.

For those who wish to try this modification the following brief description of the two grasses is given.

Rough-stalked Meadow Grass.—This is a splendid "bottom grass" for good land. It commences growth early, gives a good supply of leafy and palatable herbage but does not produce much keep during drought. It is relatively shallow-rooted, and hence should not be tried on thin light land unless in a district of high rainfall. The grass attains its maximum growth about the second year and stands grazing and trampling particularly well.

Smooth-stalked Meadow Grass.—This grass is inferior to its counterpart, since it is less nutritious and does not give so much keep. It is the better grass, however, for poor, open, light land, and does particularly well on chalky soils. It is not so winter-green as rough-stalked meadow grass and does not attain full development until the fourth year.

COMPILING SEEDS MIXTURES

In compiling a seeds mixture the problem of "balance" is very important, for the success of the mixture depends not so much on the excellence of any one constituent, but on the way in which the different species live in harmony with each other and fulfil the tasks for which they are included. Every species must justify its inclusion, and full consideration must be given to the type of soil and the purpose for which the mixture is required, whether it be for hay, grazing, or for general purposes. In temporary leys the main requirements will be yield, quality and earliness, whilst for permanent pasture longevity must be added to this list.

No hard-and-fast rules can be laid down as to what constitutes the best mixture for any district or set of conditions. Too often the seeds mixture is expected to do what can only be done by manuring or cultivation, and these latter considerations play a much more vital part in the ultimate success or failure of the mixture than does the composition of the mixture itself, provided this is decided upon with a reasonable amount of common sense.

The following mixtures can be regarded as standard types and can be modified to suit individual requirements. They have all been tried and have proved successful over a number of years:—

Duration of Ley	One Year		Two Years		Three Years or More.			
Mixture No.	1	2	3	4	5	6	7	8
Italian Ryegrass	4	—	4	4	3	3	3	10
Perennial Ryegrass	14	—	12	20	14	14	9	—
Cocksfoot (Commercial)	—	—	—	—	—	3	4	—
Cocksfoot (Certified Leafy)	—	—	—	—	—	3	4	—
Timothy (Commercial)	—	—	8	—	8	—	2	10
Timothy (Certified Leafy)	—	—	—	—	—	—	2	10
Late-flowering Red Clover	4	3	3	2	3	3	3	4
Broad Red Clover	3	—	3	—	—	—	—	—
White Clover S. 100	—	2	1	1	1	1	1	—
Wild White Clover	—	—	—	—	$\frac{1}{2}$	$\frac{1}{2}$	$\frac{1}{2}$	—
Alsike	—	4	—	—	—	—	—	—
Trefoil	—	3	—	—	—	—	—	—
lb. per acre	25	12	31	27	$29\frac{1}{2}$	$27\frac{1}{2}$	$28\frac{1}{2}$	34

NOTES

Mixture No. 1. General purpose mixture giving stubble grazing and early spring bite, good crop of hay and some aftermath.

Mixture No. 2. Wolds or clover-sick land. In some areas it may be advantageous to include 10 lb. per acre of Timothy in this mixture.

Mixture No. 3. Chiefly for hay.

Mixture No. 4. Wholly for grazing.

In Mixtures Nos. 1, 3 and 4, 2 lb. Trefoil can be added on calcareous soils, and 4 lb. Alsike used in place of Broad Red Clover on acid soils and on clover-sick land.

Mixture No. 5. Specially suited to heavy soils.

Mixture No. 6. Cocksfoot takes the place of Timothy for medium and light soils.

Mixture No. 7. General purpose mixture for all average soils.

Note i. It is suggested that at least 4 lb. per acre of S. 23 or S. 101 or Kent Indigenous Ryegrass and 6 lb. of S. 24 or New Zealand Perennial Ryegrass be included as part of the seeding of ryegrass in Mixtures 5, 6 and 7.

Note ii. The quantities of Cocksfoot can be increased slightly when supplies are available.

Note iii. All these mixtures should be grazed directly after harvest.

Note iv. For direct re-seeding without a cover crop the Italian Ryegrass should be increased to 10 lb. per acre.

Mixture No. 8. For peaty soils and wet situations for Timothy hay.

PLACE IN ROTATION

The seeds crop is usually sown the first or second year after roots, in a nurse crop of corn, which, as will be shown later in this chapter, should not be too thick, in order to give the young grasses and clovers every chance. A certain amount of grazing is obtained in the first autumn on the stubble, but the main crop comes the following year.

Seeds frequently constitute the pivotal crop of the rotation and may remain down for one or more years, depending upon the general requirements of the farm.

It is usually followed by wheat or oats, although in many districts potatoes are taken, for which crop the accumulated nitrogen from the clover and the additional humus from the green material ploughed in forms an excellent preparation.

PREPARATION OF SEED BED

Since a seeds mixture is commonly sown under a cereal the cultivations are not directly designed for the seeds but rather for the cereal. This is unfortunate, for in many cases the seeds mixture is sown under conditions which, though quite suitable for the comparatively large-sized seed of the cereal, are by no means fine enough for the small grasses and clovers.

It is of the utmost importance to work the seed bed to as fine a tilth as possible by the judicious use of harrows and roller. Naturally the foundations of a good tilth are laid much earlier than this, and whenever a cereal crop is to be undersown with seeds every endeavour should be made to get the land ploughed early. This will allow plenty of time for the natural consolidation of the furrows which, after they have been well weathered, and particularly if they have been well frosted, break down to give an ideal type of seed bed. Sometimes, however, the land cannot be ploughed until spring, as, for instance, if the cereal nurse crop is to follow roots folded on, and then full use must be made of disc harrows. The final operation just before sowing the seed should be a good ring-rolling. The ideal to aim at is always "onion bed conditions" of fineness and firmness.

MANURING

An adequate reserve of lime is necessary, for clovers cannot thrive on a sour soil. In most rotations on land which requires periodic liming roots form the most convenient crop to which lime can be applied. In this case no further application is necessary specifically for the "seeds," but should there be any doubt as to the lime content of the soil the precaution should be taken of having the soil tested or giving a moderate dressing to the corn crop.

Phosphates exert considerable influence on the "take" obtained, and before drilling the corn crop 5 cwt. per acre of high grade, high soluble slag or an equivalent amount of some other phosphate should be applied. If the ley is to remain down for several years these quantities might well be increased, and on the lighter types of soil the addition of 2 cwt. per acre potash salts is an advantage, for this frequently produces an effect as spectacular as that of phosphates on heavy land. Fertilising often makes all the difference between a patchy take and a good one, but it is important to keep both phosphate and potash at the surface, where it is required by the clovers. Some farmers slag the stubble after harvest, but in most cases the earlier pre-seeding application will be found to give better results.

Under normal conditions no nitrogenous fertiliser is required prior to seeding, and in fact even on poor land care must be taken not to overdo any nitrogenous fertilising owing to the danger that the cereal may lodge and so smother the seeds. Late applications of nitrogen to the cereal crop, with the object of increasing the amount of grain rather than the weight of straw, are quite safe so far as the grasses and clovers are concerned.

SOWING THE SEED

Barley and oats are the favourite nurse crops, though in recent years wheat and cereal-legume mixtures have been commonly used. There is no doubt that wheat is not a good nurse crop. It tillers late in the season, and is well developed before conditions are sufficiently favourable for the sowing of the seeds mixture. As a result, the grasses and clovers never get a fair chance of becoming well established, and more failures and patchy takes result when wheat is the nurse crop than with any other cereal.

If wheat is used, however, a strong-strawed variety should be chosen and given a light seeding, the seeds mixture being sown as soon as weather and soil conditions are suitable in spring, and only after the desired seed bed has been prepared by harrowing and rolling. Grazing by sheep prior to sowing is an excellent practice.

Oats are more suitable as a nurse crop than wheat, but here again care should be exercised to choose a strong-strawed variety and to avoid a heavy seeding.

Barley is undoubtedly the best of cereal nurse crops, for it is relatively short in the straw and does not tiller unduly, thus enabling the seeds mixture to get plenty of light and air for development. The danger in the use of barley lies in the weakness of its straw and the fact that it is frequently grown on land in good heart—after roots sheeped on—and is, therefore, liable to lodge. In this case an application of phosphates as already suggested helps to strengthen the straw.

Cereal-legume mixtures which are grown for ensilage also make excellent nurse crops, for although the crop may be thick on the ground it is removed early in the year before it has had time to exert a smothering effect on the grass and clover seedlings.

There is considerable divergence of opinion amongst farmers as to whether the seeds mixture should be sown at the same time as the cereal or later in the season when the corn is a few inches high. Much depends, of course, upon soil and season, but there is no doubt that sowing at the same time as the cereal is one of the surest means of getting good establishment. It is true that in a wet season the grasses and clovers may be so advanced by harvest as to give trouble in the sheaves, but in the general run of seasons it is reasonably safe. On poor soils, seeding may be delayed until the corn is well up, for in this case owing to the thinness of the cereal the grasses and clovers may grow almost as fast as the corn, and not only is the green material a nuisance at harvest but the clovers may be so weakened by cutting that many succumb during winter.

The seeds may be sown in April or May with the fiddle drill, broadcast seed barrow, small seeds coulter drill, or even by hand. When the land is Cambridge rolled immediately before sowing the seed falls into the corrugations formed by the roller and can be covered with a light chain harrow. Deep covering often causes many seedlings to perish, whereas sowing on the surface and leaving uncovered results in many of them failing to gain roothold, and these die during dry weather. A more even distribution can be obtained by keeping the light grass seeds and the heavier clover seeds separate, and after drilling the former portion, sowing the latter at right angles to it. In practice, however, provided the seeds have been well mixed, sufficiently good distribution is obtained without the need for this extra work.

When weather conditions prevent sowing at the normal time, or in cases of failure, it may be necessary to sow in summer after the stubbles are cleared. Assuming a suitable seed bed can be obtained and the seeds are sown during August, this is quite satisfactory. Good results can often be obtained from a September seeding, but this is risky in some districts, for the plants may be killed by early frosts before they become well established.

When land is being sown to permanent grass, it is a good plan to sow the mixture without a cover crop or under Italian ryegrass. This enables early grazing to follow, which encourages the grasses and clovers to tiller and occupy the ground, thereby preventing any establishment of weeds. Should the land be weedy before sowing in spring it is advisable to delay seeding until August, for this allows a half-fallow to be taken and ensures a clean weed-free seed bed.

AFTER CULTIVATIONS

The seeds should be grazed in the first autumn to prevent the herbage from becoming winter-proud. A thin and weakly plant can be helped considerably by a light dressing of dung during autumn, for this not only strengthens the plant but affords some protection over winter.

Though early grazing in spring may be possible, this should not be continued too late in the year if a heavy crop of hay is to be taken. An application of 1 cwt. per acre of sulphate of ammonia or nitro-chalk in March or April will on most soils increase the yield of hay by 5 to 6 cwt. per acre. A further top-dressing at the same rate after the hay is removed ensures a second cut for hay or silage.

A good rolling in spring is generally advisable, especially after a keen winter. Consolidation is necessary to counteract any puffiness and presses stones into the soil, thus avoiding damage to the knife of the mowing-machine. Stone-picking is common in some areas.

YIELD

The yield of seeds hay varies considerably, depending upon season and management. Average crops will be in the region of 2 tons per acre, although 3 tons or more are quite common.

DISEASES

Clover Sickness.—When clover is grown too frequently on the same land it is liable to disease, and this is usually ascribed to "clover sickness." There are, in fact, two causes of this condition, one due to eelworm causing the "sickness," and the other due to a fungus causing "clover rot."

The true sickness is characterised in autumn by the failure of the clover in patches and in these places plants are paler in colour. Later both leaves and crown die away and gradually as winter advances the patches extend.

There is no cure for the trouble, and the rotation must be extended by omitting susceptible crops for a period of six to eight years in order to starve the worm out. Crops, such as sainfoin, peas, beans and vetches which are resistant to attack, can be grown in place of clover, and of these, sainfoin is the best choice provided soil and climate are suitable for the crop.

The "rot" disease also starts in autumn in patches and causes a blackening of the leaves. If the weather at this time is warm and muggy the disease spreads rapidly, and although a cold, dry spell may check it for the time being it is liable to start again in spring.

A luxuriant growth of clover in autumn always favours the spread of the disease once it starts, and hence it is advisable to graze such fields down before winter. This practice has already been advocated as a means of avoiding "winter proudness." Infection comes from old clover leys, and therefore on soils subject to this trouble it is a wise precaution to plough early and deeply to bury the fungus which is the cause of the trouble.

CRIMSON CLOVER (TRIFOLIUM)

This is one of the cheapest forage crops which can be grown when rapidity of growth and early maturity are desired. It is an annual, 1 to 2 feet in height, but is confined to the south of

England on account of its susceptibility to severe weather. The crop does best on loamy soils and the deeper soils in general. Although it is grown in chalk districts it is always on the lower gravelly soils, for on thin chalk it is not satisfactory.

VARIETIES

There are four varieties, early, medium and late strains of red trifolium and a late white trifolium. When sown at the same time these varieties are ready for consumption in sequence by the following May. Late red trifolium is ready about the same time as the late white variety, whilst early red comes to feed about a fortnight before either.

PLACE IN ROTATION

The crop is chiefly grown as a catch crop and is usually sown on the stubble after winter cereals or silage crops.

PREPARATION OF SEED BED

The stubble is merely harrowed once or twice, for elaborate cultivations producing a deep tilth are unnecessary and, in fact, undesirable.

MANURING

Manuring produces an earlier and bulkier crop, although as a rule the crop will have little, if any, fertiliser given to it. A further advantage of a light dressing of artificials is that the feed remains succulent for a longer period.

The following mixture is suggested :—

Sulphate of Ammonia .	$\frac{1}{2}$ cwt. per acre,		Ammonium
Superphosphate . .	3 ,, ,,	or	Phosphate
	—		$1\frac{1}{2}$ cwt. per acre,
	$3\frac{1}{2}$,, ,,		

which should be applied prior to sowing the seed.

SOWING THE SEED

Early red trifolium may be sown in July, August or September, the other varieties usually being sown in August or September. As a rule the earlier the seed is sown the better, as a forward plant is in better form to withstand slugs and other damage during the winter. 20 to 24 lb. of seed per acre is required, and in many instances this is mixed with Italian ryegrass to provide a crop for folding with sheep or pigs. In mixture 15 lb. crimson clover and 5 lb. per acre Italian ryegrass give good results, and when sown in June is ready for grazing in July, or can be cut for hay in August of the same year.

The seed is generally broadcast, harrowed in, and well rolled. A good firm seed bed is desirable and the seed should not be buried deeper than one inch.

UTILISATION

Sheep are usually hurdled on small areas of crimson clover, and care is necessary to feed it off before an advanced stage of growth is attained, for then the flowers are hairy and may cause the formation of hair-balls. It is ready for folding early in spring and is, therefore, of considerable value for fat-lamb production or for pushing on ram lambs. In feeding, care is necessary not to allow them on when the foliage is rimy with frost.

Any part of the crop which is surplus to folding requirements can be made into hay, but again it is essential to cut the crop before the plant becomes woody and the flowers hairy. Fine weather is most desirable, for crimson clover soon develops mildew. When harvested for seed the straw after threshing is fit only for litter, as the woodiness of the stems make it unsuitable for feeding to stock. When feeding the hay it is a wise precaution to feed meadow hay along with it to avoid any trouble with the stock which might consume too much.

SILAGE CROPS

Most crops grown for green fodder can be used for ensilage. In days gone by it was considered that such watery crops as marrow stem kale and strong-smelling crops like mustard and rape were unsuitable for ensiling, but with the introduction of the molasses method this no longer holds good.

In this section, however, it is proposed to deal exclusively with crops which are grown on arable land with the prime object of making them into silage. Such mixtures generally consist of one or more cereals, chiefly oats, with one or more leguminous plants, chiefly tares. In recent years special grass and clover mixtures have been used for silage making.

The prime necessity for an arable silage crop is that it should be reliable to enable one to estimate beforehand on a certain weight of silage being available for winter feeding. Of all crops the tare most nearly approaches the ideal arable crop for ensilage. It is easily grown, is reliable in yield, not too fastidious as regards the management and manuring of the land, and forms a palatable and highly nutritious food. Unfortunately, owing to the weakness of its stems some supporting crop is necessary, and oats or beans or both are usually grown in conjunction with it.

SILAGE MIXTURES

Various proportions of cereals to legumes are used in different parts of the country, and there appears to be no standard formula that can be adapted for general use. Moreover, because the cereals and legumes are sown in certain proportions does not necessarily ensure that that proportion will be obtained at harvest-time. Frit-fly damage, for instance, may reduce the proportion of oats; pea weevil may seriously reduce the number of peas or beans, or wireworms take the oats, leaving only a crop of peas and beans. Much depends upon the season, method of sowing, manuring and many other factors, and it is certainly unlikely that all conditions will be "just right" in any one season.

The following mixtures which have done well in the north-east of England are given as a basis upon which others may be compounded to suit the needs of any particular soil and district:—

I Average Soils. Stones per Acre		II Light Soils. Stones per Acre		III Heavy Soils. Stones per Acre	
Oats . .	10	Oats . .	10	Oats . .	8
Tares or Peas	4	Tares . .	2	Beans . .	4
		Peas . .	2	Peas and Tares .	4

In the South, autumn-sown crops are generally much more successful than those sown in spring, and here winter oats and winter vetches are used in the mixtures, the grey winter being well suited for this purpose. When beans are included in the mixture it is usual to broadcast them and plough them in some 2 to 3 weeks before sowing the rest of the crop. This gives them a longer growing period and enables the various constituents to reach the correct stage for cutting about the same time. A little rye may be included in mixtures, say 2 stones per acre, for although the fodder is rather coarse it is a good supporting crop.

With all cereal-legume mixtures it is wise to sow 10 to 20 lb. of Italian ryegrass per acre in spring, for this provides excellent grazing after the silage crop is removed, or if preferred a second cut can be taken for silage, for the oats and the tares will produce quite an appreciable amount of aftermath if a long stubble is left.

PLACE IN ROTATION

As a rule, the silage crop occupies a portion of the root break, or it may replace the root crop entirely on heavy land or under conditions where roots are a precarious and expensive crop to grow.

In recent years it has replaced to some extent the bare fallow on heavy land, for as the crop is cut in July in most seasons, it allows a bastard fallow to follow in preparation for autumn wheat. Moreover, the crop in itself can be regarded in the nature of a cleaning crop, for few can compare with a vigorous growth of oats, tares and peas in producing an efficient smothering effect on any weeds present, especially those like coltsfoot and couch grass which do not attain any great height.

PREPARATION OF SEED BED

The cultivation necessary for a cereal-legume crop is comparatively simple. The stubble is merely dunged and ploughed and the land worked down with disc harrows to prepare a tilth. The seed can then be sown towards the end of September or early October. Many farmers even go so far as to dispense with ploughing and cut the seed into the stubble with a disc drill, following this up with a light harrowing and rolling. For a spring-sown mixture the land is ploughed during the winter and left in the furrow. Cultivations will be carried out in spring as soon as the soil is dry enough to break down the furrows and prepare a seed bed.

MANURING

When farmyard manure is available it is always best to allow a moderate dressing of, say, 10 to 12 tons per acre, which can be ploughed in during autumn or winter.

Although oats will grow on land deficient in lime the leguminous crops in the mixture, the tares, peas, or beans require a sweet soil and any lime deficiency must be rectified. The lime is best applied after ploughing so that it can be worked into the surface soil where it is required by the plant.

In addition to dung and lime some phosphate is also required, and on the lighter types of soil potash too. On heavy soils 6 to 7 cwt. of high grade, high soluble basic slag or 4 cwt. per acre of superphosphate applied before sowing gives good results. On light soils 2 cwt. per acre potash salts should be given in addition to the slag or superphosphate.

Nitrogen is most important in the case of bulky crops like cereal-legume mixtures which are cut green, for here the danger of lodging does not arise. It is advisable, therefore, to apply not less than 1 cwt. per acre sulphate of ammonia or other nitrogenous fertiliser prior to sowing the seeds. This can be mixed with the superphosphate and potash salts, but when slag is used it is necessary to apply it separately. On the poorer classes of soil 2 cwt. per acre of a nitrogenous fertiliser would not be unduly generous.

In the case of an autumn-sown crop the application of nitrogen should be delayed until March or April.

Sowing the Seed

Winter mixtures are sown towards the end of September or early in October. Spring mixtures will be sown in March or April as soon as soil and weather conditions are favourable. If the normal type of drill is used for sowing a mixture including some beans, it is important to see that the beans are buried deeply enough or they may be taken by birds. There is no doubt that it is preferable to keep the beans separate from the rest of the mixture and sow them two to three weeks before the other constituents. Not only does this enable them to be placed out of reach of the birds, but it allows them to become well established before the tares which might otherwise smother them. Then, again, as already mentioned, it ensures that the beans are ready for cutting at the same time as the rest of the mixture.

After Cultivations

In spring it is usual to give the crop a good rolling to break up any surface "cap," level the land, and press any stones out of the way of the mowing-machine.

I

HARVESTING

Cereal-legume mixtures should be cut for silage when the oats have reached the "milky" stage and the legume is well podded. At this stage of ripeness the mixture contains an adequate supply of starchy material for the production of lactic acid fermentations, and there is, therefore, no need for the addition of molasses.

YIELD

The average yield of green crop from cereal-legume mixtures is 10 to 12 tons per acre, and this produces from 6 to 8 tons of silage per acre. On land in good heart and with generous manuring, as much as 20 tons per acre of green-stuff may be obtained.

Grass and clover mixtures may also be sown on arable land for silage making, and they have the advantage over the cereal-legume mixtures that a much higher quality type of silage is produced. Whereas cereal-legume silage is generally used as a substitute for hay or roots or part hay and roots, silage made from these grass and clover mixtures can be regarded more in the nature of a substitute for concentrated foods.

The following mixture, for instance, when sown on good land will give three cuts for silage in an average season, which means from eight to nine tons of silage per acre :—

Western Wolths or Express Ryegrass .	30 lb. per acre.	
Perennial Ryegrass	10 ,,	,,
Broad Red Clover	4 ,,	,,
	44 ,,	,,

The mixture can stand for two years, though it does not yield quite so well in the second year.

The following is also worth trying :—

Italian Ryegrass . . .	6 lb. per acre.	
Broad Red Clover (Dorset Marl)	8 ,,	,,
Mixed Alsike and White Clover	2 ,,	,,
Trefoil	2 ,,	,,
	18 ,,	,,

Both mixtures can be sown under a cereal nurse crop in the usual way, or under a cereal-legume to be cut for hay or silage.

The latter method has the advantage that as soon as the cereal-legume crop is removed valuable stubble grazing will be obtained, or if this is not required the field can be shut up and the aftermath cut for silage. Moreover, the early removal of the cereal-legume crop enables the grass and clover mixture to become well established.

VETCHES OR TARES

Vetches are one of the most useful crops we have for forage or ensilage, being reliable, easy to grow and of good feeding value. Now that silage is occupying a prominent role in the feeding programme on so many farms, tares are in great demand.

The crop is grown in all parts of Great Britain and thrives on a wide variety of soils from heavy to light conditions. The ideal soil is a deep loam in good heart and well supplied with lime. On poor soils the crop produces good yields of green forage if generously dunged, and many in recent years have found this to be much more profitable than leaving the old grass down.

VARIETIES

Two varieties are commonly grown, winter vetches and spring vetches. Little is known about the differences between these varieties other than the fact that the one is much hardier than the other. In the south of England it is best to sow the winter variety both in autumn and spring, whereas in the North the spring variety is generally regarded as safer.

PLACE IN ROTATION

Vetches do not occupy a fixed place in the rotation but usually follow a corn crop, to be followed immediately they are cut by a catch crop. When grown in mixture with cereals for ensilage the crop invariably replaces the whole or part of the root break.

PREPARATION AND SEEDING

When grown as a pure crop the seed is frequently broadcast on the plough seam and harrowed in. Occasionally the crop may be drilled direct on the stubble after harvest, cutting the seed in with a disc drill, but this is only possible when the land is moist and clean. Farmers who normally grow the crop for seed contend that by this method more seed and less haulm is produced. Certainly it is a useful means of filling up a thin stand of clover.

MANURING

The land should have an adequate supply of lime and be in good heart. Apart from this vetches are not unduly particular about manuring. Like most leguminous crops they respond well to applications of phosphates which tend to hasten maturity. On heavy land an application of 5 to 6 cwt. per acre basic slag, for instance, or 3 to 5 cwt. superphosphate on the lighter soils will be found beneficial. Sometimes on light sandy soils an excellent response to 2 cwt. per acre potash salts is obtained. Manuring should always precede sowing.

SOWING THE SEED

Winter vetches are sown any time after the end of September and spring vetches from February to April, but for feeding green they may be sown as late as June. When grown alone 1½ cwt. per acre of seed is required, and for mixtures including tares details will be found earlier in this chapter. The seed should be sown not deeper than 1 inch and afterwards carefully covered by harrowing, for if any seed is left on the surface, birds, particularly pigeons, are very troublesome. A good rolling to follow the harrowing completes the cultivations.

AFTER CULTIVATIONS

No after cultivations are given except perhaps a good rolling in spring when the crop has been sown in autumn.

UTILISATION

The crop offers wide scope and it may be cut and fed green, made into hay, or harvested for seed. Autumn-sown vetches are generally ready for cutting or folding towards the end of May, whilst spring-sown crops are ready in July. Thus, by sowing in breaks at different times from spring onwards a continuous supply of green food can be obtained. The ideal time to commence folding is when the plant is just coming into flower, but for hay it should be left until the pods are nicely formed.

For seed the crop is cut with a mower, fitted with a grain-lifting appliance, when the pods are full and the straw withered. Very careful turning is necessary to get the crop thoroughly dry, and in "catchy" weather it is advisable to cock it round tripods. It must not be carted until thoroughly dry, and is then stacked in narrow, well-ventilated stacks until threshing can take place. The stacks should be thatched immediately, for a good deal of seed is left on the outside and germinates once the top of the stack gets wet.

A more common practice is to grow vetches in combination with oats or beans, for these crops act as a good support for the rather straggling, weak-strawed plants, and not only enable the vetches to attain better development but greatly facilitate cutting. By reason of the difference in size of seed between, say, beans and vetches or oats and vetches, separation of the seed at threshing time is a simple matter.

YIELD

When grown alone vetches produce from 12 to 18 cwt. of seed per acre.

KALE

In recent years the kales have increased in popularity very considerably, for more and more farmers have come to realise the great possibilities of the crop as a provider of cheap and abundant succulent cattle food for winter. Few crops, indeed, can compare with it for ease of cultivation, resistance to wireworm attack, cropping capacity, and the simplicity with which it can be handled. Moreover, kale has a long period of utility during which it can remain growing, and the enormous amount of top growth produced during summer gives excellent weed suppression.

The crop can be grown over the whole range of soil and climatic conditions where roots are normally taken. When once well established it withstands prolonged drought, but naturally districts where the summer rainfall is high suit it best. Good-bodied loams, well supplied with lime, are ideal for the crop, yet it will give satisfactory yields on the thinner types of soil provided there is no stinting of manurial treatment.

VARIETIES

There are four sorts of kale commonly grown on a farm scale.

Marrow Stem Kale.—A variety with a thickened, fleshy stem, which can stand out until Christmas or even later in a mild winter. It may be either green or purple-stemmed, the former giving the heavier yield, whilst the latter is slightly more frost resistant.

Thousand-headed Kale is a much older variety than the marrow stem kale and derives its name from the mass of budded foliage it carries. The stem is not fleshy and hence the crop is more frost resistant. For this reason it is usually reserved for feeding after Christmas when the marrow stem kale is finished. It is a favourite crop for sheep folding.

Hungry Gap Kale was only introduced in 1933 and is a hybrid plant obtained by crossing late rape kale and giant winter rape. As its name implies, it fills the "hungry gap" of the year when the normal root crops are finished and the growth of grass is still not sufficient for the stock to be turned out. It is extremely hardy and can be used as late as June when the other kales have run to seed. This kale is not a substitute for either the marrow stem kale or thousand-headed varieties, and part of the kale acreage should always be allotted to the crop in order to provide sure feed late in the season.

Rape Kale.—This is another hybrid produced from rape and the ordinary curly kale. Sown in spring the crop can be cut in early winter, and if the stumps are left good second growth will be obtained in spring.

Both hungry gap kale and rape kale often give one the impression that the crop is dead in late winter, especially after severe weather. This is not the case, however, and both crops if left growing produce an abundance of keep in late spring.

PLACE IN ROTATION

Kales occupy part of the root break in most farm rotations. They can, however, be used for catch cropping, in which case it is common to sow them following early potatoes, a winter-sown silage crop, or even after a bastard fallow.

By sowing an acreage of each variety it is possible to have a continuous supply of green food from September to the following June. A start is made with the marrow stem kale in September and this is fed until December. Thousand-headed kale is then used until March or April, then the rape kale, and finally the hungry gap kale which can be fed until late June if necessary. Thus, on heavy wet land where the folding of roots is difficult kales can well replace this crop. All varieties have the advantage under such conditions that they stand up well and the edible parts are always clean. Moreover, by utilising the crop in this way the expense of lifting and clamping a root crop is avoided.

As cleaning crops the kales are unsurpassed and do well on ploughed-out grassland in good heart. Under conditions of high fertility kale is a much safer crop than the cereals, which are likely to lodge and cause trouble in harvesting.

Preparation of Seed Bed

The cultivation of the crop follows similar lines to that for swedes or turnips. Early ploughing is desirable to get a mellow and fine seed bed.

Wherever practicable an application of dung is highly desirable, and this should be applied preferably in the autumn and ploughed in. If this is inconvenient, dunging can be carried out in spring, and in cases where root crops are normally grown on the ridge the dung can be applied in the row in the usual way.

When the crop is grown on old grassland the success attained will depend to a considerable extent on obtaining firmness and fineness of tilth without disturbing the buried turf more than is necessary.

Manuring

The crop is a gross feeder, and even when grown on rich soils it still gives a satisfactory response to applications of artificial manures. The following mixtures are recommended for use in conjunction with about 15 tons of dung per acre and should be applied just prior to sowing the seed:—

	Existing Arable Land. Cwt. per Acre	Ploughed-up Grassland		
		Very good Grass. Cwt. per Acre	Average Grass. Cwt. per Acre	Poor Grass. Cwt. per Acre
Sulphate of Ammonia	2	1	2	3
Superphosphate	2	2	2	3
Steamed Bone Flour	1	1	1	1
Muriate of Potash	1	—	1	2
	6	4	6	9

In addition to the above a top-dressing of nitro-chalk or nitrate of soda at the rate of 1 cwt. per acre should be given before the final horse-hoeing. This should be scattered down the side of the rows so that the plants can utilise it immediately. On dairy farms where there is provision for collecting liquid manure, full use of this quick-acting fertiliser should be made for the kale crop. An application of about 1000 gallons per acre can be given prior to sowing the seed and a further application when the plants are singled. In the latter case, of course, it is necessary to apply the liquid manure when the leaves of the kale are wet, for when they are dry there is a danger that serious scorching may result. Used in this way "tankage" is a very valuable source of nitrogen, and a 1000 gallons may be regarded as roughly equivalent to 1 cwt. of sulphate of ammonia.

Whilst the kales are not so sensitive to soil sourness as beet, mangolds or swedes, it is always advisable to apply lime if there is a shortage in the soil. This, of course, should be broadcast after the final ploughing, being evenly distributed and well worked into the top soil.

Sowing the Seed

Sowing can commence as soon as soil and weather conditions are favourable in spring. The early sowings will produce the heaviest crops, but sowing can extend until mid-July or even August. The seed can be broadcast, drilled on the ridge or on the flat, or it may be sown in nursery beds for transplanting later.

On existing arable land, kale should be drilled at the rate of 4 lb. per acre. On ploughed-up grassland it must be drilled or broadcast on the flat, for ridging is out of the question. When drilled, the rows will be 25 to 30 inches apart and the rate of seeding 4 lb. per acre. When sown broadcast 5 lb. of seed is required, and in order to ensure uniform distribution it is advisable to increase the bulk of the seed by mixing it with some such substance as fine sand.

For transplanting 1½ lb. of seed will produce enough plants for 1 acre of land. Transplanting takes place in May or June in rows about 2 feet wide with 18 inches between plants in the rows. This method is worth considering in wet districts and in late springs when drilling is likely to be delayed. It also lessens risk from attacks of turnip fly. If the plants are purchased about 15,000 per acre will be required.

Hungry gap or rape kale should be sown from June to August, the best results in the Eastern Counties being obtained from June sowings. When sown in spring it is ready in early winter.

The seed should be sown in fine moist soil, just covered with a light harrow and then rolled.

AFTER CULTIVATIONS

It is sound practice to roll the crop at the seedling stage, for this encourages moisture at the root and helps the plants to get away. Inter-row hoeing can commence as soon as the rows are seen on the flat or even before this when the crop is sown on the ridge.

Kale which has been drilled should be singled, leaving 12 to 18 inches between plants in the row. Many farmers now omit this operation, contending that the stems of the marrow stem in particular do not become so coarse and thick when left unthinned. This is true, but on the other hand yield is generally sacrificed in this way, and to get the utmost from the crop each plant must have adequate room for development. In the case of a broadcast crop which is grown as a catch crop this is not important, for the length of time allowed for growth is not usually sufficient for the plants to develop fully. If preferred, however, a broadcast crop may be thinned by running the harrows through it. For sheep folding the crop is best left unthinned.

HARVESTING

A spring-sown crop is ready for feeding from September onwards. Sheep may be folded upon it, but for cattle the stems should be cut at ground level and the plants carted on to grass or into the cowshed. For cows it is an advantage to pass the kale through the root slicer, for this facilitates feeding and better consumption of the stems is obtained.

If the supply of marrow stem kale is greater than can be utilised by the New Year the surplus should be cut as early as possible in autumn and made into silage. Alternatively the leaf tops can be used immediately and the succulent stems stored in pits or clamps for use later in the winter.

The woody stumps left in the ground when the tops are removed often cause a good deal of trouble when the land is ploughed in preparation for the following crop. An excellent means of dealing with them is to run a potato spinner down the rows, for this effectively brings them on to the surface where they can be collected and carted off.

YIELD

The average yield is in the region of 20 tons per acre, but kale under good management yields 30 to 40 tons per acre.

Thousand-headed kale can be fed off in autumn, again in early spring and yet again in early summer, if eaten each time before the "sprout" stage.

Rape kale can be cut or grazed in early winter and produces second growth in April.

Hungry gap kale finds its greatest use in late spring when the other kales are finished. It is not uncommon to see crops 6 to 7 feet in height in June. The leaves and stems are also of use as a table vegetable. The short side-stems should be broken off about May, and tied into bunches in a similar manner to that adopted for asparagus. When boiled they are tender and juicy with a flavour similar to that of asparagus.

PESTS AND DISEASES

Apart from occasional seasonal attacks of turnip fly and root maggot, kales are singularly trouble-free crops. Rooks sometimes cause damage by uprooting the plants, but in these cases the birds are invariably in search of wireworms.

Though not immune to finger-and-toe disease kale is highly resistant.

CABBAGES

Few crops have such a wide range of use as the cabbage. It is a safe food for all classes of stock, being especially useful for milk cows, is frequently fed to pigs and poultry, is extensively used for keeping both cattle and sheep in show condition and, when suitable varieties are grown, has a good market value for human consumption. Moreover, unlike so many crops it may be fed immature if necessary, and if the stumps are left in the ground after the heads are removed fresh leaves develop which are useful for sheep. The great disadvantage of the crop is that it cannot be stored nor does it make good silage. The heads must be consumed soon after they reach full development, for they are liable to split and decay if left standing. This applies especially to the flat-topped varieties.

Cabbages contain a high percentage of water, and hence the prime need for successful growth is an adequate supply of moisture during the growing season. Under dry conditions full development is impossible, and indeed considerable difficulty will be experienced both in getting a plant established and in combating the activities of the root maggot. Provided the soil contains an adequate supply of lime, is in good heart and well drained, the crop succeeds on a wide variety of soils. Ideal conditions are found on moist, heavy soils and in seasons with plenty of sunshine.

VARIETIES

There are a large number of varieties which for convenience may be roughly grouped as follows:—

1. *Early Varieties.*—These are sown in March, planted out in April to May and are ready for consumption in August or September. The seed may also be sown in May and the plants put out in June or July following a forage crop. In these circumstances the crop is ready from October onwards. Sown in August, on the other hand, these varieties are ready about July of the following year.

Suitable varieties in this class are Winningstadt, Early Drumhead, Early Express, Early Sheepfold and Enfield Market.

2. *Late or Main-crop Varieties.*—These varieties require a long time to reach maturity, but they produce enormous crops, being used chiefly for stock purposes.

The seed may be sown in March for planting out in April to May, and although the cabbages will not be hearted until November they keep sound for several months after. More frequently, however, the seed is sown in a bed in August, and left here over winter to be planted out in April or the plants may be dibbled out in October. When planting out is left until spring the crop is not ready before September, but when set out in autumn part of the crop may be ready for cutting the following July and can be safely left out until Christmas if not required before.

In this group are the Cattle Savoys, Drumheads and Late Ox-hearts.

PLACE IN ROTATION

Being a cleaning crop cabbages usually occupy part of the root break. As they can be transplanted with success they are frequently grown in place of swedes on heavy land where good seed beds are difficult to obtain. Mangolds are then grown for late feeding. Occasionally the crop may alternate with mangolds on the same land for a number of years.

PREPARATION OF SEED BED

Stubble cleaning is necessary as for any other root crop. A heavy dressing of dung, 20 tons or more per acre, can then be applied and ploughed in. Many prefer to plough the dung in fairly shallow and cross-plough as deeply as possible later in winter, for by so doing the dung is not buried too deeply.

When the crop is being drilled, a fine firm tilth comparable with that required by mangolds should be prepared. This fine tilth is necessary because the seed is small and also because it enables the crop to grow away rapidly from the "turnip fly."

The seed is sown with an ordinary root drill at the rate of 4 lb. per acre in rows 24 to 30 inches apart, the seedlings being gapped from 18 to 24 inches apart, depending upon the variety.

As the cost of singling is about the same as for dibbling out, and the plants get a much later start when the seed is drilled, the more common method is to purchase the plants or to sow the seed in nursery beds and transplant when ready. When purchased, from 5000 to 10,000 plants are required per acre, according to spacing, the price usually varying from 5s. to 15s. per 1000, depending upon supply and demand.

When the plants are to be grown on the farm a sheltered piece of ground should be selected and a fine tilthy seed bed prepared. Superphosphate at the rate of 3 cwt. per acre should be applied during the harrowing of the bed, for this encourages good root development. The seed is broadcast at the rate of 20 lb. per acre, being lightly harrowed in and then rolled. From an acre bed sufficient plants should be obtained to plant about 20 acres in the field.

Manuring

The crop responds in a full measure to generous manuring. Dung is the basis of this treatment and, as already indicated, 20 tons per acre or more should be applied and ploughed in during the autumn or winter. When the crop is grown on the ridge the dung is frequently applied in the ridge, but this is only common in districts of fairly high rainfall.

In addition to the dung the following mixture of fertilisers should be applied prior to planting:—

Sulphate of Ammonia	. .	1 cwt. per acre.
Superphosphate .	. .	2 ,, ,,
Steamed Bone Flour	. .	2 ,, ,,
Muriate of Potash .	. .	1 ,, ,,
		6 ,, ,,

During the growing season two or three top-dressings of nitrate of soda, each 1 cwt. per acre, or other quick-acting nitrogenous fertiliser will prove beneficial. These top-dressings are best applied by hand, sprinkling the fertiliser round the plants so that the roots may immediately take it up. Where generous applications of dung have been given or on heavy classes of soil the potash may be omitted.

Planting

Planting may be carried out in any of the following ways:—

1. *On the Flat.*—The field is marked out in two directions according to the required spacing by means of a seed drill which has its coulters set to the desired intervals. The plants are then inserted at the intersections of the marks, and this enables subsequent horse-hoeing to be made both across as well as along the length of the rows.

2. *On the Ridge.*—The field is drawn up into ridges 24 to 30 inches apart and the plants dibbled in along the ridge tops.

3. *In the Furrow.*—Early crops on free draining soils are sometimes set in the furrows between narrow ridges. The furrows are drawn with the double mould-board plough and the plants are then set along the bottom. The ridges provide some shelter from frosty winds.

4. *Ploughing in.*—Here the plants are laid by hand along each third furrow slice and are covered by the next furrow. It is advisable, particularly in dry weather, to follow this up by actually pressing each plant firmly into the soil by "heeling" them in with the feet. This method of planting is impossible in windy weather.

5. *By Transplanter.*—For large acreages the Robot transplanter is now commonly used. This ingenious machine is capable of planting 12,000 per hour and is most reliable even in unskilled hands.

The soil should be firm and moist at planting time if good establishment is to be obtained. For dibbling a spade or a bricklayer's trowel is preferable to a dibble stick. The trowel should be stuck into the ground and pulled forward to leave a cavity behind. The plant is then inserted, taking care to see that the tap-root is not bent and the leaf bases are not covered with soil. The trowel is then removed and the plant "heeled" in.

AFTER CULTIVATIONS

The crop usually requires two or three horse-hoeings with perhaps some hand-hoeing. Any blanks should be filled in by dibbling, and for this purpose it is advisable to retain a small reserve of plants in the nursery bed.

YIELD

On good land a yield of 30 tons per acre may be expected, but with generous treatment and in favourable seasons yields of 60 tons per acre are by no means uncommon.

The crop is left in the field until required, and if when the heads are cut the large bottom leaves are left on the stem, a further crop of small leaves will be produced which provides excellent sheep keep. Flat-topped drumheads which are more prone to top decay should be used first and the hardy savoys left until last.

PESTS AND DISEASES

The root maggot sometimes causes serious damage to cabbage, affected plants wilting in the field and subsequently dying completely. When these are pulled up the white maggots can often be seen attached to the roots which are completely devoid of all rootlets.

Remedial measures can be adopted on a small scale, but these are, as yet, too expensive for general use on a field scale.

Club root or finger-and-toe disease which is so troublesome in swedes and turnips may also affect cabbages. Here, again, control measures are not adapted for general application to field crops, and the precaution should be taken of using only plants which are free from disease at the outset. On a small scale good control can be obtained by pouring half a pint of corrosive sublimate solution (1 in 2000) into each hole and allowing this to drain away before inserting the plant. The treatment will also check attacks of root maggots, but since this chemical is an extremely dangerous poison, great care must be exercised in its use.

RAPE

Rape can be regarded as a turnip without a swollen root, in place of which it has a stem covered with foliage. In some varieties the leaves are like those of the swede and in others rough like the turnip. It is usually folded off with sheep or cattle, but may, if required, be cut and fed green. It makes excellent silage and is frequently used as a nurse crop for grass and clover mixture when sowing land to grass, especially in the case of August seedings.

The crop does best in the cool damp districts of the North and North-west, for when sown early in the South it is susceptible to mildew. Wet, sunless seasons are not favourable, and although it grows on a wide range of soil conditions from clay to sand the crop prefers medium loams well supplied with lime. On fen soils it frequently attains a height of 4 feet.

VARIETIES

Giant Rape has a smooth leaf and long tap root and is best suited to soils in good heart.

Essex Dwarf has a rough leaf, a fibrous root and is well adapted to the heavier classes of soil.

PLACE IN ROTATION

Rape may be sown any time during spring and summer and produces feed three months after sowing. It may be used as a catch crop after early peas or potatoes or mixed with green-top turnips for autumn and winter feed, whilst it is sometimes mixed with lupins for August and September feeding. When used as a rotation crop it naturally takes the place of roots.

A mixture of 6 lb. rape and 1 lb. turnips broadcast in standing beans during horse-hoeing provides an excellent stubble bite. In August, after harvest, a mixture of 10 lb. Italian ryegrass and 4 lb. rape can be disced into the stubble to give an early spring bite.

PREPARATION OF SEED BED

Cultivations will follow similar lines to those required for root crops. Moisture is all-important for quick and regular germination and a good rolling following seeding is advisable. When grown as a catch crop care must be taken to get a reasonably good seed bed. Too frequently, only scanty cultivations are given or the soil is too dry to work satisfactorily and patchy crops are obtained.

MANURING

Liberal manuring finds a ready response from the crop, and whenever available a dressing of dung is advisable. When grown as a catch crop rape generally has to rely upon the plant food left in the soil by the previous crop and frequently this is not sufficient to give a really good yield. The soil must be well supplied with lime.

When a moderate dressing of dung has been applied the following mixture should be given prior to sowing the seed:—

Sulphate of Ammonia . .	1 cwt. per acre,
Superphosphate . . .	2 ,, ,,
	$\overline{3}$,, ,,

with a top-dressing of nitrogenous fertiliser at the rate of 1 cwt. per acre when dung is not available.

SOWING THE SEED

The time of sowing depends upon the purpose for which the crop is required and the nature of the preceding crop.

In districts subject to late spring frosts sowing should be delayed, but elsewhere a start can be made in late March or April. The heaviest crops are obtained by drilling in rows 10 to 12 inches apart at the rate of 2 to 4 lb. of seed per acre. More frequently, however, the seed is broadcast, in which case 10 to 12 lb. per acre may be required. When rape is used as a nurse crop for seeds it should not be sown too thickly if danger of smothering the grasses and clovers is to be avoided. On most soils 2 lb. per acre is quite sufficient to give a good "nurse."

AFTER CULTIVATIONS

None are necessary.

YIELD AND UTILISATION

Grazing should commence before the crop becomes very strong, and provided it is not grazed too hard recovery is rapid and several bites can be obtained. It is particularly valuable for finishing lambs or for flushing ewes at tupping time. Care must be taken, however, to prevent stock from gorging themselves, and it is unwise to turn them on to fresh rape with an empty stomach.

A yield of 10 tons of green crop per acre is obtained under average conditions.

K

Chapter Four

ROOT CROPS FOR SALE

SUGAR BEET

THE sugar-beet crop has advantages uncommon to most of our root crops. In the first place, the guaranteed price which is paid for the crop is based upon the quality of the crop and payment is made within a month of delivery to the factory. Moreover, the leaves and crowns of the roots which are left in the field are of high feeding value for sheep or cattle and for this purpose are comparable with swedes. A further by-product of the crop is the pulp which can be purchased from the factory, every grower of beet having the first call on $1\frac{1}{2}$ cwt. of pulp for every ton of beet delivered.

The normal English season is ideally suited for sugar beet growing. The long growing season permits full development of the root, thereby producing high yields per acre, whilst the relatively large amount of daylight and the comparatively cool temperature promote sugar production. The result is that we are able with good management to produce a combination of high yield and sugar content giving high yields of sugar per acre.

The most suitable soil for beet is a deep, well-drained medium to light loam, with a retentive subsoil, an adequate lime content, free from stones and from the presence of a plough pan or iron pan which would impede the penetration of the root into the soil. It is true, of course, that the crop can, and is, grown over a wide range of soils from heavy clays to light, blow-away sands. On heavy soils, however, increased difficulties of harvesting are experienced, for at that time of the year the soil is frequently wet and sticky. In addition, good seed beds are difficult to obtain on heavy soils unless the ploughing has been done early in autumn and the land given the opportunity of being mellowed by the frosts of winter. On the lighter soils, sugar contents are high but low yields are obtained.

VARIETIES

The most suitable variety for any set of conditions is the one that produces the maximum yield of sugar per acre. During recent years the National Institute for Agricultural Botany has conducted many field trials at centres throughout the country, and their recommendations which are of great value to growers are embodied in the list below.

Three types of sugar beet seed are produced by the breeders and are designated respectively, "E," "N," and "Z" strains. The "E" types give high yields of roots per acre combined with average sugar contents, whilst the "Z" types are bred for high sugar contents. The "N" types generally fall between these two extremes. For most purposes the "E" or "N" types are best suited to our conditions.

The variety Klein. E has consistently given good results in trials throughout the country. The yield is high and the sugar content is satisfactory, and this variety can be relied upon to give good yields of sugar per acre under a wide range of soil conditions. Seldom has it been surpassed by any other variety. The "N" strains can be recommended as good general purpose varieties. The "Z" strains are especially suited to late soils where the other strains would tend to give rather low sugar contents. Marster's British Hilleshog has small tops with short cone-shaped roots, and owing to its great resistance to bolting is well suited for early sowings.

On rich silt and fen soils the "E" strains are likely to produce a cumbersome amount of top which constitutes a nuisance at lifting time. Moreover, in these districts the need for feeding them on the land for manurial purposes is not so acute, and thus the smaller topped varieties such as Marster's, Webb's and Johnson's are to be preferred. On soils where there is a tendency to produce top at the expense of sugar content, and also where lifting will take place before mid-October, the high sugar "Z" strains should be grown.

Before the war the bulk of our seed came from the Continent, but it is now produced at home and growers have the choice of some eighteen strains, the best known being tabulated on page 148.

BOLTING

When sugar beet behaves as an annual producing seed in the first year, and not as a biennial as it normally does, it is said to have "bolted." Such plants are usually of two kinds, those

" E Strains "	" N Strains "	" Z Strains "
Sharpe's Klein. E. (R.). Cannell's Nos. 22 and 937. Garton's C. Johnson's Perfection "E" (R.S.). Battle's Dippe "E." British S.K.W. (L.). Goldsmith's Dobrovice (L.). Bush "E." (L.).	Johnson's Perfection N. (R.). Webb's No. 2 (R.). Kuhn. P. (S.R.). Garton's B.	Marster's British Hilleshog (R.).

S—small topped variety.
L—very large topped variety.
R—very resistant to bolting.

which bolt early in life, and those which do not start "running" until about the middle of the growing period. The former tend to be woody and fibrous, and if sent to the factory with normal roots will not only cause damage to the slicing knives but may lower the sugar content of the sample taken for analysis. These early bolters have a much lower sugar content than normal beet, and hence, should one or more appear in the factory sample for sugar analysis, the sugar content for the whole consignment would be reduced since the sample is taken as representative of the whole. Thus the grower is likely to lose money and for this reason early bolters should be pulled up and discarded. Later bolters, on the other hand, contain almost as much sugar as normal roots and can be handled in the usual way, although it is advisable to snap off the tops at the first sign of bolting. In the early days of beet growing in this country, bolting was considered a somewhat serious problem, but present varieties are highly resistant to the condition, and in any case the percentage of bolters in a crop constitutes a negligible proportion of the total crop even though the appearance may look serious. To some extent bolting is dependent upon season, for with a check in growth in the early part of the year the tendency is increased.

PLACE IN ROTATION

As a rule the crop occupies part of the root break, and about half the root shift on a four-course farm can be replaced by sugar beet without any additional labour being required. For every 25 acres of beet beyond this limit an additional two men will be required. By utilising the tops for feeding and purchasing pulp from the factory it is possible to maintain the same head of livestock as formerly when the whole root acreage was devoted to feeding roots. Thus a feeding crop can be replaced by a cash crop without sacrificing the stocking of the farm.

Under the terms of the contract a grower is not permitted to take beet on land which has grown beet or mangolds the previous year for fear of spreading the disease known as "beet sickness," a serious pest in Continental beet districts. Nor is it possible for beet to follow turnips or swedes unless the two preceding crops were not root crops. Potatoes are not considered a root crop for this purpose and thus on fen soils beet frequently follows potatoes, which crop forms an excellent preparatory crop for sugar beet.

Spring corn is the best following crop, as this allows plenty of time for lifting. The labour can therefore be utilised to best advantage and rush periods are evened out. Where wheat follows beet there is always the risk that the land will not be ready in good time to drill the wheat, a point of considerable importance in the cultivation of this crop.

Preparation of the Seed Bed

Clean land is essential for the successful growth of the crop, the young plant being very susceptible in the early stages of growth to the smothering effects of weeds. Normally beet follows a cereal crop and stubble cleaning is essential before the farmyard manure is carted out. The stubble should be shallow ploughed or cultivated to such a depth as to get under the roots of twitch and other creeping weeds. Care must be taken to keep the weeds as large as possible, for this will facilitate combing them out. To chop them into small pieces, as would happen, for instance, if a disc harrow were used, would mean that it would be well-nigh impossible to collect all the pieces up and many would therefore remain to produce plants the following year.

Subsequent harrowings work the weeds to the surface where they can be collected and burnt. It is well to remember in this connection that it is far easier and cheaper to clean a field in autumn, weather permitting, than to wait until the following spring and summer when much costly hand work may be necessary.

Early and deep ploughing is advisable to allow the winter frost to produce a fine tilth for seeding. This will also allow the furrows to settle and consolidate naturally, thereby producing a firm seed bed which is very desirable. Should the subsoil be stiff or gravelly, or a plough pan or iron pan be suspected, it is advisable to subsoil in addition to ploughing. Suitable attachments for fixing to the plough to enable ploughing and subsoiling to be carried out together can be obtained at small cost and their use is strongly recommended. A fine, firm seed bed is a good start for the crop and late ploughing should be avoided wherever possible. Care should be taken to prevent undue dissipation of soil moisture in the top soil by carrying out an excessive number of spring cultivations. This invariably results in uneven germination and a patchy crop. By far the best seed bed is a good frost mould.

Manuring

Sugar beet is a gross feeder and requires generous applications of well-balanced fertilisers in addition to an ample supply of lime.

Farmyard manure generally forms the basis of the manuring, although if it has been applied to the previous crop no further dressing need be given. The nature and amount of artificial fertilisers given in addition will naturally depend upon the condition of the land, the manuring of the previous crop, and the type of soil. For light or medium loam soils when dung has been given the following mixture will be found suitable :—

Sulphate of Ammonia or ⎫	
Nitro-Chalk or ⎬ . 3 cwt. per acre.	
Nitrate of Soda ⎭	
Superphosphate . 3 ,, ,,	
Muriate of Potash . 1 ,, ,,	

This mixture does not store well and hence should be applied as soon after mixing as possible. Evidence from innumerable trials throughout the country has shown conclusively that there is no advantage in retaining part of the nitrogenous fertilisers for application after singling. Rich fen soils may not require any nitrogen, and in cases where a light application is considered advisable nitrate of soda is recommended.

As a substitute for the superphosphate, high soluble basic slag may be used. Good results have been obtained from the use of 10 cwt. per acre of an 80 per cent. citric soluble slag which should, however, be applied in winter or early spring before sowing the seed. The use of slag is particularly recommended on soils which are not too well supplied with lime.

Trials carried out at Rothamsted Experimental Station show that on most soils sugar beet responds well to salt, and when this is used an increased yield of sugar per acre is obtained. An application of 5 cwt. per acre of agricultural salt is recommended, and this should be applied as long before sowing the seed as possible. When salt is applied as a seed-bed application germination may be affected adversely.

Liming where necessary is essential. The sugar beet is one of our most sensitive crops to lack of lime, and in all cases where a deficiency is suspected steps must be taken to remedy the shortage. Lime is best applied some months or at any rate weeks before the seed is sown so that it can become well mixed with the soil. Following liming, surface cultivations only should be carried out, as otherwise the lime will be buried to too great a depth to be of service.

Sowing

Sowing should begin as soon as soil and weather conditions are suitable in spring. When large acreages are involved sowings are spread over a period of weeks to enable the operation of singling to be likewise spaced, thus the available labour will be able to cope with the task at the right time. When this is the practice, it is very important to make an early start with sowing, otherwise the last sowings may be unduly late and the yield likely to suffer. As a general rule the first weeks of April are ideal, but it is well to remember that this depends upon the season and that nothing is gained by sowing the seed in a cold damp soil.

Unlike most of our other crops the seed is supplied by the factory who charge the grower with the bare cost. There is little gained by sowing the seed sparingly, and whilst the normal rate of seeding recommended is 15 pounds per acre, 20 pounds can be used with advantage where soil conditions are unkind as, for instance, on heavy soils which are inclined to bake on the surface, or for the earliest sowings. The seed is supplied ready dressed with one of the mercuric seed dressings as a precautionary measure against seed-borne diseases such as "root blight."

The seed should be drilled on the flat in rows 18 to 20 inches apart and at a depth not exceeding ¾ inch. Ridging is not recommended, for this practice usually results in a lower plant population—and therefore lower yield—and it favours the depredations of hares and rabbits. Although in the early days of beet growing over here drilling on the ridge was fairly common, few growers now continue to do so, having found from experience that flat drilling is much superior. Many suitable drills are available, those fitted with single-wheel rollers behind each coulter of the drill being extremely good. In most cases, however, the normal root drill will be used or the corn drill after it has been adapted for drilling the wider spaced rows. An economy in both seed and the time taken for singling can be effected by using a spacing drill, which sows the seed in small clusters at intervals instead of a continuous line as in the case of normal drills. The serious drawback to the more widespread use of these drills is the fact that should one of the little clusters of seed, spaced, say, 10 inches apart, fail to grow, the inter-plant distance is then 20 inches, and many such failures would mean a serious reduction in yield. Under good soil conditions where the seed is likely to get away well each year, the use of a spacing drill is advantageous. A recent development is the use of "sheared" or individual beet seeds separated from the fruit mechanically. Less seed is required and the labour of singling is reduced.

AFTER CULTIVATIONS

Inter-row cultivations should commence as soon as the rows can be seen, continuing as long as possible without damaging the tops. Care should be taken that the young plants are not smothered with soil in the first hoeing and it is advisable to use disc hoes for this reason. There is perhaps no cultural operation which has more influence on the final yield than that of singling, and it is essential that an early start be made. The ideal time to commence singling is when the first rough leaves are forming, although growers with large acreages may start when the plant is still in the two-leaf stage. Evidence from many field trials indicates in no uncertain manner that delay in singling is serious, and up to one ton of beet per acre may be lost for each week that the operation is delayed. Equally important to the time at which the operation is carried out is the skill with which the task is done. A space of 10 inches should be left between plants in the row, and whilst there is seldom any advantage to be gained from leaving the plants closer together than this, too wide a spacing will reduce the plant population to a point at which the yield is likely to be reduced. For the spacing recommended an 8-inch hoe is required, although a skilled worker might use a 9-inch blade.

Hand labour in chopping out can be economised by using a mechanical gapper which cuts out the unwanted plants and leaves small clumps which can be singled to one plant later. For machine gapping the plant should be rather bigger than for hand work, and after gapping the crop is left for a few days before attempting to single. This allows the unwanted plants to die and the others to straighten up, which facilitates singling. Cross-blocking performs the same function in a rather different way. Here a multiple hoe is taken across the rows at right angles to the direction of drilling, and the blades are set to leave bunches of plants about two inches in width. In either case a full "braird" is essential and no attempt should be made to adopt these methods if the plant is gappy. Another point which has considerable bearing on the yield is to leave the strongest plant in the cluster when finally singling down to one plant. It is also advisable to firm the soil around the plant which remains, for should it be damaged a check in growth is bound to result. For this reason many growers prefer to single by hand after first gapping the plant by machine or hand hoe. In any case, careful supervision at singling time is necessary, and the provision of a bonus for piece-workers is a sound investment in that it encourages more careful work. Under such a scheme each worker would single a certain plot of land on which the plant population can be checked. Where the required number of plants per chain length of row is left the bonus (say 10s. per acre) is paid, but if the number falls below the required standard a deduction of sixpence for each 5 per cent. below this figure is made.

As a rule it is necessary to aim at horse-hoeing the crop once a week, or at any rate whenever weeds are present. In order to reduce damage to the fine rootlets the later hoeings should be shallow with the hoes set not too close to the plants in the row.

HARVESTING

Under the terms of his contract a grower undertakes to deliver his crop to the factory at equal intervals throughout the lifting season, and this consideration determines the stage of the crop at which harvesting commences. Lifting usually extends from October to December. In many seasons the roots continue to increase in weight and sugar content until the end of October, and hence growers with large acreages, who of necessity must lift before this time, should aim at drilling part of their acreage early in the season with an early maturing variety. At the end of November the risk of frost damage increases, and every endeavour should be made, therefore, to get the crop lifted before then. When the crop cannot be delivered to the factory immediately it should be clamped in large heaps near to a good road.

On light soils the beet can be lifted by hand, but on other soils a horse or tractor lifter is necessary to loosen the roots in the ground before they can be pulled up. They are then pulled by hand, knocked together to remove as much soil as possible, and laid out in rows ready for topping. The top should be severed from the crown at the level of the lowest leaf scars. Here, again, efficient work is necessary, for too drastic topping is wasteful, whilst insufficient topping means the cartage to the factory of unnecessary material. Not only does this increase the transport charges, but re-topping is carried out at the factory and an appropriate deduction for "tare" made.

The crowns and leaves should be left in neat rows and not scattered over the field, especially if they are later to be folded with sheep or carted off for silage. In the former case, the sheep will walk between the rows if they are left in this way and little waste results from them being trodden into the soil. In the latter case, good silage can only be made from clean tops, and it is essential, therefore, to see that the tops are kept as free from soil as possible.

For many years now attempts have been made to perfect a machine that would successfully lift, clean and top sugar beet. Several of these machines are now being developed, and it is likely that in the near future an efficient machine will be evolved, though the problem is rendered extremely difficult by the lack of uniformity in the size of the roots to be handled.

It is in the growers' interest to send as clean beet as possible to the factory, for the price paid is for clean beet. Both tare weight and sugar content are estimated for each delivery whether it be a cart, barge, or railway truck load.

YIELD

The average yield per acre for the country as a whole is in the region of 9 tons of washed beet, but the yield on very fertile land in favourable years frequently reaches as much as 20 tons per acre. The average sugar content registers about 16 per cent., but here again wide variations exist from season to season and on the different classes of soil, it being not uncommon to record 20 per cent.

As mentioned earlier in this chapter the by-products of the crop are of considerable importance, and a 10-ton crop of roots provides under average conditions about the same weight of tops together with half a ton of dried pulp. The amount of tops produced naturally depends upon the variety, the season, and the manuring, and frequently the weight of them out-yields that of roots. As regards feeding value, the tops are equal, weight for weight, with swedes, whilst the pulp is equal to eight times its weight of swedes. Thus a 10-ton crop of beet will have an equivalent feeding value to a 14-ton crop of swedes if the tops and pulp are utilised, and in addition there is the cash return on the roots sent to the factory.

INSECT PESTS

Cut-worms or Surface Caterpillars.—These are the common names given to the caterpillars of certain moths. The grubs usually spend the day in the surface layers of the soil or hidden under stones or leaves. At night, they come out to feed, sometimes on the leaves of the beet but more frequently on the stems and roots about ground level. In severe cases the stems of small plants will be completely severed from the root and serious damage results. When the larger roots are attacked the damage generally takes the form of large cavities in the root, but at this stage serious damage is unlikely.

Control Measures.—The most effective means of control, when the cut-worms are present in such numbers as to constitute a menace to the crop, is to broadcast a poison bait composed of bran mixed with Paris green. The mixture consists of 20 to 30 lb. of bran, to which is added 1 lb. of Paris green moistened with sufficient water to make it just crumbly. This quantity of bait is sufficient to treat an acre and should be broadcast over the crop towards nightfall.

Flea Beetles.—These are small black beetles about one-tenth of an inch long, the pest being comparable with the familiar "fly" which is such a menace to turnip crops. The beetles feed on the young leaves, and if present in large numbers may ruin a crop, though such an occurrence is comparatively rare in the case of beet.

Control measures are discussed on page 200 in connection with the swede crop.

Wireworms.—When present in large numbers wireworms may cause serious damage by eating into the young root.

Control Measures are entirely cultural, and every endeavour must be made to push the plant ahead of an attack by frequent hoeings and top-dressing with nitrogenous fertiliser. An application of calcium cyanamide at the rate of 4 cwt. per acre to the seed bed one month before sowing the seed, has proved a successful deterrent in some cases. Success has attended the use of wheat as a bait crop, and the method consists of drilling wheat between the rows of beet to attract the wireworms away from the beet seedlings. The use of a soil insecticide such as benzene hexachloride has given good results.

Blister Fly.—Pale blotches or blisters on the leaves are due to the presence of the grubs of the Blister or Mangold fly which feeds on the inner tissues of the leaf. On holding an affected leaf up to the light the presence of the grub can be detected. Later the blisters become brown and withered and as a result the health of the plant suffers. A severe attack, when the plants are in the early stages of growth, may be fatal, but when the attack comes late in the season little serious damage is likely to result.

Control Measures.—These are largely cultural and consist in encouraging the plant to grow away from the pest by cultivation and by giving a top-dressing of nitrogenous fertiliser. When the plant is small rolling has proved effective, unless the soil is very light and dry when more harm than good may be done.

Black Fly or Aphis.—This is a common pest of beet particularly in dry seasons. The black fly or aphis, sometimes called "smother flies," congregate on the under surface of the leaves and, sucking the sap, cause them to curl up, wilt, shrivel and die. The aphides multiply rapidly when conditions are favourable and are extremely difficult to control because of the curling of the leaves.

Control Measures.—The pest first appears in patches, and if control measures are commenced immediately, whilst the colonies are small, the trouble may be prevented from spreading. Treatment consists of dusting with a nicotine dust of which reliable proprietary brands are obtainable. For small acreages good results can be obtained with small hand sprayers, but for large areas a horse-drawn implement is necessary. Fortunately such sprayers can be hired from the beet factories from whom the dusting material can also be obtained. It is important, of course, that the powder should reach the under surface of the leaves where the flies are situated, and the nozzles of the sprayer must therefore be placed near to the ground and the cloud of dust directed upwards.

A machine capable of subjecting infested plants to a fifty-seconds' concentration of nicotine gas which is sufficient to obtain a 100 per cent. "kill" has now been perfected. Whilst specially designed for eradicating aphis on crops grown for seed, it is likely that the machine will have a much wider application.

Beet Sickness or Eelworm.—This is the most serious of beet pests, but so far good steps have been taken to limit its spread in this country. The condition is due to the presence in large numbers of eelworms, encouraged by repeatedly growing beet or mangolds on the same land. The life history of the pest is simple. Brown cysts, the size of a pin head, are present in large numbers in infected soil and from these young eelworms hatch out. The hatching is stimulated by a substance excreted from the tips of the rootlets of susceptible plants. On emergence, the eelworms bore in to the rootlets and feeding there cause extensive injury to the rooting system. Later the female eelworms swell up, become distended with eggs and break their way through the sides of the rootlets. These develop into cysts and remain in the soil until the following spring when the life cycle begins again.

The first symptoms of attack are patches of under-sized plants in a field. The outer leaves wilt in the sunshine and later turn yellow and die, whilst the heart leaves are under-sized. On pulling up an infected root it will be found to possess a large number of small lateral rootlets forming a beard. These are known as "hunger roots" and large numbers of cysts will be seen attached to them.

Control Measures.—The beet eelworm can be prevented from establishing itself by strict adherence to rotation. Beet or mangolds should not be grown more than once in three or four years, which must be increased to five or seven years on infected land. Cruciferous crops should also be avoided.

DISEASES

Black Leg.—When a plant is attacked with this disease the seedling wilts and the root becomes blackened and thread-like. Four fungi are associated with the cause of the trouble, one being seed borne, and the others present in the soil.

Control Measures.—Against the soil types of fungi there are no control measures other than sowing plenty of seed and making every endeavour to obtain a good seed bed to encourage rapid establishment of the seedlings. As a precautionary measure against the other diseases the seed is dressed with one of the mercuric seed dressings before it is despatched to the farm.

Strangles.—As the name implies this disease causes the top to be severed from the root by a slow process of strangulation. The constriction forms about soil level and rapid growth follows both above and below this point although not immediately beneath it. As a result this constitutes a weak point and quite a large number of plants will be lost by the tops breaking off. The actual cause of the trouble has never been finally solved, but several theories have been put forward in explanation. Some research workers consider that it is a secondary stage in an attack of Black-leg, others that it is due to mechanical damage by the wind, whilst still more, that it is caused by the bites of innumerable small insects known as Springtails.

Control Measures.—Although the cause of the trouble has not been settled good control of the pest or disease can be obtained by slightly earthing up the plants as soon as signs of attack are apparent. If a long board is placed diagonally across the horse hoe this acts as a "snow plough" and will push the soil against the roots, thereby protecting the point at which the trouble is likely to occur.

Heart Rot.—In the early stages of this disease the central leaves stop growing, turn black and die. In severe cases the decay may affect the internal tissues of the root and will cause blackened cavities in the crown. It is essentially a deficiency disease due to a shortage of boron in the soil.

Control Measures.—An application of borax at the rate of 20 to 25 lb. per acre, given prior to seeding, has given good results.

Late Blight or Leaf Scorch.—In late summer large yellow patches appear on the outer leaves which become thick and brittle as the disease develops and finally turn brown. In a severe attack the yield may be reduced. The cause of the trouble is generally attributed to physiological conditions which upset the water mechanism of the plant. It is more noticeable in a drought and lack of nitrogen appears to be a contributory cause.

Control Measures.—No control measures are as yet known. In any case the trouble occurs too late in the season to permit of treatment likely to exercise very marked control on the disease.

POTATOES

The potato must be regarded as the most valuable of our spring crops, for not only does it produce high yields of human food, but any portion of the crop which is surplus to our requirements forms excellent stock food. Moreover, if required it can be made into starch or distilled; it is an excellent cleaning crop, and does well on newly broken grassland. Then, again, it is useful for small fields and industrial areas where sparrows are a pest to ripening grain. In war-time it is the nation's iron ration.

The potato crop is very subject to frost damage, and therefore early potatoes, as distinct from main-crop varieties, can only be grown satisfactorily on a large scale in districts where late spring frosts are uncommon, as for instance in the coastal districts of south-west Scotland, Pembrokeshire and Cornwall. Main-crop potatoes, on the other hand, thrive in all parts of the British Isles.

The crop is not unduly fastidious and can be grown satis-

factorily on most types of soil, but, requiring freedom for the
development of the tubers, thrives best in deep, medium to light
loams, which are rich in organic matter. Heavy soils and wet
soils are not suited to potatoes, nor for that matter are shallow
and gravelly soils. The old red sandstone and limestone soils
produce potatoes of the highest cooking quality, whilst on moss
and fen soils big crops can be produced, but the quality is poor
and the tubers are inclined to be "waxy" or "soapy." For early
varieties sandy loams which warm up readily in spring-time are
most suitable.

The crop grows satisfactorily in sour soils; indeed, the application of quicklime to soils immediately before planting may do
more harm than good by encouraging the development of
Common Scab on the tubers.

VARIETIES

New varieties are constantly being raised and introduced to
the market, but a few varieties have held their own for many
years. At one time the number of synonyms on the market was
very great, and it was not uncommon for one variety to be offered
by three or four different firms each giving it a different name.
This problem has now been thoroughly tackled by the Ministry
in conjunction with the National Institute of Agricultural Botany,
and the position with regard to varieties has been satisfactorily
cleared up.

Varieties fall into three main groups: "first earlies," "second
earlies" and "lates or main crops." For ease of reference the
varieties, together with a description of their chief characteristics,
are tabulated below:—

Name	Shape	Colour of Flesh	Depth of Eyes	Cropping Capacity	Cooking Quality	Comments
First Earlies Arran Pilot *	Kidney	White	Shallow	V. good	Good	If left to mature is a very heavy cropper.
Epicure .	Round	White	Medium	Good	F. good	Recovers well from frost.
Ulster Chieftain *	Oval	White	Shallow	V. good	Fair	Promising yields on fairly rich land.
Duke of York	Kidney	Yellowish	Shallow	Good	Good	Only popular yel-low-fleshed variety.
Doon Early *	Blunt Oval	White	Medium	V. good	Good	Earliest of the Earlies.

* Immune to Wart Disease,

Name	Shape	Colour of Flesh	Depth of Eyes	Cropping Capacity	Cooking Quality	Comments
Second Earlies						
Eclipse	Oval	White	Shallow	Good	F. Good	Matures in August.
Great Scot *	Round	White	Medium	Good	Good	Useful for mid-season or late use.
Dunbar Rover*	Oval	White	Shallow	V. good	Excellent	Recommended as an alternative to British Queen.
Lates or Main Crops						
King Edward	Kidney	White	Shallow Skin-splashed Pink	Moderate	Excellent	Favourite variety but can be replaced by heavier cropping varieties.
Majestic * .	Kidney	White	Shallow	V. good	Good	Popular, especially for chip trade.
Kerr's Pink*.	Round	White	Deep Pink skin	Excellent	Good	Subject to second growth; excellent keeper
Redskin * .	Round	White	Shallow Pink skin	V. good	Good	Similar to Kerr's Pink, but matures three weeks earlier, and is not so coarse nor so prone to second growth.
Arran Banner *	Flat Round	White	Medium	Excellent	Good	Forms tubers early and can be used as second early.
Gladstone *	Oval	White	Shallow Skin-splashed Pink	Good	Excellent	Substitute for King Edward ; should be lifted for consumption in autumn.
Arran Consul *	Oval	White	Medium	Excellent	Good	Excellent keeper fit for consumption until May.
Ulster Supreme *	Oval	White	Shallow	Excellent	Good	Lord Derby Gold Medal, 1948.

* Immune to Wart Disease.

SELECTION AND PREPARATION OF SEED

The use of healthy seed is of vital importance in the production of maximum yields of potatoes. Good cultivation and generous manuring very naturally exert a considerable influence on the yield of the crop, but all efforts in these directions can be nullified by planting disease-ridden tubers. All growers are familiar with the good results obtained by planting "new seed" as compared with seed that has been grown on the farm for several years. Seed which has been grown for several seasons in the same district generally shows a high percentage of stunted plants with mottled or rolled leaves, and these on lifting produce only a few small-sized tubers at their roots. It is now known that these plants are infected with one or more of the maladies classified under the general term "virus diseases," and that the use of seed from these infected plants will carry over and increase the trouble in ensuing years. Thus the great need for using virus-free stocks of potatoes.

Carefully selected seed grown in Scotland, Ireland, Northern England and Wales, and certain isolated parts of Western England is known to be reliable and will give uniformly good results. The superiority of this seed is due largely to its freedom from virus diseases which are transmitted by greenfly from diseased to healthy plants during the summer months. In these districts greenflies are far less troublesome than in other districts where potatoes are grown. Once-grown seed from such stock can also be relied upon if the parent crop was healthy; in fact, a crop grown with once-grown seed from, say, Yorkshire or Lincolnshire, or own-saved seed, frequently gives better results than the new seed. When saving seed for planting the following year, however, it is essential to keep the parent crop healthy by removing all plants which show indications of virus disease, namely, those in which the leaves are rolling up, or are mottled in colour, or the growth is poor and stunted. This practice, known as "roguing," should be carried out when the plants are well above ground, being repeated before the end of June or July.

IMMATURITY

In Scotland crops for seed are lifted before the plants have completed their growth, for in these northerly districts the haulms do not die off naturally as commonly happens further south, but they are killed by frost. It was thought at one time that the superiority of Scotch seed might be due to lifting the crop green-top, and experiments were carried out in England to investigate this point. At the Kirton Experimental Station increased yields of over 2 tons per acre have been obtained by using immature seed, and what is more it was found that the stocks kept their vigour much longer.

Lifting for seed purposes, therefore, should take place just before the tops begin to turn yellow—indicating that the crop is ripening off—and the tubers should be placed in sprouting boxes as soon as possible. By lifting at this time there is, of course, a small loss in yield, but this is more than compensated by the increased yield the following year. The seed should be kept in a cool place out of the direct rays of the sun, being transferred to the chitting-house later on.

The more common method of obtaining seed potatoes is to take them from the pit or clamp during the winter when the ware tubers are being sorted for sale. Experiments at Kirton have shown, however, that better results in most seasons can be obtained by boxing the sets at lifting time.

In order to ensure a supply of clean and healthy seed the Ministry have instituted various schemes of certification in the seed potato districts, and it is obligatory on seed merchants to state in writing at the time of the sale the certificate number of the seed potatoes.

SEED POTATO CERTIFICATION

In order that merchants and growers may readily understand the significance and value of the different kinds of seed potato certificates issued by the Agricultural Departments in the United Kingdom and Eire, these Departments have agreed on a common system of certification. Certificates are issued after inspection of the growing crops, and when seed from a certified crop is sold or offered for sale for planting in England and Wales, the seller must quote to the buyer the letters and number of the relative certificate.

Certificates are of three kinds: "SS" (Stock seed) which is seed of the highest grade intended mainly for seed production, "A" (first quality commercial seed) and "H" (healthy commercial seed). After the certificate letter, the country of origin is indicated thus: Scotland "(Scot)," England "(E)," Wales "(W)," Northern Ireland "(Nor.Ir)," Eire "(Eire)" or Isle of Man "(I.O.M.)." Finally, "N.I." is added in the case of those varieties which are not approved as immune from Wart Disease. Thus a certificate designated "A (Scot)" would indicate seed potatoes of first quality commercial standard grown in Scotland and of a variety immune from Wart Disease; "H. (E) N.I.," healthy commercial seed potatoes grown in England but of a variety not approved as immune from Wart Disease.

The field inspection standards adopted by the several Departments for the issue of these certificates are now in very close agreement.

The attention of all seed potato merchants and growers is drawn to the Seeds (Amendment) Regulations, 1944, which lay down a new classification for seed potatoes and set out the particulars which must be stated on every sale or exposure for sale of seed potatoes in England and Wales.

The new classification is divided into the 3 groups (1) "certified," (2) uncertified (English or Welsh once-grown) — an intermediate group for seed potatoes obtained from an uncertified crop which was grown in England and Wales from a "certified" stock, and (3) "uncertified." In the case of the "certified" classes, the reference letters and number of the relative certificate must be quoted. The full classification is:—Certified (Scotch), Certified (Northern Ireland), Certified (Eire), Certified (English), Certified (Welsh), Certified (Isle of Man), Uncertified (English once-grown), Uncertified (Welsh once-grown) ; Uncertified (Scotch), Uncertified (English) and Uncertified (Welsh).

When ordering seed potatoes, growers should state the variety, class of seed, country of origin and size of tuber required. The quantity of seed required to plant an acre of land is dependent upon the size of the seed used, and tuber size varies considerably between the different varieties and from season to season. As a rule, 1 ton of seed is sufficient for one acre. For earlies planted in 24-inch rows with a foot between the setts, 25 cwt. will be required, whilst for main crops in 28-inch rows with 16 inches between the setts, 18 cwt. may be plenty.

The most economical seed potato is about the size of a hen's egg and should weigh not less than two ounces. The use of large seed whilst giving a greater total yield per acre results in a lower percentage of ware or saleable tubers. Small setts produce a few large-sized tubers but the total yield will be low. Seed potatoes are sold according to a specified size of riddle which must be declared by the vendor, as, for instance, $1\frac{1}{4} \times 2\frac{1}{4}$, which means that the setts pass through $2\frac{1}{4}$-inch mesh riddle but remain on the $1\frac{1}{4}$-inch riddle.

CUT SEED

It is not always possible to obtain the ideal size of seed, and large tubers (or when stocks are scarce) should then be cut. Weight for weight cut setts are equal in yielding capacity to whole tubers of comparable size and will generally give a rather higher percentage of ware.

In cutting large tubers for seed it is advisable to make the cut lengthwise, leaving one or two healthy eyes or sprouts on each half. If the cut setts cannot be planted immediately, to prevent loss of moisture they should be covered with damp sacks and kept in a cool place. It is best to plant them cut side down, preferably when the soil is damp, covering as soon as possible.

When planting is likely to be delayed the following method should be adopted. In making the cut leave about $\frac{1}{4}$ inch at one end uncut as a sort of hinge. The cut surfaces should then be placed together again and the tubers left in a cool dark place. Thus, the cut surfaces are kept moist and in a few days' time a layer of protective cork will have sealed them over and this prevents any drying out in the field. When planting, the two halves are merely pulled apart, leaving only a small unhealed surface.

The practice of rubbing the cut surfaces in lime or ashes is not advised, for these substances have a drying effect and tend to draw water from the tuber. In the past poor results from the use of cut setts has frequently been accounted for by the use of this method. Some varieties appear to do better than others after cutting, but with good management any variety may be cut successfully.

When the seed arrives on the farm it should be placed in wooden trays for sprouting or, if this is impracticable, spread out on a wooden floor where it is safe from frost but can get ample light. Failing this, it should be clamped outdoors, for to leave it in the bags in which it arrives invariably means that long thin sprouts are produced which frequently grow through the bags and entwine one with another. This represents so much wasted effort for the potato and results in loss of vitality and yield.

SPROUTING

The practice of sprouting seed potatoes is very sound and results in an increased yield, frequently up to 2 tons per acre. The chief advantage of sprouting in boxes or trays lies in the fact that only strong-growing tubers, likely to do well in the field, are planted, and that all diseased tubers can be discarded. This means fewer misses in the rows with a resulting higher yield. A further advantage is that if unfavourable weather conditions prevent planting at the normal time, the delay is not reflected in a reduced yield if the potatoes have been sprouted, for they will still be growing though they are not planted. There is evidence that sprouting improves the eating quality of a crop, presumably because it shortens the growing period and thereby allows the crop to reach maturity, at which stage it is at its best.

For large quantities of potatoes special glass chitting-houses can be erected, but for small quantities simple glass-houses or even a barn will give good results. Provision must be made for heating the house in cold weather, for the temperature must not fall below 40° F. Small paraffin stoves are quite suitable for this purpose and need only be lighted when there is a danger of frost. Two such stoves are sufficient for a house 20 feet×40 feet ×8 feet.

Light is essential for the production of short sturdy shoots. Good ventilation, but freedom from draughts, is also necessary, and during the winter it is advisable to turn the boxes occasionally so that all the tubers have an equal chance of getting plenty of light.

Three boxes per cwt. of seed is the normal allowance, although four allows better placement of the tubers. The boxes should be placed in tiers, allowing 15 inches between the tiers with a central gangway, 3 feet wide, to allow easy working. Sixteen boxes per tier can be accommodated in a house measuring 8 feet to the eaves, and as the boxes measure 30×18 inches the size of house required to hold any particular quantity of setts is a matter of simple calculation. Most growers use their chitting-houses for tomatoes in the summer months.

The secret of successful chitting lies in getting short sturdy sprouts about 1½ inches long. This means boxing in October to bring them along slowly, but should this be impracticable the temptation to force late-boxed tubers by means of heating must be rigorously rejected. If greenfly happen to collect on the sprouts during the winter the house should be well fumigated with nicotine.

PLACE IN ROTATION

There is no fixed rule as to the position potatoes should occupy in the rotation and it generally varies according to the district in which they are grown. Being a cleaning crop they often follow a cereal, but in many districts it is common to take them after a clover ley. In special cases, such as for instance in the early potato-growing districts of Cornwall and Ayrshire, they are grown on the same land each year, catch crops of Italian ryegrass, rape or broccoli being the only change. In other cases where the soil conditions are particularly suited to the crop, the rotation is designed to include a high proportion of potatoes which may come every three years. Normally, however, the crop occupies part of the root break.

Two factors which may make land unsuitable for planting with potatoes are firstly the presence of eelworm cysts and secondly large numbers of wireworms in the soil. Eelworms cause potato "sickness," but it is unlikely that this pest will be a source of trouble excepting in potato-growing districts where the crop is taken frequently on the same land. Wireworms reduce the market value of the crop by boring into the tubers, but in either case if the soil is suspected of harbouring these pests it is well to have it examined by the county advisory entomologist (see Appendix I).

The crop does exceptionally well after a long ley or old permanent grass. When the grassland is in good heart, growing a cereal crop may be risky on account of the danger of lodging, but with proper cultivation the decaying sod is an ideal source of plant food for potatoes.

PREPARATION OF SEED BED

Potatoes demand a deep, friable tilth. The soil need not be broken down so finely as for other crops, however, for there are good opportunities for working the land after planting has taken place. When potatoes follow a cereal the preliminary work is similar to that for any root crop and usually commences with stubble cleaning as already outlined. This is followed by deep winter ploughing with suitable cultivation in spring to secure the necessary tilth. Consolidation of the soil is not necessary, so that rollers need only be used to crush large clods.

In the case of temporary leys the land is often ploughed quite shallow in autumn, and left until early spring when a deep cross-ploughing is given. Should the soil be a deep light loam, deep ploughing with a digger, fitted with a skim coulter, may be all that is necessary. In other cases, double ploughing may be practised, and here two ploughs follow each other. One takes the sod to a depth of about 3 inches, turning it into the bottom of a deep furrow previously left by the second plough. The latter in turn will cover it with 8 or 9 inches of soil as it follows the first plough. This ensures that the turf is well buried and unlikely to be brought to the surface by subsequent operations.

On old grassland it is advisable, before ploughing, to break up the surface by means of disc harrows, pitch-pole harrows or heavy cultivators. It is much easier to cut the turf up before ploughing than after, and in experiments carried out in Yorkshire in 1939 at six centres, the average total yield of tubers was 221·7 cwt. per acre on land which had not been cultivated before ploughing, whereas on land cultivated before ploughing the average yield at the same centres was 238·5 cwt. per acre.

After the turf has been broken up by harrowing, the land should be ploughed as deeply as possible without bringing up subsoil. Obviously, the earlier the land can be ploughed in autumn the better is the chance of getting the furrows well weathered and the soil mellowed by the frosts and rains of winter.

The normal practice in most districts is to draw the land up into ridges in spring and plant the potatoes in rows. In most cases farmyard manure and artificial fertilisers are applied immediately before planting begins. Good results are sometimes obtained on light soils by dibbling potatoes on the flat on land ploughed and prepared just as it would be for corn. Another method is to plough them in, planting the tubers in the bottom of every third furrow and placing them under the edge of the previous furrow slice so as to escape damage from the furrow horse.

The actual cultivation necessary to break down the furrows and prepare a suitable tilth for ridging depends upon the type of soil and whether the land was previously arable or grassland. In any case work should not commence until it can be carried traight forward and planting completed, for if potatoes are to go in well the land should be moderately dry and in a fertile state. Usually two or three strokes of a heavy cultivator, together with the use of a ring roller if the land is cloddy, are sufficient to obtain the necessary tilth. In the case of old grassland, however, the cultivations must be more gradual so that no large clods of unbroken turf are brought to the surface.

When a deep loose tilth has been obtained, the land should be drawn up into ridges 6 inches deep and from 26 to 30 inches wide for main crops down to 20-24 inches for earlies. This operation should be completed for main-crop potatoes by the end of March or early in April, but more ridges should not be drawn out than can be dealt with in a reasonably short time or there is danger of them drying out. The most rapid method is to use a three-row ridger, but for small acreages the more common implement to use is the ridging plough. The advantage of this implement is that it can be used for ridging up, for splitting the rows to cover the "seed," for earthing up, and, by substituting prongs for the ridging body, for lifting the crop as well. The tractor-drawn ridgers can be used for splitting the ridges if the tractor wheels can be adjusted to run on top of the furrows.

MANURING

The basis of the manuring for the potato crop should be a good heavy dressing of well-rotted dung. This is invariably true except perhaps after rich old pasture, or where it is possible to use seaweed or a green crop for ploughing in as a substitute. Dung, supplemented by artificials, can generally be relied upon to give better results than a heavy dressing of dung alone or a heavy dressing of artificials alone.

In many districts, particularly in the North, the common practice is to apply the dung in the drills in spring after ridging. The artificial fertilisers are then applied on top of the dung, the setts planted and the ridges split to cover them in. There is no doubt that this gives excellent results, but in the South, and to an increasing extent in the North, the usual procedure is to apply the dung in late summer or autumn to the clover aftermath, or the stubble, and plough it in. Where cattle are fed indoors until late in the season, supplies of dung will be available for autumn application in this way, but the chief advantage lies in reducing the amount of work necessary in spring, which after all is the busiest time of the year. All too frequently planting in spring is held up because dung must be carted out and spread.

The response to farmyard manure is well shown by the results obtained at ten centres in Yorkshire in 1939. Plots to which farmyard manure had been applied gave 232 cwt. of tubers per acre, as against 197 cwt. per acre where farmyard manure was not given. The normal application is 12 to 15 tons per acre, but where supplies are plentiful this can well be increased to 20 tons per acre.

Few crops respond better to applications of artificial fertilisers and in many districts 15 cwt. per acre of mixed tillage is applied. Carefully conducted trials have shown, however, that 12 cwt. per acre is about the economic limit when applied in conjunction with 12 tons of dung in a district with 24 inches rainfall. In manuring potatoes it is important to keep a balance between the three-plant foods, nitrogen, phosphates and potash, all of which are required. Failure to do so is likely to result in the production of excess haulms at the expense of tuber production.

For second earlies and main crops the following mixture has given excellent results under widely varying conditions of soil and climate:—

Sulphate of Ammonia	.	.	2 parts by weight.
Superphosphate	.	.	. 3 ,, ,,
Muriate of Potash	.	.	. 1½ ,, ,,
			6½ ,, ,,

In addition to dung, this mixture should be applied at the rate of 4 cwt. per acre for poor land, 6 cwt. per acre for average, and 8 to 10 cwt. per acre for good land. If dung is not available these quantities can be increased by about 50 per cent.

Many prefer to use one of the concentrated complete fertilisers now available, in which case it will be found that in most cases 3 cwt. per acre C.C.F. No. 2 is likely to give comparable results with 6 cwt. per acre of the above mixture.

This home-made mixture should be applied soon after mixing, for otherwise it is likely to set hard in the bags. The addition of 1 cwt. of steamed bone flour per acre to these ingredients will act as a drier without materially affecting the balance of the mixture for practical purposes.

For main crops on black land it is generally conceded that the emphasis should be on the phosphatic portion of the mixture and the following is then suggested :—

Sulphate of Ammonia	. .	2 parts by weight,
Superphosphate . .	.	4 ,, ,,
Steamed Bone Flour . .	.	1 ,, ,,
Muriate of Potash . .	.	1 ,, ,,
		8 ,, ,,

which may be given at rates up to 15 cwt. per acre.

For early potatoes which have to be forced to maturity rapidly, it is common to give up to 12 cwt. or more per acre of fertiliser in addition to as much organic manure as possible. The latter may take the form of dung, seaweed, shoddy or a green crop. The general opinion is that the mixture should be rich in nitrogen and phosphate without undue emphasis on the potash, and the following is recommended for soils other than black fen :—

Sulphate of Ammonia	. .	4 parts by weight,
Superphosphate . .	.	5 ,, ,,
Muriate of Potash . .	.	1 ,, ,,
		10 ,, ,,

applied at the rate of 10 cwt. per acre.

On black fen soils the practice is still common of applying phosphate only, say up to 10 cwt. per acre, of superphosphate. This may still be justified, but there is evidence, on certain black fen soils at any rate, that the use of nitrogen and potash in addition may be advantageous.

Obviously it is not possible to give mixtures suitable for all soils and districts, and growers should find out for themselves which mixture suits their land best, using the above suggestions as a basis upon which to plan their trials.

The artificial manure is usually applied after the ridges have been made and before the seed tubers are planted. Where dung is applied in the row it should be spread on top.

PLANTING

Planting may be done by hand or machine, the former method still being the more common. Machines for planting sprouted or unsprouted setts are available, the Albion, Robot and Bamlett being good examples. The advantage of a machine is largely a question of speed and enables the work to be carried out with fewer hands. The latest type of planter draws the ridges, fertilises, plants and covers the setts. All planting machines require skilled attention and a close watch during operations. Hand labour is still the most common method of planting, however, and provided skilled workers are available is reasonably rapid, for ten women can plant eight acres of sprouted seed in a normal working day.

Spacing depends upon the variety and the purpose for which the crop is grown, first earlies being spaced 12 inches apart in the rows, second earlies 14 inches, and main-crop varieties 16 inches. In the case of Arran Banner and Majestic, however, the tubers frequently grow too big to be marketable, and with these varieties, therefore, it is advisable to space the tubers not wider than 12 inches in the row. Planting should follow closely on ridging up and the ridges are then split back, it being essential to split all rows that are planted each day. When setts are left in the field they should be protected from night frosts.

AFTER CULTIVATIONS

About a fortnight after planting, light harrows should be run over the land to level the ridges and kill small weeds. Not more than 3 inches of soil should be left covering the setts. Harrowing can be continued so long as there is no risk of the young potato sprouts being damaged.

When the potatoes have come through the ground, horse-hoeing between the rows should be carried out to keep the soil loose and check weeds, and this should be continued as frequently as is necessary until the tops almost meet in the rows, when earthing up should be completed. Before this is done, however, any weeds in the rows should be removed by hand-hoeing. A fortnight after earthing up the operation can be repeated with advantage, for any tubers which are exposed to the light turn green and are unsaleable.

HARVESTING

As far as practicable the crop should be lifted in dry weather, especially if the haulms are attacked by Blight. Failure to observe this precaution may result in many of the tubers being infected with the blight spores which fall from the leaves, and these tubers will rot in the pit or clamp.

In a very few early districts lifting commences at the end of May, but the main early potato season begins about mid-June. Lifting of earlies is frequently done by hand-fork, which has the advantage that no damage is done to the tubers—the skins are tender at this stage—and since the crop is lifted "green top" the haulms would be troublesome to other lifting implements. Early potatoes are sent to market right away; main crops, on the other hand, are stored in "graves," "pits," "pies" or "clamps" to be sorted over and marketed at a later date.

Lifting is generally accomplished nowadays by means of a spinner or digger, although for small acreages the ordinary plough or a ridging plough, the breast often replaced by special prongs, is used. With a spinner about 3 acres a day can be lifted, and 14 pickers are required to keep pace with the machine working in both directions. After lifting, the harrows are run over the ground to expose any tubers that have been buried by the soil. These are then collected and should be stored separately, as they are certain to be bruised or damaged by the harrows and may not keep so well.

A potato clamp is generally 4 feet to 4 feet 6 inches wide, and is carried up as high as is practicable with sides at an angle of 45°. The potatoes are covered with 6 to 8 inches of wheat or rye straw with a spadeful of soil here and there to hold it in place. After a few weeks when respiration or "sweating" has finished, the clamp is covered with about 8 inches of soil, leaving wisps of straw protruding through the top for ventilation purposes. Needless to say, the site of the pit or clamp should be chosen with care, being near to a road, and dry in winter time. Since frost is always more likely to enter from the windward and north sides, these should receive special attention when soiling down. Separate clamps should be made for different varieties.

Though this is the traditional method of storage it has its drawbacks, namely, once the tubers get wet in a clamp, though they can be dried out, trouble develops and rot spreads. Furthermore, the subsequent dressing for sale has to be done outdoors and is frequently postponed because of bad weather. Mr. James Keith of Aberdeenshire, who grows some 120 acres annually, largely for the English seed trade, has successfully stored his crop in sheds, which are also used for housing and sprouting. These measure 45 feet by 100 feet, and one shed is allowed to each variety, the tubers being spread over the floor in a layer 3 to 5 feet deep. A covering of straw prevents greening, protects them from frost, and prevents moisture or sweat condensing on the top tubers and trickling down and damping the remainder. Mr. Arthur King has used this method of indoor storage successfully for several years now on his moorland dairy farm at Ilkley, Yorkshire, but in this case an old cowshed is used for the purpose. The American method of storing potatoes in well-insulated but cheaply constructed containers in which the air is well circulated has been tried out in this country with successful results. This would appear to be a development likely to have far-reaching results on the storage of potatoes in this country.

YIELD

The average yield of marketable potatoes varies from 6 to 8 tons per acre, but on good soils in favourable seasons 16 tons and over can be obtained.

PESTS

Wireworm.—Wireworms can cause serious damage to potatoes in so far as they affect the saleability of the crop, and even low populations of wireworms can cause extensive tuber injury.

On land known to have a high wireworm population it is advisable to either grow early varieties which will be lifted before the autumn feeding period of the wireworms begins, or if main-crops are involved, to examine the crop periodically from the end of August onwards. As soon as it is evident that the tubers are being attacked the crop should be lifted. This will obviate the holing of large numbers of tubers and reduces the risk of the trouble being continued in the clamp.

It is not uncommon to find the "setts" in spring badly infested with wireworms soon after they have been planted. Fortunately, in most cases, this is not likely to cause serious damage, if any, for soon afterwards the spring feeding period of the wireworm ends and they leave the tubers for the lower layers of the soil.

Root Eelworm.—The most serious pest of potatoes is the root eelworm, which has attained a magnitude comparable with that of the beet eelworm on the Continent. In many cases, owing to the high infestation of the soil, potato growing is ruled out until the land has been rested for several years.

The symptoms of an attack are unmistakable. The plants are unthrifty, dwarfed, and contain at the root only a few small-sized tubers. Confirmation of the presence of the pest can be obtained by an examination of the roots for the cysts which can be found on them from June onwards.

The description of the cysts and the life history is similar to that already given in the case of the beet eelworm.

Control Measures.—Considerable control can be obtained by rotational cropping, and two crops of potatoes in succession should not be taken on land that has once shown signs of eelworm. On such land it would appear that the minimum period that ought to elapse between one potato crop and the next is four to seven years.

In all cases where eelworm is suspected, an examination of the soil for cysts should be made before planting potatoes again. Seed tubers from infected land should not be used, for the adhering soil may carry cysts.

SLUGS

In some seasons slugs can cause serious damage to potatoes both in the field and in the clamp. Tubers damaged by this pest have small holes on the outside which give access to larger inner cavities. An attack is unlikely in a dry season. Slugs are encouraged by dung lying exposed on the stubble during winter and they breed in this during the winter months, the increase in population reaching a climax the following autumn when an attack on the potato crop may be made. Good control has been obtained in the Lothians by the use of the Meta-bran poison bait which has already been described in connection with slug damage on cereals (see page 54), and in some cases as many as 12,000 slugs per acre have been killed in the potato crop by the application of 25 lb. per acre of the poison bait.

Colorado Beetle.—This dangerous foreign pest of potatoes is not present, so far as we know, in this country, and it is a matter of great importance to potato growers that if it should gain entry, it is not allowed to establish itself. It is always possible for a limited number of Colorado beetles to gain entry, particularly in the neighbourhood of seaport towns, and potato crops adjoining such towns would be most likely to be infested first.

Both adult beetles and their grubs feed upon the plant foliage during the summer. The beetle is similar to a ladybird in shape but larger and is striped along the back with black and yellow stripes. The grub is reddish-yellow with some black spots. Any insects resembling this description found feeding upon potato leaves should be regarded as suspicious, and specimens, packed in a tin box, should be sent at once to the Ministry of Agriculture along with details of where found.

No attempt at control should be undertaken by the grower, as such measures might have the unfortunate result of dispersing the beetles and so making ultimate control more difficult.

DISEASES

The potato is subject to a serious epidemic known as Potato Blight which occurs to some extent in most years, though the amount of damage done is dependent upon season and the measures of control taken by the grower.

The symptoms of this disease are easily recognised. Dark green blotches appear on the leaves which quickly turn dark brown or almost black. The blotches are surrounded by a delicate, white, powdery mould, especially on the under surface, which is really a mass of spore-bearing filaments that have grown out through the pores of the leaf from the internal spores which are killing the tissues and causing the discoloration. These spores are blown by the wind to other plants, causing further infection under warm, moist conditions but succumbing in dry weather. The disease can spread at an alarming rate, for the interval between infection and the production of a new lot of spores is only a matter of hours or, at the most, a day or so. In a severe attack the haulms may be killed completely, but whatever the scale of attack there is always a danger of many of the spores falling to the ground where sooner or later they will reach the tubers and infect them. Infected tubers have dark, slightly sunken, irregular areas on the skin and when cut, the flesh is discoloured, being a characteristic foxy-red. Moreover, should the production of spores be still going on when the crop is lifted, the tubers may come into contact with them and become infected.

The disease is carried on from year to year by infected tubers which may be planted unwittingly by ground-keepers from the previous crop, or from diseased plants on the site of an old potato pie. The year 1936 was one of the worst blight years in living memory and the disease made its appearance exceptionally early, and continued unchecked and with ever-increasing intensity until the end of the season. There are grounds for hoping that resistant varieties will shortly be available.

Control Measures.—Preventative measures consist in spraying the tops with Bordeaux mixture (copper sulphate and lime) or Burgundy mixture (copper sulphate and soda) or one of the many proprietary fungicides now on the market.

The fungicide may be applied as a solution by spraying or in powder form by dusting, the choice of method to adopt depending largely upon the availability of an adequate water supply. Spraying is generally more effective than dusting and should be used wherever possible, though dusting is much simpler and more rapid and requires only one man.

For dusting, 1 cwt. of fungicide will do at least 5 acres. The active blight destroyer is the copper compound and when purchasing a dust fungicide it is important to ascertain the percentage of copper it contains. The best results are obtained by using dusts which contain 20 per cent. of copper expressed as metallic copper and so fine that at least 90 per cent. of the powder passes through a 100-mesh sieve. It is necessary to see that no free soluble copper salt is present or scorching of the foliage results.

Satisfactory horse-drawn machines or small hand or knapsack

M

sprayers are on the market for either liquids or powders. Whichever is used, however, it is important to cover the under surfaces.

In mixing up either Bordeaux or Burgundy solutions the following procedure should be followed:

Using a 40-gallon wooden barrel (metal must not be used) pour in 35 gallons of water. Now place 4 lb. of copper sulphate (bluestone), 98 per cent. pure, in a muslin bag and suspend it in the water to dissolve.

For Bordeaux mixture, 2 lb. of freshly burnt quicklime should be slaked in a bucket and worked into a paste, water being added until 5 gallons of solution are obtained; if more convenient, 3 lb. of hydrate of lime can be mixed with 5 gallons of clean cold water.

Now pour the lime solution through a strainer into the bluestone solution, stirring well all the time. The mixture is now ready and must be used fresh.

For Burgundy mixture, 5 lb. of washing soda (98 per cent. pure) is dissolved in 5 gallons of water which is then added to the bluestone solution, again stirring vigorously.

Before application the solution should be tested for free copper salt by holding the clean bright blade of a pocket knife in the mixture for a minute or two. If it darkens or turns coppercoloured, more lime or soda solution should be added or the spray will scorch the foliage.

When the foliage is still small 50 gallons of solution per acre will be sufficient, but when the plants are in full leaf as much as 100 gallons per acre may be required. In practice the use of proprietary compounds which can be mixed directly with water in the spray tank are much more convenient, and only slightly more expensive than mixing one's own solution.

No hard-and-fast rules can be laid down as to when spraying should take place, but since the treatment is preventative and not curative it should be done before the trouble begins or at any rate at the first appearance of the disease.

The middle of July may be regarded as about the average time for the first application, though many growers like to give the first application just before earthing up in late May or early June. As soon as it is known that blight has broken out in any district, spraying should commence. The number of applications necessary will depend upon the weather, and whilst two may be sufficient in some cases eight may be necessary in others. The intervals between spraying will be generally about 14 to 21 days. Wet sprays are best applied in the daytime when the foliage is dry, avoiding if possible bright sunshine. On the other hand, dry dusting is best carried out early in the morning or late evening when the foliage is dewy.

Spraying in districts where the atmosphere is fouled with industrial fumes or in seasons when greenfly are present in large numbers may cause serious scorching of the leaves. If there is any doubt as to the advisability or not of spraying it is best to seek advice from the nearest advisory centre (see Appendix I).

Quite apart from the measures taken to control the disease on the leaf, contamination of healthy tubers from a blighted crop should be prevented by delaying lifting until three weeks or more after the tops have died down completely, by cutting off the tops and waiting for two or three weeks after they have dried up before lifting, or by scorching the tops off with sulphuric acid 2 to 3 weeks before lifting. The strength of the acid solution will vary from 10 to 15 per cent. depending upon the vigour of the haulms. No harmful effect on the tubers has been noted from the use of acid provided it does not come into contact with them.

Wart Disease.—This disease transforms the eyes of the tubers and frequently the entire tuber into a monstrous growth resembling pieces of dirty cauliflower. When the crop is harvested these growths break off, and the infection can persist in the soil for many years. Fortunately, many varieties are immune from attack (see Table of Varieties, pages 160-1) and on infected land only these varieties can be planted. Under the Wart Disease Order, the disease is a notifiable one, and all varieties are tested to determine whether they are immune from or susceptible to it.

Corky Scab.—Potatoes affected by this disease may have small scabby patches, powdery or corky in appearance, or the growths may be of considerable size and deep cankers may be present. The organisms causing the trouble can live in the soil for a number of years, and hence potatoes should not again be grown on land known to be infected for a considerable period. The disease is more prevalent on wet land than on dry and an application of lime merely aggravates the trouble. No varieties are immune and care must be taken not to use affected tubers, for these transmit the disease.

Common Scab.—Although the scabs in this disease are merely superficial they spoil the appearance of the tubers and its commercial value. Excessive liming may cause a serious outbreak of common scab, and on land subject to this trouble a large measure of control can be obtained by spreading dung in the bottom of the drill rows. Any green material such as grass clippings or even ploughing in a green manure crop helps to control the trouble.

VIRUS DISEASES

These are frequently known as the "Degeneration" diseases, because infected crops rapidly decline in vigour and cropping capacity. Sap-sucking insects transmit these diseases in much the same way as malaria and hence the necessity for efficient roguing of a crop from which seed is to be saved (refer to page 162). The insects commonly believed to be responsible for Virus are greenfly and leaf-hoppers.

The degeneration diseases may take the following forms :—

Leaf Roll.—The upper leaflets become rolled and stand stiffly erect or the lower leaflets are markedly rolled and brittle.

Mosaic.—This results in a mottling of the leaves, whilst in some varieties (King Edward, Arran Crest, Epicure) the growing point of the haulm turns brown and the plants usually die. In several cases there is pronounced puckering of the leaves which curl downwards.

Leaf Drop Streak.—This type of Virus disease results in the leaves becoming mottled followed by a blackening along the veins. Finally they turn yellow and the lower ones wilt and drop off, whilst the crop has the appearance of ripening unduly early.

Control Measures.—The only method of control is to purchase seed from districts in which greenflies are scarce, or from crops known to be free. When home-grown seed is used, systematic roguing of the crop should be carried out.

CARROTS

Carrots flourish under all English climatic conditions, but a deep sandy or loamy soil free from stones is essential. On these soils fine seed beds can be obtained, and the crop can be lifted with greater ease than on the heavier types of soil. A gravelly soil produces fanged and badly shaped roots, whilst on light, blow-away sands the crop is liable to suffer badly in a period of drought and heavy rain or wind may cause the seed to be buried too deeply. Deep soils are essential for shapely roots and any trace of a pan must be broken up by subsoiling. The crop does well on peaty and fen soils.

VARIETIES

Varieties grown for human consumption are generally classified according to their shape and form, namely, long, intermediate and stump-rooted. In general the intermediate and stump rooted varieties are most favoured, for long tapering roots are more difficult to lift and are not favoured by the market salesmen because of the room they take up in packing and storage. For stock-feeding purposes the yellow and white-fleshed varieties produce much heavier yields. The following are amongst the most popular varieties:—

White Belgian . . . A heavy yielding white-fleshed variety grown solely for stock purposes.

Red Altrincham . . A heavy cropper, red-fleshed, with shorter and blunter roots than the other types.

Stump-rooted Intermediate ⎱ General purpose varieties of good
James Intermediate ⎰ colour and quality.

Long Altrincham ⎱ Suitable for deep sands—and for canning
Long Red Surrey ⎰ when sliced.
Early Market . . . Quick-growing variety for the bunching trade.

PLACE IN ROTATION

Carrots generally do best after potatoes but they are also frequently taken between two corn crops, thus acting as a cleaning crop. In East Nottinghamshire the crop frequently follows turnips folded by sheep. Owing to the slow germination of the seed it is essential that the land be clean, for on foul land the young seedlings may be smothered by weeds, one of the worst offenders in this respect being spurrey or louse grass. It is because potatoes leave the land in very clean condition that they form such an excellent preparatory crop.

PREPARATION OF SEED BED

If the crop follows a cereal the stubble is cleaned in the normal way as recommended for the root crops. This is followed by a deep ploughing in November, the open furrows being turned in to keep the land level, and is then left in the furrow over winter to mellow.

In spring, the first treatment is to apply the artificial manures which are worked into the soil with the seed bed preparations. Where annual weeds are a nuisance the cultivation of the land is left until these have germinated so that the subsequent working kills them.

Success in carrot-growing depends in a large measure upon getting the right type of seed bed, which should be fine, firm and moist. To this end straight-tined harrows are used across the furrows to break the surface crust, and these are followed by chisel-toothed harrows to give the necessary depth of cultivation and break down any lumps. Straight-tined harrows are again used, then the ring-roller. If these operations fail to produce a perfect seed bed the whole sequence is repeated, any weeds brought to the surface in these operations being collected by hand and carted off.

MANURING

It is generally conceded that farmyard manure should be applied to the previous crop and not direct, for the application of fresh dung produces coarse, fangy roots. Moreover, when the humus of the dung is well incorporated with the soil it helps to retain moisture in the soil which is so vitally important on many of the typical carrot soils. If applied in the year of cropping not more than 10 tons per acre of well-rotted dung should be given, being spread in autumn and ploughed in.

The crop is by no means so susceptible to a shortage of lime as sugar beet, nevertheless most carrot soils tend towards lime deficiency, and where the crop is grown as part of the normal root break liming should be carried out according to routine practice. The following mixture of artificials will be found suitable when given as a seed bed application :—

Sulphate of Ammonia	.	1	cwt. per acre.
Superphosphate	. .	2	,, ,,
Steamed Bone Flour .	.	1	,, ,,
Muriate of Potash	. .	1	,, ,,
		5	,, ,,

The phosphate may, if necessary, be applied in the form of high soluble slag and potash salts or kainit may replace the muriate of potash mentioned above, but these should be applied 2 to 3 weeks before drilling the seed if possible. When the plants are 2 to 3 inches high they can be top-dressed with nitrate of soda at the rate of 1 cwt. per acre. Many growers give two further applications of nitrate later in the season, but care must be taken not to overdo the top-dressing or the roots are liable to split, which seriously reduces their saleability. Moreover, when growth is unduly forced the roots do not keep so well. The nitrate of soda is usually applied by hand down the side of the row. Although sulphate of ammonia can be used in place of nitrate of soda its use is not favoured, for if carelessly applied it is liable to scorch the foliage.

Sowing the Seed

The seed is drilled on the flat in rows 12 to 20 inches apart, but in many northern districts it is common to drill on the ridge. A Scottish practice is to sow double rows, 4 to 6 inches apart, on the top of 27-inch ridges. Trials conducted by the Midland Agricultural College in 1940 indicate that the maximum yields are obtained from 15 and 18 inch rows, but in practice 20-inch rows are more favoured because of the difficulty of horse-hoeing between narrow drills.

The seed is small and very difficult to sow because of its spiny covering. A large proportion of the seed sold has the spines rubbed off by machinery, but where unmachined seed is used it is customary to mix it with fine earth or sand or dry wood ashes to soften the spines and allow the seed to run more freely through the drill. It is an advantage also to fit rubber feed spouts on the drill to obviate the risk of seeds lodging in the spouts. The main thing is to get a continuous row of sown seeds, using the minimum amount in order to avoid the necessity for thinning the plant at a later date.

Carrot seed is slow in germinating and the seedlings are very delicate, hence, as already mentioned, clean land is essential if the crop is not to be smothered with weeds. Sowing should not take place before conditions are favourable for growth, for this again allows the crop to get away well. The normal time is from mid-April onwards, though in the Eastern Counties sowing is frequently postponed deliberately, for a late crop stands a better chance of missing the annual attack of carrot fly. The seed rate is generally 5 to 6 lb. per acre but many growers try to sow as little as 3 lb. When sowing takes place on the flat, some barley or oats mixed with the carrot seed will, by reason of its quicker germination, indicate the position of the rows and enables inter-row cultivation to commence at an earlier date. It is quite a good plan to soak the seed before drilling, or to mix it with moist sand and leave it for a few days to allow the seed coat to soften, and thus hasten germination. In either case, it is necessary, of course, to make certain that the seed is sufficiently dry to permit drilling before a start is made. Recent work has shown that it is possible to even allow the shoots to break through the seed coat before drilling takes place and by this means get a rapid establishment of the plant. Few of the shoots appear to be damaged during the subsequent drilling and this is a procedure that carrot growers who have difficulty in getting a plant might try out for themselves.

AFTER CULTIVATIONS

With good growing weather the rows of seedlings should appear about 14 days after drilling, although it frequently takes three weeks for them to come through. As soon as the rows can be seen horse-hoeing should commence, care being necessary to avoid burying the plants. Three or four such hoeings are given.

By the time the plants reach the second leaf-stage, hand-weeding in the rows is necessary and this operation will be repeated later in the season when necessary. Owing to the risk of carrot fly, which is attracted by the characteristic smell evolved from bruised carrot plants, thinning is not regarded as sound practice, and what is more, should not be necessary with the low seed rate recommended above. Later in the season some growers may rough thin by hand and the thinnings are then sold green top in bunches for human consumption.

Experiments carried out in 1940 by the Midland Agricultural College into the problem of thinning the crop have given results which support the contentions of practical growers, namely, that thinning is not economical. The figures obtained in these trials indicate that when thinning to 4, 6 or 8 inches between plants as compared with bunching at 5-inch intervals or leaving the crop unthinned, the highest yield per acre is obtained from the unthinned crop.

The final operation consists of earthing up slightly in early September to cover the shoulder of the roots and stop them from greening, at the same time checking weeds.

HARVESTING

The crop is usually ready for lifting from August onwards but the main crop will be lifted from October to December, and most growers endeavour to get the roots under cover before any danger of frost is likely. Some, however, leave a small portion of the crop in the ground after slightly earthing them over. The roots keep better in this way and when lifted in late winter or early spring the crop commands a good market. There is always the danger of frost to take into account, however, and during the winter of 1939 and 1940 several crops in the North were completely ruined.

The early crop is usually pulled out of the ground by women, but for the main crop the method is usually adopted of cutting off the tops to leave about $\frac{1}{2}$ an inch above the crown, whilst the crop is still in the ground. The roots are then forked out by hand and pitted, after the fashion of potatoes, in small heaps each about 4 feet wide and 3 feet high. Afterwards the heaps are covered with straw and then soil.

Wherever possible, lifting should be done in dry weather and the use of a sugar-beet lifter considerably hastens the task, especially when large acreages are involved. Good ventilation should be left in the heaps until all danger of over-heating is past.

For market purposes it is customary to wash the carrots and many growers have their own plant for doing this work. Some markets, on the other hand, prefer unwashed roots, and in any case that portion of the crop which is lifted before October is seldom washed because the skins are too tender.

YIELD

The average yield per acre is in the region of 10 to 12 tons, but on good land, suitably manured and in favourable seasons, crops of 20 tons per acre or more are common. On several farms in Yorkshire in 1940 the crop averaged over 25 tons per acre and in all these cases the crop was unthinned and grown in rows 20 inches apart.

INSECT PESTS

Carrot Fly.—This is by far the most serious pest, the grub of which burrows into the roots causing them to become brown or "rusty" and finally rotten. The attack of the "fly" does not as a rule begin until the end of May or early June, and young seedlings about that time may be seriously damaged. On the other hand, an early sown crop that is well forward may escape injury in some districts, although in Yorkshire experienced carrot growers affirm that sowing after mid-May is the best way of avoiding the pest.

Roots that are seriously damaged are not only unsaleable but will rot in the clamp. It is in dry seasons when growth is not so luxuriant, and particularly in a young crop that is not getting away, that the carrot fly is most injurious.

The trouble can be recognised easily. In the early stages of growth the leaves turn reddish, then yellow, and finally wither and die. When an affected plant is pulled up the maggots can invariably be seen protruding from holes in the root.

Control Measures.—It is unwise to grow carrots out of rotation or in a field that is in close proximity to one that has carried carrots or parsnips the previous year. Promising results have been obtained by spraying the headlands with a sodium fluoride-molasses bait to kill the flies.

PARSNIPS

The demand for parsnips is somewhat limited, for they do not appeal to the public taste quite so much as carrots. The crop has the advantage, however, that it can be left in the ground until required for use and that it is easy to grow and produces good yields.

The conditions required for successful growth are comparable in all respects with those required for carrots. Deep, fertile and well-cultivated land allows of free root development and produces long, well-shaped roots which are good to sell. The crop will grow quite satisfactorily on heavy soils, but under these conditions lifting is much more expensive.

VARIETIES

The hollow-crowned parsnips are the most widely grown, but the common cattle parsnip is sometimes grown as food for stock, notably in the Channel Islands. For market purposes it is important to choose the right variety and several of these offered are vastly superior to the hollow-crown variety. Of these the following are recommended :—

Hollow Crown Improved.　A good general purpose variety.

Improved Marrow .　Notable for its fine quality.

Offenham　.　.　A half-long variety, wide in the shoulder and very convenient to pack.

Tender and True　.　Of good quality and relatively resistant to canker.

PLACE IN ROTATION

In most cases parsnips will occupy part of the normal root break. They do well, however, when the crop follows potatoes or roots.

PREPARATION OF SEED BED

As with carrots, soil that has been dunged for the previous crop is preferable, the presence of fresh dung giving rise to forking in the roots. Where, however, dung must be applied direct for the crop it is best spread in autumn and ploughed in.

In early spring a seed bed should be prepared by cultivating, taking due care to keep the frost mould on the surface. Particularly on the heavier classes of soil is it important to avoid late ploughing, which results in so many seasons in the production of a cloddy seed bed.

MANURING

Lime is necessary for this crop and so, if the soil is deficient in this respect, a good dressing of lime should be given after ploughing, being well worked into the surface soil by cultivating.

Before sowing, the following mixture of fertilisers should be applied :—

Sulphate of Ammonia . .	1	cwt. per acre.
Superphosphate . . .	3	,, ,,
Muriate of Potash . . .	1	,, ,,
	5	,, ,,

A top-dressing of sulphate of ammonia should be given after singling.

SOWING THE SEED

In the warmer districts of England or in very favourable seasons the seed may be sown during the last week of February. More frequently, however, seeding takes place during the first fortnight in March. The seed should be sown at the rate of 7 lb. per acre on the flat in rows 15 to 18 inches apart, placing it in drills about one inch deep.

AFTER CULTIVATIONS

The plants should be thinned to stand 6 to 8 inches apart as soon as they get into rough leaf. The normal procedure on a field scale is to gap them into bunches with a hoe, and then single to one plant by hand. The soil should be pulled up to the plants to cover the crown and prevent attacks of carrot fly. During the summer several inter-row hoeings may be necessary to keep the crop clean.

HARVESTING

Parsnips are best left in the ground until required, in fact most housewives concede that the flavour of the root is better following frost. If more convenient, they can be lifted and clamped in October and November as for carrots, and it is always well to have a portion of the crop clamped for fear that severe frost will prevent lifting later on. The crop cannot be pulled by hand owing to the depth to which the roots penetrate into the ground. Thus hand-forking is necessary, or on a large scale the crop can be ploughed out or eased from the ground with a sugar-beet lifter. When the hand fork is used it must be pushed in vertically to avoid breaking the root, and if the crop is ploughed out the plough should be set to a depth of 12 inches and so adjusted that the row of parsnips to be lifted is 3 inches from the outer edge of the last furrow. In this way the roots lie on top of the turned furrow and can be easily picked out by hand. The tops are then cut off close to the crown.

YIELD

The yield varies considerably but as a rule 12 tons per acre can be expected. Under good soil conditions and with generous fertilising much heavier crops are obtained. For some markets the roots are washed like carrots but in other cases unwashed roots are preferred. It is perhaps hardly necessary to add that only clean, well-trimmed roots of good shape and size and free from damage should be marketed. Fanged or cankered roots should be used for cattle-feeding, for which purpose they have a considerably higher feeding value than carrots. It is interesting to note in this connection that for many years parsnips have been used for dairy cows in the Channel Islands where they are valued for the production of milk and butter. Small quantities can be boiled and fed to pigs.

Chapter Five

ROOT CROPS FOR FEEDING

TURNIPS AND SWEDES

In recent years the wisdom of growing turnips and swedes as a source of animal food for winter use has been contested by both farmers and feeding experts. Staunch adherents to the crop have been ranged against those who have advocated its complete replacement by purchased concentrates and from time to time the cry has been made that the crop is both old-fashioned and unprofitable. It is true, of course, that on heavy soils where swedes and turnips are an unreliable crop, cereal-legume mixtures for silage are much safer. Then again, on many farms it has been found possible to replace the root crop by sugar beet, thereby increasing the cash output of the farm whilst still maintaining the same head of livestock by utilising the beet tops and pulp. In spite of these alterations many farmers have stuck to the crop with dour determination and to-day, when we require a much greater measure of self-sufficiency on our farms, the despised "roots" are once more occupying an important position in the economy of the farm.

It is generally agreed that roots are much more than the mere sugared water claimed by those who cry that the crop is doomed. They are succulent and palatable at a time of year when other appetising foods are difficult if not impossible to obtain. In addition, they are one of the most important cleaning crops in the rotation and when folded on by sheep are a sure means of maintaining the fertility of light land.

As both turnips and swedes require very similar treatment they will be classed together under the term "roots" for the remainder of this chapter.

Roots thrive best in a cool, moist climate and the best quality and highest yields are obtained in Scotland, Ireland and the North and Western regions of England. Suitable climatic conditions are essential for a full crop, and in hot, dry weather attacks of turnip "fly" and mildew disease take serious toll of the

190

plants. Sunshine is not essential, but once the plants begin to meet in the rows an abundant supply of rain is required.

Deep, free-working light loams resting on a fairly firm, well-drained subsoil are ideally suited to the crop. The "sheep and barley" lands of the Wolds and Norfolk are typical of large areas where the crop, though never heavy, grows to good advantage and, in fact, the maintenance of fertility of these light soils depends upon good crops of roots for folding. Heavy soils and wet soils seldom yield good crops, for under such conditions it is difficult to obtain the fineness of tilth so necessary for even germination. Peaty soils must be well drained and limed before good results are obtained.

VARIETIES

Turnips, which have rough hairy leaves, can be grouped into three main classes: white, soft yellows and hardy yellows.

1. *White Turnips* contain only about 8 per cent. of dry matter and, although the heaviest croppers amongst turnips, are only of poor feeding quality. They are rapid in growth and are often grown as catch crops or for filling up headlands. They do not keep and are not frost resistant. Well-known varieties in this class are:—

Lincolnshire Red . A quick-growing variety for autumn and early winter use.

Greystone . . A good cropper for early feeding.

Pomeranian White . A heavy cropping and early maturing variety.

2. *Soft Yellow Turnips.*—These contain about 9 per cent. of dry matter and are slightly better keepers than the white turnips.

Fosterton Hybrid . A rapid-growing, early maturing variety.

Early Sheep Fold . A good cropping, early variety.

3. *Hardy Yellow Turnips.*—These contain about 10 per cent. of dry matter and are hardy and frost resistant. They are, in fact, little inferior to swedes in both feeding value and keeping quality.

Aberdeen Yellow is the best-known turnip in this class of which there are two types: the Green-top and the Purple-top.

The Bruce (purple-top) and the Wallace (green-top) are
strains of yellow turnips which are markedly resistant to
"finger-and-toe" or "club root" disease.

Swedes can be subdivided into three groups, namely: Purple-
top, Bronze-top and Green-top varieties.

1. *The Purple Tops* contain about 11 per cent. of dry matter,
and though they are the least hardy of the swedes produce the
heaviest yields and are the quickest growers. Favourite varieties
are Tipperary, Magnum Bonum, Magnificent, Majestic, Super-
lative and Purdy's Purple Top.

2. *The Bronze Tops* are intermediate in character, between the
Purple Tops and the Green Tops. They contain about 12 per
cent. dry matter and the class includes such well-known varieties
as Darlington, Gateacre, Caledonian and Carboy.

3. *The Green Tops* not only produce the best quality swedes,
having about 13 per cent. dry matter, but they are also the
best keepers. Slow to mature, they are the smallest croppers.
Good varieties are Lord Derby, Keep-well, Old Kinaldy and
Conqueror.

Wilhelmsburger is a green-topped variety very resistant to
"finger-and-toe," extremely hardy and an excellent keeper.
Danish Herning is another swede which has shown itself very
resistant to disease.

White-fleshed swedes are also available, but these are not well
known and have not been so widely tested as other types. Some
are very heavy yielders with keeping qualities and frost resistance
comparable with the more common purple-topped varieties.

In general, one can say that differences between the many
varieties of swedes are by no means so marked as in the case of
other crops. Soil, season and cultivation are of prime importance,
and when a variety has proved consistently good under any
particular set of conditions there is generally little reason for
growers to change to other varieties.

PLACE IN ROTATION

Roots are the principal cleaning crop of the rotation and hence
come between or after two straw crops. Under most conditions
the crop does not come more frequently than once in four years,

although, provided the soil is regularly limed, they can be grown continuously on the same land. Frequently by far the most efficient method of cleaning land foul with weeds is to take two root crops in succession. As a rule a spring cereal follows roots for, especially when they are folded off with sheep, it is not possible to get wheat or winter oats sown early enough. Occasionally the crop may be carted off in time to follow with an autumn-sown cereal.

PREPARATION OF SEED BED

Soils on which roots are grown vary so widely in character that it is impossible to lay down any standardised sequence of cultivations for the crop. In general, however, field work may be roughly grouped under two main motives, firstly the cleaning of the stubble and secondly the preparation of the seed bed.

Autumn cleaning follows fairly general lines in most root-growing areas. The land is shallow-ploughed or cultivated immediately after harvest and the "twitch" is dragged to the surface where it can be collected and burnt. If not done in autumn, cleaning must be performed in spring when, in most seasons, the weather may not be so favourable. Moreover, autumn cleaning eases the pressure of spring work.

Following this preliminary work subsequent operations will depend to a considerable extent upon whether dung is to be applied in autumn or spring. Climate is the determining factor here, and in districts of low rainfall autumn dunging is practised, whilst in the wetter districts of the North it is common to apply the dung in spring.

An autumn application of dung is followed by deep ploughing. Some prefer to plough shallow first and cross-plough deeper later in winter, for in this way the dung is placed, sandwich-fashion, at not too great a depth below the surface. Where stiff or impervious subsoils are experienced it is an advantage to subsoil at the same time as ploughing.

On medium and heavy soils in particular it is wise to avoid spring ploughing, since this brings raw soil to the surface which does not have sufficient time to mellow and fall to a fine frost-mould before a seed bed is required. As a result, cloddy seed beds follow and this invariably gives rise to uneven germination.

N

It is usual, therefore, to rely on heavy drags and cultivators to break down the furrows and prepare a deep fine tilth.

In the dry districts of the South, and especially on heavy soils, the land is ridged immediately after the initial deep ploughing in autumn, the ridges running at right angles to the furrows. During the winter, when fine spells of weather permit, the ridges are split and re-split several times. This exposes a comparatively large area of land to the weathering influences of frost, rain and drying winds, allows the free passage of rain water, and produces a fine tilth in spring, leaving plenty of time for the ridges to settle before seeding takes place.

When spring dunging is intended, it is usual to plough deeply in autumn and leave in the furrow over winter. In spring, the land is shallow-ploughed once or twice, and if perennial weeds were not removed by stubble cleaning, or are still present in large quantities, this is followed up by dragging to bring the weeds to the surface.

They are then rolled up with chain harrows, collected and burnt. The land is then ridged, well-rotted muck spread in the rows, the ridges split to cover the muck, and the land is ready for sowing.

The dung should be covered up as soon as possible, since it rapidly loses ammonia to the atmosphere as it dries and abstracts valuable moisture from the surrounding soil. A Yorkshire method that gives good results is to chain-harrow the ridges down after mucking to cover up the dung and help to retain the moisture. It is then usual to wait for a shower, after which the ridges are split and the seed drilled immediately.

There is no doubt, however, that in all cases where it is practicable the dung should be applied in autumn or winter and ploughed in. Some slight manurial loss may follow from the winter rains washing out the soluble nitrogenous matter in the dung, but it is safe to say that this is more than counterbalanced by the improvement in tilth which is obtained when the dung is intimately mixed with the soil. Each year many failures can be attributed to the dung, applied in the row, becoming dry. Then when the young seedlings reach this dry insulating material in the centre of the row, growth is slowed down and the plants are liable to "fly" attack. Many instances of thin and patchy crops in dry districts have been remedied by changing the spring application of dung to an autumn application and drilling the seed on the flat instead of the ridge.

Time must not be lost in spring by intensive cultivation nor must moisture be lost by undue harrowing which only causes the surface layers to dry out. Far too often the plea is made "if only I had been able to drill a week earlier I should not have lost the crop," and it is true to say that more failures result from sowing too late than from any other cause. Those who doubt this statement should reflect on their own experiences, when in the majority of cases it will be recalled that the early sown crops have succeeded whilst the late sown ones have fallen prey to "fly" and mildew.

MANURING

Lime is essential and on all soils where periodic liming is necessary the root crop can be regarded as the most convenient crop to which it can be applied. The lime should always be applied after the final ploughing so that it can be worked into the surface soil where it is at hand for the young seedlings to acquire it readily. Sour soils devoid of lime are fatal to this crop, and even if "finger-and-toe" disease is absent the plants can never thrive unless the soil is sweet, but will remain stunted and of poor development.

Whenever possible a dressing of dung should be given to the root crop, not so much from the standpoint of plant food, as from the improvement in texture and water-holding capacity which is brought about. No crop is more affected by soil poverty, and if dung is not available reliance must be placed on the use of artificials alone. In general, however, the best results will be got from a moderate dressing of dung of about 15 tons per acre supplemented by artificials. Phosphates are all-important and frequently prove the limiting factor in yield. About 4 cwt. per acre of superphosphate will meet the requirements of the crop on average soils. For light soils the addition of 1 cwt. per acre muriate of potash is advisable, whilst on the heavier classes of land 4 to 6 cwt. basic slag (high soluble) may replace the superphosphate.

When slag is used it should be applied a few weeks before sowing the seed. If dung is not available, 1 cwt. per acre sulphate of ammonia should be given in addition to the dressing of super-phosphate recommended above.

For both swedes and turnips a good start in life makes all the difference between a good yield and a moderate or even poor one. Rapid growth in the seedling stage is of enormous advantage especially during dry weather, for it is the crop which "sits on the fence" that is so liable to attacks from flea beetles. Frequently an application of quick-acting phosphate, such as superphosphate, will bring the crop to the hoe two or three weeks earlier than would be the case without this treatment.

SOWING THE SEED

In all the typical root-growing districts the crop is grown on the ridge, the rows being about 26 inches apart. In dry districts and on the lighter types of soil, however, drilling on the flat in rows 20 to 24 inches apart is common, and this practice is extending. As to which method is best much depends upon the soil and climate and not a little upon local custom. From time to time heated controversies rage between the advocates of ridge work and those who prefer drilling on the flat. The chief advantage of the ridge is that it enables horse-hoeing to commence before the rows appear, which is very useful on weedy land. On the other hand, there is no doubt that unless the land is ridged with great care dry clods and soil are pushed to the top of the ridge and then, when the seed is sown, germination is likely to be very patchy. On clean land flat drilling is quite satisfactory, and there is no doubt that in dry weather one can frequently obtain a plant on the flat when conditions are much too dry on the ridge. Many workers contend that hoeing and singling are much easier when the crop is sown on the ridge than when it is drilled on the flat. This is a debatable point, but careful enquiry fails to indicate that these operations are done any more skilfully or quicker in the case of ridge work, and it would seem that custom is the determining factor.

Seeding takes place from mid-April to July, depending upon season and district. The usual time for swedes is during the latter half of May, turnips being sown about a fortnight later. In hot dry districts where early sown crops are liable to mildew, however, seeding may not commence until the end of June. In order that singling may be conveniently spaced over as long a period as possible, the crop is generally sown at intervals of a week in convenient breaks. The average seed rate is 4 lb. per acre for swedes and 3 lb. for turnips. Here again, however, local experience frequently indicates much lighter seedings, and under ideal conditions of tilth and growing weather 1 lb. per acre of seed is ample. Where good stands are invariably obtained a thick seeding is a nuisance, for it makes singling very difficult. On the other hand, under adverse conditions and where the "fly" is apt to be troublesome a good thick plant is a decided advantage. Another point of considerable importance with "swedes" is to drill only good "bold" seed which will produce lusty plants. To buy cheap seed is the height of folly.

After drilling, it is almost always advisable to roll, preferably with a ring roller, and this applies both to flat and ridge work. The roller attached to some ridge drills ("bobbin drills") is a travesty and can never take the place of the ring roller.

AFTER CULTIVATIONS

As soon as the rows of seedlings can be seen on the flat, and even before this on the ridge, horse-hoeing should commence to keep weeds in check. Disc hoes are preferable for the first hoeing, especially on the flat, for it is then possible to avoid smothering the seedlings in the soil. Once the plants are in rough leaf the sooner they are singled the better. This operation can be performed by hand-hoe or entirely by hand, depending largely upon the custom of the district. In recent years gapping machines have been used to an increasing extent, and after the plant is gapped singling to one plant may be done by hand or hoe. The plants should be left 8 to 10 inches apart. Inter-row hoeings can continue through the season until such time as the growth of the tops makes this inadvisable. Deep hoeings late in the season may be harmful.

HARVESTING

White turnips are ready in September and early October, and these are usually fed together with their tops on grass or they are folded off with sheep. Yellow turnips follow next in order of maturity, and lastly come swedes which are ready for lifting about November. A portion of the swede crop may be folded off and a portion stored for late feeding, or in mild districts the roots can be left growing until required. When the crop is lifted and protected from frost it is usual to adopt one of three ways. They may be stored on the field in small clamps each containing one day's supply, they may be carted to a convenient site and stored in large broad clamps not deeper than about 3 feet 6 inches which are well protected from frost, or they may be ploughed in. The last method is undoubtedly the best in that the roots keep their freshness and succulence, but a good deal of additional labour is necessary to clean the roots after lifting, an operation carried out, of course, in the winter months when the soil is not in the same dry friable condition that it might have been in October or early November. Storing in this way is quite simply done by ploughing out a furrow, pulling two rows of roots and placing them in the bottom, and then ploughing a furrow back to cover the roots and protect them from frost. The tops should be left above ground, and as long as the weather remains mild the roots will continue to grow. If the tops can be kept green in this way they are excellent for ewes which are suckling early lambs. An easier but less effective method is to run the plough down the rows in October or November and earth up the roots.

Before storing in a clamp the roots are topped and tailed, but this trimming should not be drastic, for there is evidence that the keeping quality of the roots is impaired by so doing.

In all cases where the bulk of the roots are left in the field a good supply must be kept at home for use in bad weather.

That the method of storage influences keeping quality very considerably is indicated by the results obtained in the following experiment carried out in the winter of 1939-40 which, it will be recalled, was exceptionally severe in January and February.

Treatment	Percentage Sound Roots on 12th March 1940
1. Left growing in the field	3
2. Left growing but earthed up in November .	12
3. Pulled and ploughed in as described above .	70
4. Pulled, topped and tailed and clamped in 4-load heaps in field with good covering soil	87
5. As No. 4 but stored in large clamp . .	94

A bronze-top variety of swede was used, and the pulling and subsequent treatment was carried out between the 10th and 12th November.

YIELD

The average yield for the country is in the region of 14 to 15 tons per acre, but in the good root-growing districts yields under 20 tons per acre would be considered poor. In the South of England and on thin soils the yield is a good deal lower than the average, but it is doubtful if under such conditions the crop can be justified.

GROWING FOR SEED

Turnip and swede seed is easily grown on the farm. At lifting time individual roots should be selected which are of a good shape, with a single top and single root, and having a convex crown. The latter is important from the keeping point of view, for roots with a concave or hollow top hold the rain and are liable to rot. The skin should be smooth and tender and the roots free from any sign of disease. Selected roots may have cores taken from them for analysis if desired, but on a farm this is usually considered unnecessary.

The selected roots should be carefully stored over the winter and planted out in spring, giving each plant a square yard of ground. If a sheltered spot is available pitting is unnecessary and the roots can be planted out in autumn.

Seed stems form early in summer, and the small top branches should be removed to encourage side development. Moreover, as cross fertilisation is easy the crop should be grown at least a quarter of a mile from any other crop of the same family likely to flower.

As soon as the seed is ripe the stems should be cut and stored in a dry airy shed until they are brittle, when the seed can be knocked out quite easily. It is important to riddle the seed obtained very carefully, and to discard all small and badly developed seeds which would produce weakly plants when sown. Before storing the seed should be rubbed in paraffin.

Seed obtained in this way is known as "stock seed," and on a commercial basis it would be sown in late summer or early autumn and allowed to run to seed the following summer. Frequently, however, the plants from a nursery bed are transplanted in February or early March into rows 28 inches wide with 12 inches between plants in the rows, or quite often the stock seed will be drilled in rows 22 inches apart using about 2 lb. of seed per acre. Later the plants are singled to 12 to 18 inches apart.

Commercial seed is grown chiefly in the South-Eastern and Eastern Counties, and a good crop produces about 10 cwt. of seed per acre. Farmers who contemplate growing seed for sale are advised in their own interest to communicate with a seeds merchant before commencing the project, for it is always wise to have a market for seed before growing it.

Insect Pests

"Fly" or Flea Beetle.—Few crops suffer so much and so consistently from any pest as does the root crop from "fly" or flea beetles. The small jumping beetles are mostly black with a yellow stripe down each wing case.

The damage is so well known as to require little description. The seedlings are attacked as soon as they appear through the ground, and in severe cases even before they are clear of the soil the beetles are gnawing the shoots. Once the plant reaches the rough-leaf stage it is generally safe, but in very dry seasons when growth is slow a crop may even be seriously attacked at this advanced stage. When this happens the leaves are punctured with innumerable little holes.

The seriousness of an attack depends upon prevailing weather conditions. During spells of drought and hot sun when the seedlings are struggling for existence the fly finds them easy prey, and a crop can be entirely eaten off as it appears. On the other hand, when the weather is moist and warm the growth of the leaves is much more rapid than the beetles can cope with and the plants escape serious injury.

Control Measures.—Much depends upon the condition of the seed bed and the strength of the young plants. If care is taken to get a really fine, firm seed bed, good bold seed is used, and the land has enough moisture for germination, the crop stands a good chance of survival even where the fly is present in large numbers. On the other hand, if the seed bed is dry and cloddy or a small-sized sample of seed is sown, the plants will often succumb when the beetle population is by no means so great.

In practice the common method of control is to re-sow until such time as a plant is obtained. The low rate of seeding and small cost of the seed makes this a practical proposition in many cases. In some seasons, however, three or four sowings may be necessary before a "plant" is obtained, and a factor often lost sight of is that re-sowing means loss of time, in fact, the season may be so far advanced before a plant is finally obtained that it is then too late for swedes, and reliance has to be placed on turnips which do not keep through the winter. Thus farmers are strongly advised to adopt control measures in order to secure a crop at the first sowing.

Many of these methods are of doubtful benefit yet have sufficient support amongst farmers to justify trial. The seed may be treated, for instance, with paraffin or turpentine (only wood turpentine must be used) before sowing with the object of temporarily disguising the smell of the germinating seeds which is supposed to attract the beetles. Proprietary seed dressings which work upon the same principle are also available. When paraffin or turpentine is used 1 fluid ounce (about two tablespoonfuls) should be stirred into 7 lb. of seed.

A more recent dressing consists of mixing one gallon of kerosene, 4 lb. of paradichlorbenzene, and 1 lb. of naphthalene and using two tablespoonfuls of the mixture to each pound of seed, treating the seed the day before drilling and spreading out on sacking overnight to dry.

As soon as the crop begins to appear dusting with lime or slag (3 cwt. per acre) may act as a deterrent. A "beetle catcher" is also of use. This consists of an axle about six feet long supported about 1 foot from the ground by a pair of old cycle wheels. Bags are then attached to the axle in such a way that they trail along the ground when the machine is pushed forward. The bags are covered with tar, and as they sweep along the ground the beetles are disturbed, jump forwards and upwards, and so stick to the tar. The efficiency of the method depends upon keeping the sacks freshly covered with tar, for the tarred surface quickly becomes coated with soil. Left to themselves few farm workers take the necessary trouble and hence the remedy is never wholly satisfactory.

Spraying with a paraffin and soft soap solution just before the plants emerge is also useful, but this involves the cartage of large quantities of water and hence is seldom used.

The most recent treatment is to dust the seedlings with a derris dust containing 0·2 per cent. rotenone at the rate of 56 lb. per acre.

A mixture of 50 per cent. naphthalene and 50 per cent. "colloidal" silica, applied at the rate of 55-65 lb. per acre, has given good results.

Dusts containing 3 per cent. nicotine have given a good kill in hot weather but are less satisfactory at low temperatures. The rate of application should be 40 lb. per acre unless conditions are very favourable, when as little as 20 lb. per acre may be sufficient.

These materials not only kill the beetles but mitigate further attacks. Still sunny days when the beetles are active should be chosen, and if rain or high wind follows the dusting the application must be repeated.

It should always be remembered that charlock is the feeding-ground for the beetles in early spring, and hence the weed should be ruthlessly eradicated from arable fields.

There is little doubt that the introduction of a cheap, efficient dusting machine would materially assist in controlling this pest, especially if the work was carried out by contractors at an all-in reasonable cost.

DISEASES

"*Finger-and-Toe*" or "*Club Root.*"—This disease is the cause of abnormal swellings on the roots, and occurs on soils deficient in lime, especially in the North. The germs of the disease can persist in the soil for a number of years and hence control presents a difficult problem. Affected plants appear unthrifty, the leaves tend to wilt, and on close inspection the malformation of the roots can be seen.

Control Measures.—Whenever practicable, the rotation should be lengthened or the land put down to a ley for a number of years. The lime deficiency should be remedied, preferably by an application of lime to the preceding crop. When roots have to be grown on land known to be infected, a resistant variety such as Wilhelmsburger or The Bruce should be selected and a light dressing of lime applied to the seed bed. Since charlock and other weeds of this family are attacked by the disease it is essential that they be suppressed. It need hardly be mentioned perhaps that diseased roots should on no account be thrown on to the manure heap, for by so doing the disease can be spread to every field.

MILDEW

In dry seasons, especially in the Southern Counties, a powdery mildew may attack the leaves and in severe cases will completely destroy them.

Control Measures.—In districts where this disease is prevalent it is usual to sow swedes a month later than would normally be the case, later sowings suffering less than early ones because there is less leaf by the time the hottest and driest part of the season is reached.

When seedlings are attacked they should be singled out at once, and given every encouragement to develop rapidly by frequent horse-hoeing.

MANGOLDS

The mangold is one of our most valuable sources of winter food for all classes of livestock. Not only is the crop capable of producing a large bulk of cattle food per acre, but it is more reliable than swedes or turnips, keeps better, and is less subject to pests and diseases.

Mangolds do best in dry sunny districts, and hence are grown extensively in the Midlands and Southern Counties of England. Once established, the crop can withstand prolonged periods of drought, especially when grown on the heavier types of soil, but in cold, wet and sunless seasons the results are disappointing.

Satisfactory crops can be grown on a wide variety of soils, but it is on deep rich loams that the plant excels. On poor, thin soils it fails utterly, although with suitable treatment surprisingly good results can be obtained even on the lighter types of land.

VARIETIES

As with turnips and swedes the number of named varieties of mangolds is very large, and it is an impossible task to describe them individually.

They can, however, be divided roughly into four groups according to their shape, namely globes, tankards, intermediates and longs. The globes are spherical in shape and grow entirely above ground, thus being well suited to the shallower soils and greatly facilitating pulling at "lifting time." Within this group subdivisions according to colour can be made, these being yellow, orange and lemon globe varieties.

Tankards have parallel sides which round off sharply at the neck and the root. The yield of this type is lower than for the other groups, but the feeding quality is excellent. Red and golden-coloured varieties are available.

Intermediates, as the name indicates, are intermediate in shape between the globes on the one hand and the longs on the other, being a somewhat elongated oval in shape. Yellow, orange and red varieties are obtainable.

Long varieties are spindle-shaped, being three or four times as long as they are broad, and red or yellow in colour. Although they go far down into the soil more than a foot of the root still stands above ground, and hence the type is rather susceptible to frost. On heavy land the roots are difficult to lift, whilst stony soils are unsuitable for their full development. On good, deep soils with generous manurial treatment this group will produce enormous yields, although the roots are somewhat coarse and fibrous and have a lower feeding value than other sorts.

Mangolds have a high water content which varies quite considerably between different varieties. Thus it is important in selecting any particular variety to choose one which will produce a high yield of dry matter per acre. Tonnage per acre, therefore, must not be the only consideration, for one frequently finds that a lower yielding variety but with a high dry-matter content is more profitable than one which gives a spectacular yield of roots that are largely composed of water, for it does not pay to cart water about the farm in the disguise of mangolds. It is not uncommon, for instance, for a given weight of one variety of mangolds to have twice the food value of the same weight of another lot of mangolds. Hence *quality* as well as *quantity* must be considered.

In recent years a large number of varieties have been tested in field trials by the National Institute of Agricultural Botany, and among the varieties tested Kirsche's Ideal has been outstanding in that it has produced over 7 cwt. of dry matter per acre more than the average of all the other strains. This variety is of the tankard shape and has white flesh and a yellowish skin below ground but greenish above. The roots lift easily but the tops, being more profuse than most other types, are difficult to twist off when topping is done in this way. It is a good keeper and is well worth a trial on all farms.

Regarding other named varieties little can be said except that a variety which has proved by experience to do well under certain soil and climatic conditions is worth sticking to, always bearing in mind the fact that the best variety is one which produces the greatest yield of *dry matter* per acre, and at the same time is of good keeping quality.

PLACE IN ROTATION

Mangolds occupy part of the root break in most districts, being used for late feeding when the other roots are finished. Where soil and climate favour mangolds and not swedes the former may replace swedes and turnips entirely. As the crop keeps well into the following summer, on farms where sugar beet is grown, it is common to feed the beet tops and pulp until Christmas to replace swedes and follow on with mangolds after the turn of the year.

Quite frequently the crop is grown on the same piece of land each year. This practice has the advantage that it enables a convenient site to be chosen near to the farm buildings, which reduces the labour and time entailed in carting the crop home. In addition, by growing them continuously the land is maintained in clean condition at little cost and the fertility of the soil is maintained at a high level. Hence big yields are obtained.

As the crop has to be sown early it is impossible to take mangolds after a forage crop consumed in spring.

PREPARATION OF SEED BED

Mangolds may be grown on the flat or on the ridge, and the sequence of operations necessary to produce the desired tilth for seeding is determined largely by which of these methods is adopted. It is well to bear in mind, however, that mangolds prefer a stale seed bed, and hence all the major cultivations should be done some considerable time before seeding takes place. This enables the land to become firm by natural settlement, and undue reliance need not be placed on the use of the roller.

Where necessary stubble cleaning should be carried out as for swedes. The farmyard manure can then be applied and ploughed in fairly shallow, to be cross-ploughed deeper at a later date. On strong land it is a common practice to plough in autumn and ridge up immediately afterwards, the ridges running at right angles to the ploughing. The dung is then spread in the drills and the ridges are split to cover it, the field being left in this condition over winter. All that is then necessary in spring is to harrow the rows to break down the clods which will have been well weathered, distribute the artificials, run up the ridges again and the land is ready for sowing. In some cases, instead of applying the dung in the rows in autumn it is left until spring and then, during the winter months when conditions are favourable, the ridges are split and re-split, thus exposing the soil to the full weathering influences.

In dry districts and on the lighter soils it is usual to apply the dung in autumn and plough it in, work up a tilth in spring with heavy cultivators, and drill the seed on the flat. On all the heavier types of soil spring ploughing is inadvisable, for it brings unweathered soil to the surface which will dry into hard clods and prevent the necessary fine seed bed being obtained. The objection to growing on the flat is that since mangold seed germinates very slowly it enables weeds to get ahead, horse-hoeing being impossible before the rows can be seen. This is not the case, of course, when the seed is sown on the ridge, in which case inter-row cultivation will commence as soon as weeds appear.

Manuring

Mangolds respond readily to high farming, and what is more they pay handsomely for generous treatment. The basis of the manurial treatment should be a good dressing of dung, and if supplies are available 20 tons per acre is not too liberal. Dung alone is not sufficient, and even when the land is known to be in good heart one or more top-dressings of nitrogen should be given in addition.

As a general rule, however, a moderate application of a well-balanced fertiliser, given prior to seeding, will be found beneficial and the following mixture is suggested :—

Sulphate of Ammonia	.	1 cwt. per acre.
Superphosphate	. .	2 ,, ,,
Steamed Bone Flour .	.	1 ,, ,,
Muriate of Potash	. .	1 ,, ,,
Common Salt .	. .	3 ,, ,,
		8 ,, ,,

At singling time ¾ cwt. per acre nitrate of soda should be given with a further top-dressing at the same rate about six weeks later. In place of the nitrate of soda, nitro-chalk or sulphate of ammonia may be used.

Lime is essential to success, and any shortage must be rectified before the crop is contemplated.

SOWING THE SEED

The seed is really a "fruit," and enclosed within the rough and tough outer coat are 2 to 4 small shiny seeds. This outer coat renders germination difficult, and in dry weather the plants may take several weeks to appear. Frequently they "come at twice" which is annoying, for it means that the crop requires singling at two different times.

For this reason many farmers soften the seed coat by soaking the seed for 24 hours before drilling. Care is necessary in this case to allow the superficial moisture to drain away and the seed to partially dry before it is drilled, otherwise the seeds stick together and uneven drilling results.

The rate of seeding varies from 6 lb. per acre under good soil conditions to 10 lb. per acre for poor seed beds. It should be sown not deeper than one inch in rows 26 to 28 inches apart on the ridge or 20 to 22 inches on the flat. Surplus seed keeps well and can be used the following season.

The time of seeding varies from mid-April in the Midlands to mid-May in the Southern Counties, while too early drilling causes a large number of plants to "bolt" or send up flowering stems.

At the risk of undue repetition it might be emphasised again that one of the surest means of getting a full plant is to drill only on a fine, firm and moist seed bed that has been prepared some time before seeding actually takes place.

When the plant is patchy it must not be assumed that the remainder of the seeds will not appear, and under the conditions it is better to single by hand and not disturb the soil in the gaps as would happen if hoes were used. Frequently plants will appear at intervals extending over several weeks, and what in the first instance appears a very poor and gappy plant may ultimately become a full one.

During damp weather gaps can be filled in by transplanting

seedlings, but during dry spells it is safer to use cabbage or kohl rabi for filling up the rows.

About six weeks after drilling the crop is ready for singling, by which time the first pair of rough leaves will be forming. About a foot is left between plants in the rows, though tankard varieties may be gapped somewhat narrower. The method of singling varies from district to district, some doing it in one operation by hand-hoe, others gapping first and singling later by hand, whilst in other cases the whole operation may be done entirely by hand.

Inter-row horse-hoeing can commence as soon as the rows are seen for flat work or before this when the crop is grown on the ridge, and this will continue during the season until the growth of tops is prohibitive. In order to permit horse-hoeing to begin before the mangolds actually appear, it is sometimes customary when the crop is being put in on the flat to mix a little rape or turnip seed in with the mangold seed. This germinates readily, enables the rows to be seen and the plants are removed when the crop is singled.

Should "bolters" appear in any great number it is advisable to go through the crop and cut the flowering stems off. If bolting is allowed to proceed unchecked the flowering heads draw on the reserves of food in the root and the yield is reduced.

HARVESTING

The crop shows signs of ripening when the lower leaves begin to droop, and since it is unable to withstand any but very light frosts, it is usual to lift the crop towards the end of October. If by some mischance the roots do get frosted they should not be touched until the frost has gone right out of them, for it is fatal to clamp them in a frosted condition as they would merely rot. After gently thawing out, frosted roots should be clamped separately, so that a watch can be kept on them and permit them to be used first.

In most districts the tops are screwed off by hand, and if a knife is used care must be taken not to trim the top too close to the crown. Nor should the roots be "tailed" or even loaded into the carts with a fork, for such injuries cause the root to bleed and permit the entry of decaying organisms, resulting in many roots rotting in the clamp.

Mangolds are generally stored in large clamps which should be immediately covered with a good covering of straw or bracken. Many a good crop has been lost by an unexpectedly early and severe frost when the clamp is still exposed. The roots may be stored in large buildings, against walls or stacks, but sure protection against frost must be provided. Outside clamps should be covered with at least a foot of straw and then soil, good ventilation being left till "sweating" has finished.

GROWING MANGOLD SEED

The seed is sown in July or early August in a well-prepared nursery bed, to which superphosphate at the rate of 6 cwt. per acre has been applied and well raked in. Seed can be broadcast at the rate of 20 lb. per acre or drilled in rows 12 inches apart.

The plants should be large enough to transplant in October, but they can be left in the bed until early spring if conditions are not favourable for autumn transplanting.

The land on which they are to be grown should receive a good dressing of dung which can be ploughed in. Prior to planting out the following mixture of artificials should be applied and worked into the surface of soil:—

Sulphate of Ammonia	.	$\frac{1}{2}$ cwt. per acre,	
Superphosphate	. .	3	" "
Muriate of Potash	. .	1	" "
		$4\frac{1}{2}$	" "

this being followed by rolling.

The land should then be marked off with a drill in two directions with the coulters set to allow each plant a square yard of room. The plants are dibbled in at the points of intersection, preferably during showery weather.

The advantage of autumn transplanting is that if some of the plants fail to survive the winter they can be replaced in spring, and moreover, by then they will be well established and as soon as the growing weather arrives good headway is made.

During the growing season weeds should be kept in check and the plants assisted with a dressing of nitrate of soda applied at the rate of 1 cwt. per acre. When the leading shoot is running up for seed it should be nipped off to encourage the development of the side branches.

o

The crop is cut with a hook when the seeds begin to harden and is tied in bundles and stooked to dry.

Carting must not take place until the crop is thoroughly dry, and the stack must be thatched immediately unless threshing is done from the field.

On a large scale, when economies in the cost of transplanting are necessary, the usual procedure is to fallow a field until July and then drill the crop in the normal way. The treatment of the crop follows usual lines, except that instead of lifting the plants in autumn they are left in the ground and allowed to produce seed the following year.

It is commonly thought that seed production should be confined to the dry, sunny districts of the South, but recently excellent results have been obtained in northern areas.

The yield of seed varies from 10 to 20 cwt. per acre.

YIELD

The average yield of roots is only about 20 tons per acre, but on land reasonably well treated 30-ton crops can be grown with ease and with care in getting a full plant, and when favoured with a good season yields in the region of 50 tons per acre are quite common.

It is essential that mangolds should be allowed to ripen before being fed to stock, for if fed in an immature state animals scour badly. In order to allow full time for the necessary changes in the root to take place it is not usual in practice, therefore, to feed mangolds before Christmas. Nor should they be fed to male sheep, as they tend to produce urinary disorders.

Though it is usual to leave the tops in the field and plough them in, when keep is scarce they may be fed or converted into silage.

PESTS AND DISEASES

Mangolds are subject to the same insect pests and diseases as sugar beet. These have been fully dealt with in connection with the sugar-beet crop, and in the event of a serious infestation reference should be made to the control measures outlined on pages 155-159.

KOHL RABI

This crop is not grown extensively in Great Britain, but in certain districts it is able to thrive under conditions of drought unfavourable for other root crops. Strictly speaking, it is not a root at all but a swollen stem, and as it grows well out of the ground is very popular for folding with sheep, as they can consume practically the entire plant. It is excellent for milk cows, for there is no danger when it is fed of tainting the milk which sometimes happens with turnips. It is also very valuable for pigs.

Kohl rabi is commonly known as the "bulb of dry summers," which aptly describes its drought-resisting properties, and for this reason it is popular in the eastern and southern parts of England. The crop does best on the stiffer loam soils, but on account of its great resistance to "finger-and-toe" disease it is often grown on fen soils where the large amount of organic matter in the soil, combined with a not inconsiderable shortage of lime, make this disease quite common. Kohl rabi is not suitable for cold, wet soils but does reasonably well on light land in districts of high rainfall.

VARIETIES

Two varieties are commonly grown, one in which the leaves and bulbs are glaucous-green, the other being reddish-purple. Some strains have short tops which are suitable for drier and warmer conditions; others have large tops which are more suited for colder soils and, being very hardy, are useful for late feeding.

PLACE IN ROTATION

The crop occupies part of the root break.

PREPARATION OF SEED BED

In growing kohl rabi the land is prepared as for roots, although the crop, unlike swedes and turnips, is invariably drilled on the flat. There appears to be no reason why in cooler and moister districts the crop should not be grown on the ridge if this method is preferred.

Sometimes the seedlings are raised in a nursery bed and transplanted. To encourage rooting an application of superphosphate at the rate of 6 cwt. per acre is usually given to the bed, and 2 lb. of seed provides sufficient plants for an acre of land. In view of the ease with which the crop can be transplanted there would appear to be considerable room for its extended use for the purpose of filling in gaps in mangold and swede crops.

MANURING

So far as manuring is concerned the requirements of the crop are closely akin to those of the mangold.   In addition to a moderate application of dung, say 15 tons per acre, the following mixture of artificials should be applied and worked into the seed bed prior to sowing :—

Sulphate of Ammonia	.	1 cwt. per acre.
Superphosphate	. .	2 ,, ,,
Steamed Bone Flour .	.	1 ,, ,,
Muriate of Potash .	.	1 ,, ,,
		—
		5 ,, ,,

At singling time 1 cwt. per acre nitrate of soda or some other nitrogenous fertiliser should be given.

SOWING THE SEED

The seed is sown in April on the flat in rows 20 to 24 inches apart at the rate of 4 lb. per acre.

When the plants are transplanted from the nursery bed this is done in May or June when soil and weather conditions are favourable for such work.   The tap roots should be cut off before planting, leaving only the shallow fibrous roots.   It is advisable to do this in order to avoid planting with the long tap root up-turned which in practice so frequently happens, for a plant with an upturned root can never thrive.   A spud or builder's trowel should be used in preference to a dibber, and the plants, once in position, should be heeled in.   A skilled man can plant out at the rate of 20 per minute, 2 feet apart in the rows, but a rate of 10 per minute is good average work.

AFTER CULTIVATIONS

Horse-hoeing between the rows should commence as soon as possible, and when sufficiently forward the plants can be singled to a distance of about 1 foot apart in the rows.

Inter-row cultivation continues, as with other root crops, as long as it is possible to do so without damaging the tops.

HARVESTING

The roots stand frost fairly well and may be left growing in the field until it is convenient to feed them.   On the other hand, they can be lifted and stored in a like manner to swedes, should this be more convenient.

YIELD

20 tons per acre is a good crop which, when compared with the high yields of swedes and mangolds that are quite common, may not seem very encouraging. It must be remembered, however, that the crop is generally grown under conditions so dry that the other root crops would be a failure or at any rate would give only poor yields.

Chapter Six

MISCELLANEOUS CROPS

LINSEED

LINSEED is grown both for its seed and for its fibre. Since 1939 the acreage of this crop has greatly increased, for the seed is required as a source of oil and the fibre for ropes and canvas, both of national importance. When the crop is grown for seed it is generally referred to as Linseed, but when grown for fibre it is more common to call it Flax.

Linseed requires a comparatively low rainfall and a warm climate, and is confined, therefore, very largely to the South-Eastern Counties. Much, of course, depends upon the season, and with favourable conditions good crops are grown in the North. Any good medium soil is suitable, but since the crop is unable to withstand drought, sandy soils and those which are subject to drought are quite unsuitable. Whilst in the normal way heavy soils would fulfil the requirements in so far as they retain moisture and are not so liable to dry out in a period of drought, owing to the difficulty of obtaining the necessary fineness of tilth for a seed bed, the crop is not usually grown on these soils. The ideal soil is one that is light enough for barley yet has sufficient body for wheat, although quite good crops have been grown on poor chalky soils with suitable fertiliser treatment. There is a considerable danger of lodging on very rich soils.

VARIETIES

The best varieties for seed production are:—

Redwing, Bison and Royal.

When imported seed is used, care should be taken to dress it carefully or ensure that this has been done by the seedsman from whom it is obtained, for otherwise there is a danger of introducing foreign weeds on to the farm. As the seed readily absorbs moisture and loses vitality it is essential to store it in a cool dry place. Recent trials indicate that Royal, Bison and Redwing—in this order—are superior to La Plata and give increased yields,

214

more even ripening and, being longer in the straw, easier harvesting. Redwing is the first to ripen and most suitable for late districts.

PLACE IN ROTATION

Linseed commonly follows a straw crop and does well after wheat. On the lighter soils which lack body it is best to grow it after roots which have been fed on. It forms an excellent nurse crop for seeds or may be followed by wheat, which appears to do well following linseed. Wireworms practically ignore the crop, and hence it is one of the most suitable crops for growing on ploughed-out grassland, especially when the wireworm population is known to be high. Rabbits are also indifferent to it, and for this reason it has decided possibilities on ploughed-out grassland in the region of woods infested with rabbits, for it enables a crop to be obtained pending the extermination of this pest.

PREPARATION OF SEED BED

The crop only takes some 10 weeks from seeding to maturity, and hence every endeavour should be made to get the land into good condition for rapid growth. To ensure clean land the stubble should be cultivated immediately after harvest to encourage weed seeds to germinate and facilitate the removal of any "twitch." The land can then be deeply ploughed and left in the furrow over winter to mellow. In late February or early March the furrows should be broken down, and by means of cultivators, harrows and the roller a fine, firm seed bed prepared.

MANURING

A soil in high condition is not necessary, and the crop is generally grown on the reserves of plant food left in the soil by preceding crops. In order to assist early and even ripening, however, a moderate dressing of phosphates and potash is helpful and the following mixture is recommended :—

Superphosphate	.	. 2 cwt. per acre.
Muriate of Potash	.	. 1 ,, ,,
		3 ,, ,,

the quantity applied depending upon the condition of the land. Poor soils may require 6 cwt. per acre, whereas when generous use has been made of both phosphate and potash for previous crops 2 cwt. per acre of the mixture should be adequate.

SOWING THE SEED

The seed should be sown when a suitably fine tilth has been prepared and as early as possible. On the lighter soils in the South sowing will begin in March, but on the heavier classes of land and in the North, April sowings may be necessary.

The seed can be broadcast by hand or fiddle drill, a seed barrow, or even with a corn drill the spouts of which have been set about 6 inches apart. Before commencing to drill it is advisable to test out the drill, for not all drills can sow this slippery seed thinly enough. To test the drill the driving wheel should be jacked up and jam pots placed under each coulter. If some seed is then placed in the hopper and the wheel turned a fixed number of times, seed will collect in the jars. By simple calculation it is possible to check up the rate of seeding by weighing the seed in the pots and multiplying by an appropriate factor.

When broadcast, 117 lb. of seed per acre (2¼ bushels) is required, but when drilled only 91 lb. (1¾ bushels) is necessary. The seed should be covered lightly with a single harrowing, for if buried deeply (more than 1 inch) uneven brairding is likely. When the crop is to be undersown with a seeds mixture the latter should be sown at the same time as the linseed. A light rolling then finishes the operations.

AFTER CULTIVATIONS

Linseed is not a good smother crop, and for that reason the use of clean land has already been advocated. When drilled the crop may be horse-hoed, but great care is necessary not to disturb the roots unduly. When the seed has been broadcast hand-pulling of the weeds may be necessary.

HARVESTING

The crop ripens unevenly but matures in the stook. Hence, when the stems have turned yellow, the lower leaves have fallen, and the earliest bolls (seed capsules) are ready, cutting should commence. The seed in the ripe bolls at this stage is bright and plump and pale-brown in colour. If the crop is left until all the bolls are in this condition a high percentage of the seed is lost by shedding when the crop is handled.

The crop may be cut with a binder or combine harvester. The sheaves should be made fairly small to facilitate drying in the stook. As soon as the crop is dry it should be carted, stacked and thatched.

The lower part of the stem is very wiry and the knife of the binder or combine should therefore be set fairly high.

The seed is difficult to thresh out, and on this account the sheaves should be fed slowly and the drum carefully adjusted. Fine riddles are necessary to deal with the seed.

The straw is unsuitable for feeding, and owing to its wiry nature does not rot down well when used as bedding. It is better, therefore, to use it as a covering for root or potato clamps.

The chaff can be used for making linseed jelly or may be fed direct to stock. Ewes in particular are very fond of it, but owing to its high oil content (3 to 5 per cent.) it should be fed with care.

The seed may be crushed for home consumption or sold, the vendor having the option of obtaining a small quantity of linseed cake for each ton of linseed delivered. In practice this will be found the most convenient way of dealing with the bulk of the seed at any rate, for, whilst the ordinary grist mill or oat crusher may be used for grinding, most farmers find that the large amount of oil expressed is a nuisance, even though the seed is first mixed with an absorbent such as crushed oats or chaff.

YIELD

The average yield is about 10 cwt. per acre of seed, 8 to 9 cwt. per acre of chaff, and 20 to 30 cwt. per acre of straw.

Good crops may yield up to 1 ton per acre of seed.

INSECT PESTS

Linseed is generally a very trouble-free crop to grow. Occasionally, however, leatherjackets (grubs of the Daddy Longlegs) attack it in the young stage. A poison bait composed of 1 lb. of Paris green and 25 lb. of bran per acre broadcast over the crop gives good control.

FLAX

Flax is only grown on contract for the processing factories, the price paid being dependent upon the type of contract undertaken, of which, however, there are three types.

As might be expected the climatic and soil conditions suitable for flax-growing are comparable to those already indicated for linseed. There is, however, one point of difference, namely, that in the case of flax, the land selected for the crop is subject to the approval of the factory concerned. Land infested with redshank, thistles or charlock should be avoided, for these weeds may ruin the quality of the crop.

VARIETIES

Improved stocks of pedigree seed such as Liral Monarch are now available which surpass in yield of fibre by as much as 50 per cent. the varieties grown 20 years ago. The seed is supplied by the factory at a fixed price and only such seed can be used.

PLACE IN ROTATION

On fat land flax produces a coarse type of fibre with a low percentage yield. Hence it is unwise to grow the crop following roots and more generally it follows a straw crop or seeds. Following a clover ley two crops may be taken in succession, the second crop often being a good deal better than the first.

It is inadvisable, however, to take flax after a long ley which is full of clover and has been well sheeped, for under such rich soil conditions there is a grave danger of the crop lodging. As flax is ready for pulling between the normal hay and corn harvests, an opportunity is given for following it with a catch crop of Italian ryegrass, rape, or six-weeks turnips.

PREPARATION OF SEED BED

Clean land and a fine, firm seed bed, such as is required for onions, are essential for good results. The sequence of cultivations necessary to obtain this ideal have already been dealt with under Linseed, and it is, therefore, unnecessary to repeat them here.

MANURING

Direct dunging is inadvisable for fear of lodging, although it is an advantage if the previous crop has received a dressing of dung. Lime also is best applied to the previous crop.

For average conditions the following mixture of artificial manures is recommended:—

Sulphate of Ammonia	.	½ cwt. per acre.
Superphosphate	. . 2	,, ,,
Muriate of Potash	. . 1	,, ,,
	3½	,, ,,

The use of potash is important in that it prevents the yellowing of the crop in spring and improves the quality of the fibre.

SOWING THE SEED

Uniform growth is essential and hence uniform seeding is vitally important. This implies careful drilling on a well-prepared seed bed, for ideally all the seed should come through evenly and at the same time, and this is impossible on a cloddy, loose tilth. The seed can be drilled with a light corn drill or a Suffolk drill with the coulters set closely together. Some factories hire out suitable drills or even do the work for farmers, and in many cases it is advisable to make use of this service.

The seed can, of course, be sown broadcast, though this method always suffers by reason of the fact that all the seed cannot be placed at a uniform depth and broadcasting such a slippery seed is not an easy job.

Seeding should take place as early as possible from March to May depending upon locality, seasonal and seed bed conditions. In the South a start may be made in late March, whilst in the North sowing may not be possible before May.

The seed should not be buried deeper than ½ to 1 inch and should be covered by a light harrowing and rolling.

AFTER CULTIVATIONS

When the crop is 1 to 2 inches high a light rolling often proves beneficial, for it encourages growth by aiding the supply of moisture which reaches the roots of the plants. Freedom from weeds is most important, so much so in fact that some factories refuse delivery of a crop which contains more than 5 per cent. of weeds or such impurities as white straw or wild oats. Thistles and redshank constitute a nuisance in the processing of the flax, and efforts to keep them in check are, therefore, essential. When charlock is present it should be eradicated by spraying with a

3 per cent. copper sulphate solution. Weeding in all cases should be done before the plants are 6 inches high, the workers wearing rubber boots to avoid damaging the crop as they would do with hob-nails.

HARVESTING

The crop is ready for the harvesting when the lower third of the stem has changed from green to yellow and the leaves in this region have fallen. Seeds in the older capsules at this stage are changing from green to a brownish tint at the apex. It is important that this stage of maturity should not be passed before the crop is harvested.

Formerly it was common to pull the crop by hand, but pulling machines are now available and these are to be preferred. Under the terms of the contract growers can hire machines from the factory, the charge made depending upon whether the machine is supplied with service or tractor and crew are provided by the farmer. The introduction of these machines has lightened the task of pulling enormously, for whereas one-sixth of an acre per day was considered reasonable for hand-pulling, a machine will average 5 acres pulled and tied. Under favourable conditions it may deal with as much as 10 acres in the day.

Pulling machines also tie the crop into sheaves or "beets" and these must be stooked up immediately for, if left on the ground, flax spoils very quickly. Stooking is the same as for corn, six sheaves being put together.

Flax must be straight and even in the root ends, and hence when the crop is being stooked it is well worth while to straighten and butt down the beets. Care and attention to these small points will avoid undue waste in processing which is vitally necessary in the national interest.

If the weather is poor when pulling commences the crop can be "hutted" either by building the sheaves round tripods or by putting them into small circular stacks built to a point with successive single rounds of sheaves. The butts of the sheaves should slope downwards and outwards.

The delivery of the crop to the factory varies with different contracts. It may be delivered direct from the field or stacked and thatched near to a good hard road until such time as the factory can accept delivery.

YIELD

In the best flax districts of Northern France, which are comparable to our own flax-growing areas, less than a 3-ton crop is regarded as moderate. Over here, however, 2 to 2½ tons per acre is an average yield, though every endeavour must be made to increase this by care and attention to the cultivations and preparation of the seed bed, which is the all-important factor.

The normal yield of cleaned and dried seed is 2 cwt. per ton of crop.

BUCKWHEAT OR BRANK

Buckwheat is a quick-growing crop which, being seldom attacked by pests, is very useful as a first crop on newly broken grassland. Moreover, it can follow corn crops which have failed or may be sown in late and backward seasons when there has not been sufficient time to prepare for other crops. Now that the problem of feeding poultry is so acute, small acreages of land in odd corners in fields might very well be sown with this crop.

The crop prefers warm and sunny climatic conditions and is most commonly grown in East Anglia and the Fens. Small acreages are grown, however, in most districts to provide pheasant cover. It gives best results on well-drained sandy loams, failing to thrive on cold, wet soils. A big point in its favour is that it does well on light sour soils where even rye would fail, but under such conditions it is only natural that poor yields are obtained. On land in very good heart the danger of lodging is considerable.

VARIETIES

Common buckwheat is the only variety marketed in this country and is an annual plant growing to a height of about 3 feet in 12 to 14 weeks.

PLACE IN ROTATION

The crop occupies no fixed place in the rotation and as a rule is grown as a catch crop. It may be grown as a forage crop or for green manuring, and may then occupy part of the root break. On the other hand, should it be grown for grain it is likely to follow a white straw crop.

PREPARATION OF SEED BED

No special requirements are necessary for buckwheat, and the normal sequence of ploughing, cultivating and harrowing to prepare a seed bed are all that is necessary. A fine tilth is desirable, but good results may be obtained merely by discing in cases where the crop is grown after a corn crop that has failed.

MANURING

On well-farmed land and fen soils no manurial treatment will be necessary and, in point of fact, may even be dangerous in that the crop is very susceptible to lodging.

On poor soils, however, a general fertilising is necessary and the following mixture is recommended:—

Sulphate of Ammonia	.	1	cwt. per acre.
Superphosphate	. .	2	,, ,,
Muriate of Potash	. .	1	,, ,,
		4	,, ,,

SOWING THE SEED

Buckwheat is very sensitive to frost and must not, therefore, be sown until all danger of this is over. The seed is preferably drilled not deeper than ½ to ¾ inch at the rate of 100 lb. (2 bushels) per acre. If sown broadcast 150 lb. (3 bushels) of seed will be required.

The seed should be lightly harrowed in and the land well rolled. As a rule no further attention is given, or is necessary, during the growing period.

HARVESTING

The crop should be cut when the majority of the seeds are ripe, which in a normal season is towards the end of August. There will probably be some flowers still present when the correct ·stage for cutting is reached. Owing to the difficulty of drying the succulent stems when they are tied into sheaves the common practice is to cut with a scythe, self-delivery reaper, or even a binder without string, and to allow the crop to lie for a few days to assist the drying. It is then tied and stooked, and when in dry condition carted and made into small stacks with faggots or layers of dry straw between successive layers of sheaves to assist the final stages of drying out. When used for game it is frequently left unharvested and the birds allowed to help themselves. Careful watch on the crop must be kept when it is ready for cutting or whilst it is in stook, for birds of all kinds are fond of the grain and will quickly strip a crop.

YIELD

10 to 20 cwt. per acre of grain is normally obtained. The straw can be used for all ordinary purposes.

Buckwheat may also be grown in conjunction with other crops. For instance, a mixture of 60 lb. of lupins and 25 lb. of buckwheat per acre makes a useful mixture for folding with sheep, whilst the following mixture has given good results when mown green for cattle in August:—

Buckwheat	.	.	.	50 lb. per acre.
Peas	.	.	.	60 „ „
Rape	.	.	.	4 „ „

MUSTARD

Mustard may be grown as a forage crop for folding off or ploughing in, or as a seed crop for the production of mustard oil or condiment. For seed, it is usually grown under contract.

The crop can be grown under a wide range of climatic and soil conditions. It requires, however, to be harvested in dry weather when grown for seed, and hence for this purpose the crop is confined to the Eastern Counties. For forage purposes, however, climate is not a factor of any great importance, and the crop is grown to some extent in most districts.

Lime is necessary for the crop and it frequently refuses to grow under sour conditions. It does best in rich alluvial soils and is a favourite crop in the highly farmed potato districts of eastern England.

VARIETIES

Two species are commonly grown, Black or Brown Mustard and White Mustard, but only the latter is grown for forage purposes. A blend of both seeds is used for the production of the ordinary table mustard.

1. Growing for Seed

Place in Rotation

Mustard grown for seed commonly follows potatoes, but it may also follow ploughed-up grassland, for which purpose it is well adapted in that it is highly resistant to wireworm attack. Two crops may then be grown in succession followed by potatoes and then another mustard crop. Frequently the crop is taken after a fallow on heavy land and prior to taking wheat. On light land it is sometimes taken after roots and before barley. In this way a better malting sample of barley is obtained, for the mustard taps the richness of the soil.

Preparation of Seed Bed

A fine firm tilth is required, and the soil should be cultivated in such a way that this requirement is obtained.

Manuring

Following potatoes it is unlikely that any manurial treatment will be necessary. When, however, the crop follows a cereal the application of 3 to 4 cwt. per acre of superphosphate or 5 to 6 cwt. per acre basic slag (high soluble) is advisable. On poor land a good general manuring is necessary, and under these conditions it is well to apply a moderate dressing of dung in autumn and plough it in, following this up by an all-round fertiliser in spring prior to sowing the seed. The following mixture is recommended:—

Sulphate of Ammonia	1	cwt. per acre.
Superphosphate	3	,, ,,
Muriate of Potash	1	,, ,,
	5	,, ,,

Sowing the Seed

The seed should be sown from February to April not more than ½ inch deep in rows 15 to 18 inches apart, 4 lb. of seed per acre usually being ample for the black variety and 8 lb. for the white. The white mustard is not so hardy as the black and must not, therefore, be sown until danger of frost is over. Early sown crops are to be preferred, for they stand a chance of coming to maturity before the cereal crops on the farm are ready for cutting.

The seed should be lightly harrowed in or the coulter ridges may be left and the plant rolled when the seedlings appear.

AFTER CULTIVATIONS

As soon as the plants are in the rough-leaf stage the crop should be thinned to 10 inches between plants in the rows, which may be done by taking the steerage corn hoe across the rows or by cutting the superfluous plants out with an 8-inch hoe. Weeds should be kept in check by inter-row cultivation.

HARVESTING

Great care is necessary in choosing the time for cutting the crop. If this is done too early the seeds will be green and shrivelled, whereas by leaving until the crop is too mature may result in serious losses from shed seed. Old growers say that the crop should be cut when the pods have the brownish tinge of a hare's back. The crop can be cut by hand, reaper or binder, but in any case the stubble should be left fairly long to keep the crop off the ground. Tied loosely and in small bundles these may be left on the ground for a day or two to kill, being turned first thing in the morning when damp to prevent shedding.

If the crop is stooked, as soon as the outer side of the sheaves is dry they must be carefully turned to get the other side dry.

When perfectly dry the crop can be carted and stacked or stored in a loft. Sheets should be put over the cart bottoms to collect any seed that is knocked out, and the crop is best stacked on a sheet. The seed which collects in the carts should be thrown on to the stack from time to time, for it matures better when scattered in this way.

It is usual to make narrow stacks about 4 yards wide. Thatching should be completed immediately, for the stack is open and rain enters easily.

YIELD

10 to 12 cwt. per acre of seed is commonly obtained, but under good conditions this may be increased to as much as 20 cwt. per acre. The chaff may be used for feeding, but the straw is of no value.

P

2. Growing for Forage

White mustard may be grown for green manuring or as a catch crop, and when folded with ewes has a high reputation for flushing them at tupping time. It is frequently grown after early potatoes, with the object of utilising the surplus plant food left in the soil and so preventing the valuable nitrates from being washed out of the soil. It is also useful as a catch crop after early peas or beans or for sowing on stubbles.

The seed should be broadcast at the rate of 20 lb. per acre or drilled at 15 lb. per acre. A fine, firm seed bed is necessary and the seed need only be lightly harrowed in and rolled.

Given good growing weather mustard is ready for grazing about six weeks after seeding, but it should be grazed down before growth becomes too rank. Since white mustard is susceptible to frost it should be fed off in early autumn.

When the crop is grown for green manuring it is necessary to roll the crop down before ploughing commences and to fix a drag chain on to the plough in order to roll the green material under the furrow. Care must be taken to prevent the crop from seeding, for if this is permitted the plant can rapidly develop into a "weed" pest.

LUPINS

Lupins are not widely grown and their use is confined almost entirely to light, poor land in the Eastern Counties. On these soils the crop is extremely useful as a soil improver, for not only does the crop utilise the nitrogen of the atmosphere, but by rapid growth produces an abundance of green material which, when ploughed in, adds valuable humus to light, hungry soils.

The crop thrives under a variety of climatic and soil conditions. It is, however, essentially a light land crop, and though the yield is dependent upon an adequate rainfall quite appreciable growth is obtained in dry seasons.

Varieties

White, yellow and blue lupins are available, of which the blue appears to be the most reliable, and the white to yield best. The sweet lupin is a recent introduction suitable for grazing. It may also be grown as a grain crop, the seed containing from 27 to 40 per cent. protein according to variety.

PLACE IN ROTATION

On poor light land lupins may form an important crop in the rotation. At the Tunstall Light Land Experimental Station, for instance, it has been shown that when lupins are grown once every four years considerable benefit is obtained in the subsequent crops, and it has been estimated that an average crop contains as much nitrogen as 9 to 15 tons of dung.

For green manuring the crop can be grown after a bastard fallow or an early crop of potatoes or peas.

PREPARATION OF SEED BED

Little difficulty is experienced in preparing a seed bed on the light soils on which lupins are commonly grown. Usually the land is ploughed, cleaned if necessary, harrowed, and is then ready for seeding.

MANURING

The fact that lupins grow on sour, poor land should not imply that such conditions of poverty are desirable. No crop, even lupins, can grow to full benefit unless it receives adequate supplies of plant food, and when the crop is grown for "building-up" purposes it is essential to ensure a full crop by the use of fertilisers.

A suitable dressing would be:—

Superphosphate	. .	2 cwt. per acre,
Muriate of Potash	. .	1 „ „
		$\overline{3}$ „ „

which should be applied prior to sowing the seed. If the land is very deficient in lime it is advisable to give an application of some form of lime in moderate quantity after the final ploughing.

SOWING THE SEED

April is usually the best month for sowing. When the crop is sown in March there may be danger from late frosts, whilst if seeding is delayed until May the seed may not ripen satisfactorily in a wet year, although this is of no consequence if the crop is being ploughed in. As a catch crop it may be sown from May until July, and even an August sowing will often give a fair crop for ploughing in.

For seed, the crop should be drilled in rows about 20 inches apart at the rate of 90 to 120 lb. of seed per acre, but when grown for folding or ploughing in, 90 lb. is generally adequate. The seed may be broadcast if more convenient than drilling.

AFTER CULTIVATIONS

The crop may be horse-hoed if this is considered necessary.

HARVESTING

When the crop is grown for seed production it is cut when ripe with a binder. Care must be taken not to leave it to become too mature before cutting, for the pods are then likely to split and shedding losses may be high. The pods are liable to wear the binder canvases rather badly, and hence lupins are often cut with a mower or put-off reaper. The crop may be tied by hand or harvested loose, the latter procedure being facilitated by the fact that the crop hangs well together.

When fit, carting and threshing are carried out as for beans.

YIELD

12 to 18 cwt. per acre of seed.

Great care is necessary in feeding lupin seed to sheep and not more than ¼ lb. per head per day should be fed to ewes, and it must not be fed to ewes in lamb.

Folding off can also be a risky business, because the plant contains a poisonous principle. Shepherds who are used to the crop experience no difficulty in folding, but when grown for the first time it is essential to allow the sheep only limited access to the crop. They should not be put on when very hungry, nor is it safe to allow them to remain too long, being accustomed to it very gradually. When lupins are required for grazing it is far better to sow the sweet variety which is non-poisonous.

As a green-manure crop for poor thin soils it is, certainly, pre-eminent, and for the reclamation of light sandy soils it should have a much wider use.

ONIONS

In normal times the onion is regarded as a market-garden crop and is not grown extensively on a field scale. The needs of the times, however, demand a considerable increase in home production and this can only be met by introducing the plant to the farm field. Fortunately, provided the right soil and climatic conditions are at hand, little difficulty should be experienced in growing good crops which incidentally will add substantially to the cash output of the farm.

The crop is not unduly affected by climatic conditions and can be grown in most districts provided conditions are favourable for harvesting. Districts which normally experience a low late-summer rainfall are ideally suited for onions, since this enables the bulbs to ripen and permits them to be left in windrows to dry out after pulling.

Provided there is adequate scope for the rooting system the crop does well on most soils. Heavy clays which produce unkindly seed beds, or poor shallow sandy or chalk soils where the crop is liable to suffer from drought, should be avoided. Soils which are in good "heart" as a result of good management over a number of years are undoubtedly most suitable and under such conditions the crop is likely to yield well.

VARIETIES

The crop may be grown in one of three ways, either by sowing the seed in autumn and transplanting in spring, by transplanting in spring from seed grown under glass, or by sowing the seed in the open in spring.

The variety selected is determined by the method of growing, and the following list of proved strains of good keeping quality can be used with confidence :—

For Autumn Sowing.—Reliance, Autumn Queen, Solidity, A1, and selected varieties of the Giant Zittau type.

For Spring Sowing under Glass.—Ailsa Craig, Premier.

For Spring Sowing in Open.—Up-to-date, Bedfordshire Champion, Market Favourite, Density, Rousham Park Hero, Banbury, James' Long Keeping, Nuneham Park.

PLACE IN ROTATION

Since onions have not been grown widely on a field scale in this country before, there is no fixed place in the rotation allotted to them. The crop requires, however, very clean land in good heart, and hence it is likely that following roots would be the most convenient place in rotation.

PREPARATION OF SEED BED

Tradition has always demanded and practice confirmed that onions should be grown on a fine, firm tilth. On a small scale great pains can be taken to ensure the degree of firmness necessary, but in the field reliance must be placed on natural means of consolidation, and this implies and demands early ploughing. Moreover, since the crop does best on a deep tilth it is advisable to subsoil at the same time as ploughing, if there are signs of a "pan." The land should then be left to mellow over winter in the furrow.

As soon as the soil is dry enough in spring, cultivators and harrows should be employed to break down the furrows and produce the required deep tilth without burying any of the fine frost mould. Light harrows and roller should then be used to fine down the surface, a fine top tilth on a firm foundation being essential for sowing outdoors.

MANURING

Generous but judicious manuring is necessary if the bulbs are to mature properly and to keep well. "Old hands" advocate that in the case of a spring sown or planted crop the dung should be applied on the furrow in early spring and worked into the soil by cultivating. When this method is adopted it is, of course, essential to use only short, well-rotted dung. For autumn-sown transplants the dung is best given to the previous crop.

The fertilisers applied must be well balanced, for an overdose of nitrogen spoils both the marketing and keeping qualities of the crop. The following mixture is advised and should be applied before seeding at the rate of 6 to 8 cwt. per acre:—

Sulphate of Ammonia	.	.	.	1 part.
Superphosphate	.	.	.	3 parts.
Muriate of Potash	.	.	.	1 part.

SOWING THE SEED

The seed should be drilled in rows 12 to 15 inches apart and about 1 to 1½ inches deep as early in March as soil conditions are considered suitable. Where it is intended to keep the crop clean by horse-hoeing, wider spacings must be used and then 20-inch rows are necessary. To avoid thinning heavy seedings are inadvisable, and in most cases 5 lb. of seed per acre is quite adequate to obtain the desired plant population of from 6 to 9 plants per foot of row. It is important to drill when the soil is loose and dry and to follow up with the roller.

In order to facilitate inter-row cultivations many growers adopt the practice of sowing a little rape with the onion seed. This germinates rapidly and enables the rows to be seen at a much earlier date than is possible when the onions are sown alone. Not more than 1 lb. of rape seed per acre is necessary for this purpose.

RAISING PLANTS

For transplants the seed may be sown in August in the open or under glass in January. For August sowing the seed should be sown fairly thinly in a well-prepared seed bed which should receive a good dressing of potash or wood ashes, for this hardens the plants and helps them to stand the winter. About 2 lb. of seed per acre to be planted should be allowed.

Plants obtained in this way are usually transplanted the following March, and when well established are given the fertiliser dressing recommended above.

For January sowings the seed is sown in shallow boxes, sowing thinly to avoid the necessity for pricking out the seedlings. About ½ lb. of seed per acre to be planted will be required. Care should be taken in preparing the compost with which to fill the boxes, and the best results are obtained by mixing 3 parts of sifted loam with 1 part wood ash, plus a little bone-meal and fine sand.

After sowing the seed the boxes should be watered, covered with a sheet of glass, and placed in a temperature of 50 to 60° F. The seedlings should be maintained at this heat for three weeks after they appear, when they can be transferred to a cold house and later to cold frames, slowly hardening them off.

Transplanting usually takes place about the first week in April, care being taken to set them firmly in rows about 18 inches apart with 4 to 8 inches between the plants in the rows. The latter spacing depends upon the size of the bulbs required.

After Cultivations

Careful hand-hoeing is necessary to keep down weeds, although horse-hoeing is possible when the rows are spaced more than 18 inches apart. Great care is necessary in these operations, however, for if the stem is damaged the plants do not bulb properly, and for this reason most growers rely entirely on hand-work. From the very start weeds must be kept in check and a good surface tilth maintained throughout the season. Bolters should be pulled out as they appear.

Harvesting

The crop is ready for lifting when the foliage has died down completely. Ripening starts with the autumn-raised plants about mid-August and extends into September or October for spring seedlings.

The bulbs should be lifted when ripe and laid out in rows on their sides to dry off, being left until the surface skin is loose, the flesh firm, and the necks and roots completely shrivelled. During unsettled weather the bulbs must be collected up after lying out for a week or ten days. Considerable experience is necessary to determine when an onion is perfectly "fit," and when the crop is grown for the first time great care should be taken to see that the bulbs are really dry for storage, as otherwise they will not keep. When a potato chitting-house is available this makes an excellent drying shed and the onions can then be placed in the trays and packed in tiers until fit.

The bulbs should be stored in a cool airy shed and placed on slatted racks not on the ground. Glass-houses are not suitable, and when handling the bulbs care is necessary to prevent bruising them, which adversely affects the keeping quality.

The crop is graded for sale into large ($1\frac{3}{4}$ inches and over), mediums ($1\frac{1}{4}$ to $1\frac{3}{4}$ inches) and "picklers" (less than $1\frac{1}{4}$ inches), being marketed in half-bags (56 lb.) or bags (112 lb.).

Yield

The yield is subject to considerable variations and is dependent upon seasonal and manurial conditions and the variety grown. Autumn-sown crops yield up to 12 tons per acre, but spring-sown crops usually average no more than 6 tons per acre.

GRASS AND CLOVER SEED PRODUCTION

A considerable increase in the home production of grass and clover seeds will be necessary in the next few years in order to supply the demand for seeds mixtures for short and long leys consequent upon the increase in arable acreage and the more general adoption of the system of ley farming. There is likely to be a good market for herbage seeds, and farmers are strongly advised to seriously consider the possibilities of a crop which adds to the cash output of the farm.

When grown for seed, grasses and clovers require no special treatment or implements and do well under varying conditions of soil and climate. Many farmers have already had experience of producing red and white clover seed and this should now be extended and grasses added to the list. The following recommendations apply to "commercial" strains of grasses and not necessarily to pedigree strains, many of which require special technique.

Herbage crops can be grown for seed in most districts even when the rainfall is 40 inches or more, but undoubtedly a sunny climate with a moderate summer rainfall is best. Good medium loams suit the grasses which require a somewhat higher plane of fertility than is necessary, for the clovers and clay loams, well supplied with lime, are ideal for both classes of crop.

PLACE IN ROTATION

A herbage crop should be grown on clean land in good heart, after roots being the ideal place in the rotation. As a rule the crop is sown under a cereal, and not only is it important to select land free from indigenous weeds but also to have it free from grasses and clovers that might remain from a former ley. Obviously this does not matter so much if a farmer is merely growing for his own use, but when the seed is to be marketed it is necessary to take great pains to have the land free from such adulterants. In many cases it is necessary to go even further and make sure that the crop is not contaminated with hay seeds carried by stock, or in the dung, or blown into the field from passing waggons, or from feeding hay to sheep folded on the roots.

PREPARATION OF SEED BED

A fine firm tilth is highly desirable, but this has already been dealt with at some length in Chapter Three. Every endeavour should be made to get the seedlings away rapidly, and with this object in mind a good rolling before and after sowing is advisable. A fine frost mould forms, of course, the perfect seed bed, and wherever practicable the heavier classes of land should be ploughed before Christmas.

MANURING

Lime is essential for all herbage seeds whether grasses or clovers, but liming is best carried out for the preceding crop, for this allows ample time for it to be worked into the soil. In addition, phosphates are required on most soils with the addition of potash on the lighter types. An application of 5 cwt. per acre of high soluble slag or superphosphate should be given prior to sowing the nurse crop, and if potash is required, 1 cwt. per acre muriate of potash.

Regarding nitrogenous fertilisers it is unlikely that the clovers will require any, but for perennial ryegrass 1½ cwt. of sulphate of ammonia per acre should be given immediately the nurse crop is removed, with a further 1 cwt. per acre the following April or May if the spring is dry and backward. Cocksfoot and timothy should receive 2 cwt. per acre of a nitrogenous fertiliser in spring.

SOWING THE SEED

Perennial ryegrass is generally sown in spring under a cereal nurse crop and to facilitate harvesting is mixed with a little timothy, cocksfoot and clover. Especially is this the practice if the crop is to be left down for a number of years.

In Ireland, from whence comes a good deal of our perennial ryegrass seed, the following mixture is used:—

Perennial Ryegrass	35-42 lb. per acre.	
Cocksfoot	8 ,,	,,
Timothy	4 ,,	,,
Late-flowering Red Clover	2 ,,	,,
Wild White Clover	1 ,,	,,

but in this country it is more usual to sow:—

Perennial Ryegrass	16-24 lb. per acre.	
Timothy	5 ,,	,,
Wild White Clover	1 ,,	,,

Seeding can take place from mid-March onwards as soon as weather conditions are favourable.

Italian ryegrass is usually sown alone under a cereal nurse crop in spring. In some districts it is a common practice to sow it as a catch crop under rape after early potatoes or other vegetable crops. The rate of seeding varies from 44 to 50 lb. per acre.

To obtain the maximum benefit from cocksfoot it should remain down and be harvested for several years. This is not possible, however, unless it is kept free from weeds, and hence the best method is undoubtedly to drill it in rows about two feet apart on the flat. The seed can be drilled with the ordinary root drill at the rate of 7 lb. per acre. In some cases it is preferable to sow the seed without a cover crop, when it is advisable to include about $\frac{1}{2}$ lb. of white mustard which, germinating quickly, indicates the position of the rows and enables horse-hoeing to commence before the grass comes through. This is especially necessary in dry and backward springs when weeds grow away rapidly and are liable to smother the slower growing grass. The mustard must not be allowed to flower but should be mown or grazed before reaching this stage. On land subject to charlock the inclusion of white mustard is useless and it is better to use crimson clover.

Timothy is commonly sown broadcast under a nurse crop of oats and is particularly suited to deep heavy loams which are not subject to drought. From 12 to 18 lb. of seed per acre is required, which is usually mixed with about 2 lb. per acre of broad red clover. It can also be sown in drills like cocksfoot, using 4 to 5 lb. of seed with a small amount of white mustard or crimson clover. The seed is extremely small and great care is necessary to avoid burying it too deeply. Rolling before and after seeding is essential and only the lightest of chain harrows should be used for covering the seed.

The management in the case of red clover for seed production is dependent upon the type of clover being grown. Broad red clover produces more seed at the second cut, and hence the usual practice is to take an early hay crop or graze it down in spring and then put the aftermath up for seed. Late-flowering red clover, on the other hand, produces very little aftermath and hence the first crop is used.

The seed is usually sown in April, being drilled under a cereal nurse crop at the rate of 14 lb. per acre, or it may be broadcast, as in the south-western seed-growing areas, mixed with a few pounds of ryegrass. The late-flowering red clover does particularly well when grown in conjunction with about 5 lb. of timothy, the difference in seed size between the clover and grass enabling them to be easily separated at threshing.

Wild white clover seed may be obtained from an old pasture and certified as Grade A under the Ministry scheme if the pasture has been down for ten years or more, or it may be grown on arable land in temporary leys as "once grown" seed. In the latter case 7 to 12 lb. per acre of seed will be sown with about 4 to 7 lb. of perennial ryegrass. This gives good grazing before the field need be shut up for seed production and the two seeds are easily separated at threshing.

AFTER CULTIVATIONS

If the seed is drilled in rows inter-cultivation is carried out periodically in order to keep the land free from weeds. When the crop is to be left down for a number of years, as for instance with cocksfoot or wild white clover, manurial treatment is necessary and the crop should be treated as if it were an arable one. Farmyard manure is not commonly applied for fear of introducing weed seeds, and the dressings of fertilisers given naturally vary according to the nature of the land. On poor soils a complete dressing is called for, whilst in other cases nitrogen applied as sulphate of ammonia or nitro-chalk is all that is likely to be necessary. One or more applications of nitrogen per year may be given.

As to the correct time to shut a field up for seed production, seasonal and local conditions play a large part and the farmer must use his judgment. Ryegrass, for instance, can be lightly grazed until March, whilst it is generally better to leave cocksfoot and timothy alone unless growth is very forward. The clovers, on the other hand, may be grazed until May or June.

Moderate autumn grazing is generally desirable for both grasses and clovers, although in the first seeding year care is necessary in the case of cocksfoot and timothy where, unless growth is very forward, the crop is best left to get well established.

HARVESTING

Considerable skill is necessary to determine when the crop should be cut. In the case of perennial and Italian ryegrasses cutting can commence when the heads have turned brown and the straw is yellowish or silvery. At this stage of maturity a few seeds are left in the palm of the hand when the heads are simply grasped, and most growers wait for the earlier maturing heads to shed a few seeds. Italian ryegrass usually ripens about ten days later than perennial.

Cocksfoot is deemed fit for cutting when the heads are grey-white and the upper part of the straw is yellow; timothy when the heads are lightish brown, the seeds well filled and the chaff has lost its green colour. In both cases a small amount of shedding is permissible before cutting commences.

Grass crops can be cut with a mower and tied by hand into small sheaves, or if preferred a binder, adjusted for tiny sheaves, may be used. In either case by cutting first thing in the morning or in the late afternoon when the foliage is damp, losses from shedding are minimised. The sheaves must be stooked at once, allowing 4 to 6 sheaves to a stook. These remain out until fit for carting which may take from 7 to 14 days, depending upon weather conditions. Should the weather be unsettled it is best to build the sheaves, after fielding in the stooks, into small cocks, each holding about a small load. The heads of the sheaves should point inwards with the tops of the cocks protected by an inverted sheaf or two. Under very favourable conditions it may be possible to thresh straight from the field, but normally it is usual to stack the crop until fit for threshing.

Red clovers are ready for cutting when the flower heads have turned brown, and when on rubbing out a few heads in the palm of the hand the seeds are firm, plump and the purple coloration is well developed. The crop is cut by the mower, and after hand-turning several times is carted when fit. Brush-wood is used in the stack to avoid heating.

In the case of white clover the crop is cut when the majority of the heads are brown, and a few bright yellow seeds can be rubbed out in the hand. Although the flowers may appear brown the small stalks of the individual florets which constitute the "head" should not be completely brown or brittle.

Should the crop be very short—as frequently happens in the case of old pastures—some difficulty may be experienced in dealing with it. A metal tray fixed behind the cutter bar of the machine enables the crop to be "put off" in small heaps. These must be carefully turned by hand to avoid shedding, and when fit should be put into small cocks to give better protection against the rain.

When carting herbage crops it is advisable to lay a sheet over the cart bottom to collect any seed that is lost during loading and forking.

YIELD

The following table indicates the average yields per acre for the various crops :—

Perennial Ryegrass . . .	5-6 cwt. per acre.
Italian Ryegrass . . .	7 ,, ,,
Cocksfoot	$3\frac{1}{2}$-4 ,, ,,
Timothy	4 ,, ,,
Late-flowering Red Clover . .	260 lb. per acre.
Broad Red Clover . . .	260 ,, ,,
Wild White Clover (old pasture) .	60 ,, ,,
Wild White Clover (once grown) .	150 ,, ,,

DISPOSAL OF SEED

When a farmer is a member of a Seed Growers' Association the problem of finding a market for the seed does not arise. In all other cases it is advisable to consult a reliable seed firm before embarking on the project. Quite naturally seedsmen are reluctant to purchase seed unless they are familiar with the history of the crop and how it has been grown. The source of the stock seed is also of vital importance. It is, therefore, a wise precaution to have a contract with a firm willing to buy the crop. Growing herbage seeds in the hope of finding a market privately after the crop has been harvested is likely to lead to disappointment.

Chapter Seven

THE CROPPING PROBLEMS OF TO-DAY

AT the present time the cropping of the farm calls for very serious consideration, and modifications to normal practice are essential in order to meet the needs of the State and the individual. Every farmer is confronted with the problem of making his farm more productive and at the same time as nearly self-supporting as possible. This is rendered necessary by the drastic reduction in imports of both human and animal feeding stuffs which prior to 1939 amounted to no less than 23 million tons per annum. The nation must now rely more upon its own soil to produce essential human foods like milk, potatoes, sugar, and vegetables and also replacements for the concentrated cattle foods which can no longer be obtained from abroad. Not only must farmers supply these foods, but in doing so must surmount the innumerable difficulties of post-war farming, an acute labour shortage, limited supplies of fertilisers and feeding stuffs, and curtailment of essential equipment. Following the intensive arable cropping of the war years, a large acreage of land is likely to be sown down to long leys in the interests of fertility maintenance. Then, too, the need for additional supplies of meat and milk requires a considerable increase in livestock numbers, which are needed, indirectly, to utilise the larger acreage of grassland which is likely to result from the relaxation of cropping orders.

Great as these demands are the fulfilment of them is not impossible, for the productivity of our soil can still be considerably improved. It is necessary, however, for each man to prepare careful plans for cropping and stocking, to make the fullest use of the findings of agricultural research, to improve boldly and take risks if necessary, and above all to be prepared to revolutionise his whole method of farming.

It would be as well perhaps at this juncture to have a clear picture of national policy before us. Milk has first priority, and the maintenance of output in winter is especially of the utmost importance. Essential human foods must be ensured by allocating specified acreages in certain cases to each crop, and into this category wheat, potatoes and sugar beet fall. As far as possible the livestock population must be supported by utilising all by-products such as straw, tail corn, beet tops and surplus vegetables, by growing an adequate acreage of grass and clover and forage crops, and by improving all the poor grassland that remains after the needs of the human population have been met by ploughing out the necessary good grass. A further considerable contribution can be made to the national larder by raising the average yield per acre of all crops both arable and grass.

CROPPING PLOUGHED-UP GRASSLAND

The prime need when grassland is ploughed for arable cropping is to get it into rotation as quickly as possible. Good grass might well carry two or three straw crops before a restorative crop of roots or clover is necessary. Less fertile grass can be sown to seeds after one corn crop, whilst poor grassland is likely to benefit from immediate re-seeding with a seeds mixture or pioneer crop to provide animal grazing, for this gives the soil new vitality via the dung and urine of the stock. When the fertility has been restored in this way rotational cropping can follow with every hope of success.

The decision as to when to re-seed with a grass and clover mixture, or whether to take a root crop before doing so, varies from farm to farm. The seeds ley is one of the surest means of maintaining fertility and of cleaning the land, though many farmers prefer roots. Where the latter procedure is adopted dung should be applied wherever possible, for the humus content of the soil must be maintained at all costs if cropping capacity is to be kept at a high level. Alternatives to dung have already been discussed in an earlier chapter, but it is likely that the practice of green manuring will have to be considerably extended. In present circumstances, for instance, it is good policy to under-sow all cereal crops with a cheap mixture of grass and legume. This provides not only valuable stubble grazing for sheep or cattle, but helps considerably in keeping weeds in check. A mixture of 10 lb. of Italian ryegrass and 2 lb. of trefoil per acre is ideal for the purpose and should be sown at the same time as the cereal if the latter is spring-sown. When a spring-sown cereal follows, such a mixture provides not only autumn grazing but a useful bite during the winter and early spring before the land need be ploughed. It can also be sown in beans, in which case it should be broadcast and worked in during the last scruffling between the rows.

For many the great bogy attached to ploughing out grassland is still the wireworm. It is true, of course, that the pest has taken considerable toll of crops in the last few years, but it is equally true to say that a good deal of the damage could have been avoided. Proper cultivation, suitable manuring, and early and generous seeding on a good seed bed all help a crop to withstand attacks and ultimately to beat the enemy. When grassland is ploughed the first and logical thing to do is to obtain an estimate of the wireworm population. Teams of entomologists are available for this purpose and farmers should take advantage of this free service. A field that is safe for cropping can contain up to about 600,000 wireworms per acre. If the population is in excess of this a crop less susceptible to attack such as peas, beans or flax should be grown, whilst in cases of very severe infestation it may be advisable to re-seed direct to grass. Under poor conditions of cultivation and fertility considerably less than 600,000 wireworms per acre may be dangerous, for then the seedlings are frequently weak and impoverished and quickly succumb to the pest.

The first crop after ploughing out is not necessarily the most damaged and in many cases the second suffers more. It is frequently better, therefore, to take a resistant crop in the second year, and flax, peas or even transplanted Brassicas are suitable. This is particularly true in the case of poor, matted grassland, for here the wireworms live on the organic material for the first season and attack the crop in the second year when supplies of food are getting scarce. Time of ploughing has an indirect effect in this connection, in many cases late ploughing being advisable in order to leave the old turf for the wireworms and so enable the crop to grow away. Early ploughing, by encouraging the rotting of the turf, deprives the pest of food and it has no alternative but to attack the crop. Time of seeding is also of importance, since the wireworm after the spring feeding period generally rests over summer in the deeper layers of the soil until the autumn feeding period begins. Thus a late-sown crop of barley may escape injury, and for this reason it is a good plan to patch up a thin wireworm-ridden crop of wheat or oats with barley or even re-drill with this crop.

In dealing with old grassland great care is necessary to get soil consolidation. Ploughing must be well done to ensure that the old turf is completely buried and prevent grass and weeds from growing between the furrow slices. It is also essential to connect the top soil with the subsoil if the danger of drying out or "malting" of the seedlings in a period of drought is to be avoided. Ploughing is better delayed until the furrows are well wetted, for when they are dry it is difficult to get good consolidation. The removal of all top growth prior to ploughing by burning, mowing or grazing greatly facilitates good work, and on badly matted land pre-treatment with heavy disc or pitchpole harrows is advisable.

Many means are available to ensure good covering of the old turf and adequate consolidation of the furrow, such as the fitting of skim and disc coulters to the plough, double ploughing, the use of the furrow press, a weighted cart-wheel, or even the roller.

In most cases the disc harrow is the ideal implement for breaking down the furrows to form a seed bed. Not only does it chop up the furrows without lifting them or bringing the old mat to the surface, but ensures good consolidation.

Manuring is a vital necessity on much of the grassland ploughed out for cropping. We are prone to speak glibly about tapping the reserves of fertility stored up in old grassland, but are apt to lose sight of the fact that much of the grassland to be cropped is desperately poor and seriously short of lime. Even in the case of good average grassland an application of a quick-acting fertiliser frequently produces a marked response in the crop and thoroughly justifies the expense involved.

Where the grassland is of indifferent quality and clover is either absent or only present in small amounts, phosphates are essential. An application of 2 to 3 cwt. per acre superphosphate or 3 to 4 cwt. basic slag can make the difference between a full crop and a patchy one, and in addition 1 to 2 cwt. per acre of a nitrogenous fertiliser applied partly as a seed-bed dressing and partly as a top-dressing is a sound investment. A large percentage of our arable and grassland is under-fertilised, and confirmation of this can be seen daily as one travels about the country.

When first quality grassland, full of clover, is ploughed for cropping with cereals the risk of lodging must be faced. An application of superphosphate, say 2 to 3 cwt. per acre, to the seed bed may help the crop to stand, but it is also essential to select a strong-strawed variety. Frequently, it is safer to take a crop or two of potatoes or sugar beet, however, before risking a cereal crop under conditions of high fertility.

FERTILISER PRACTICE

We have by no means reached the limit of nitrogenous fertilising and indeed are no more than at the threshold of its possibilities. Grassland can and must receive more generous applications, forage crops can utilise it to full advantage, and even in the case of cereals and leguminous crops there is considerable scope for its more general use in greater amounts.

Recent work indicates that small applications of fertilisers in close proximity to the seed may be as effective as the normal heavier doses applied broadcast and worked into the surface before the seed is sown. Fairly conclusive evidence is now available from trials in many parts of the country showing that 2-3 cwt. per acre of, say, superphosphate, applied with a combine drill, will give as good results as double this quantity when broadcast on the surface. Moreover, there is evidence that combine drilling gives a sturdier plant which rapidly establishes itself and is better able to withstand adverse conditions and insect attack.

Supplies of dung are becoming strictly limited by reason of the increased acreage of arable land which requires periodic applications. The substitution of green manuring and other alternatives has already been discussed. Such supplies of dung as are available should be reserved for the root crop, for when roots receive dung and a short-term ley is incorporated in the rotation, it is unlikely that the humus content of the soil will be depleted unduly. Much more attention must be paid to the making and storage of dung, which constitutes an important national supply of vital plant food.

TREATMENT OF DERELICT LAND

Derelict land is of tremendous potential value to the nation. The ploughing of good grassland for human food is definitely

limited by the amount of land available, whereas there is unlimited
scope for the cropping of derelict land, so extensive has it become
in the last two decades.

Much of this poor land is unsuitable for immediate cropping.
The neglect of years means lack of fertility, and in many cases it
is advisable to re-seed to grass or put under a pioneer crop before
an arable crop is contemplated. By folding with cattle and
sheep, dung and urine are added to the impoverished soil and
fertility is brought back. Nor must one lose sight of the fact
that stock food obtained in this way liberates better grassland for
arable cropping and the production of direct human food.

Acres of gorse, thorn and bracken-infested land still exist in
many counties, and the poorest of this land can be reclaimed in
the short space of months once the plough has been introduced.

Fertilising, however, is a prime necessity and following
ploughing lime, phosphates and nitrogen should be applied.
As far as liming goes a generous dressing, well distributed, should
be the aim, and various waste limes such as "limestone dust"
which are available at low rates are admirably suited for the
purpose. In the establishment of a ley slag is pre-eminent and
½ ton per acre dressing of high soluble slag is ideal. Difficulties
of supply, however, may necessitate the use of superphosphate
and enforce a reduction in the rate of application to as low as
2 cwt. per acre. Both lime and phosphate should be applied
on top of the ploughing and worked into the soil by disc-
harrowing.

Nitrogen is vital in reclamation work, and prior to sowing
the seed 1 to 2 cwt. per acre of sulphate of ammonia or nitro-chalk
is necessary. This will induce rapid growth and provide early
grazing. Where the poverty of the land is such that a pioneer
crop rather than a seeds mixture is indicated the following can
be tried:—

Italian Ryegrass	. . .	10 lb. per acre.
Rape	. . . . .	2 ,, ,,
Hardy Green Turnips	. .	2 ,, ,,
		14 ,, ,,

Sowing can take place from April to August and grazing is
usually possible in an average season about eight weeks later.

Subsequent treatment depends upon the original poverty of the soil and it may be necessary to repeat the pioneer crop for another season. Then a tilth should be worked up with disc harrows to avoid bringing the old turf to the surface, and a further application of nitrogen given prior to sowing the seed. Often quite a good cover of Italian ryegrass is present at the end of the first year, in which case it is sufficient if rape and turnips are disced in without further cultivation.

In some cases re-seeding will follow the first "pioneer" crop and then ploughing is generally necessary. This should be shallow in an endeavour to leave the original herbage undisturbed and followed up by a good discing to provide a fine tilth for seeding. During this operation it is not extravagant to give a further light dressing of lime and slag where supplies can be obtained, but most certainly additional nitrogen is essential.

The seeds mixture can be sown under a nurse crop of Italian ryegrass (10 lb. per acre) or rape (2 lb. per acre). To economise in seed is likely to jeopardise the resulting "take," for it must be remembered that the soil conditions are still far from ideal. A mixture that has given uniformly good results in the North in the re-seeding of poor land is :—

Italian Ryegrass . . .	10 lb. per acre.
Perennial Ryegrass . . .	20 ,, ,,
Cocksfoot . . .	10 ,, ,,
Late-flowering Red Clover	4 ,, ,,
Wild White Clover . . .	1 ,, ,,
	45 ,, ,,

Under moist peaty conditions the cocksfoot can be replaced by 6 lb. of timothy. On poor land where an expensive seeds mixture cannot be justified in the first instance the following is useful :—

Perennial Ryegrass . . .	28 lb. per acre.
Crested Dogstail . . .	8 ,, ,,
Wild White Clover Cleanings .	4 ,, ,,
	40 ,, ,,

The seeds mixture may be sown in spring or summer, the decision as to time of seeding being determined by locality and rainfall. In districts where early summer droughts are frequently experienced it may be safer to postpone seeding until July or August. The land must be firm for sowing and the seed lightly covered and rolled in. Grazing, preferably with young cattle or sheep, should commence as soon as the herbage is about four inches long.

CROPPING FOR SELF-SUFFICIENCY

A reduction in the acreage of grassland does not necessarily mean that fewer livestock must be carried. In many cases where the land was formerly understocked a definite improvement in both quality and stock-carrying capacity is noted when the grass is more intensively grazed. On the other hand, when it is already carrying stock up to the hilt, special measures are necessary in order to provide sufficient winter fodder and summer grazing to offset any loss of meadow or pasture ploughed up for priority cropping.

Many farms carry some low-grade grassland which by ploughing out and direct re-seeding can be brought into line in the minimum space of time. Under favourable weather conditions it is by no means uncommon for fields so treated to be grazed six to eight weeks after re-seeding and a spring sowing then provides a well-established sward by autumn. Even in the first season the stock-carrying capacity of re-seeded land is considerably greater than poor permanent pasture, and experience in recent years in most counties has demonstrated that the head of live-stock need not be reduced if for every three acres of permanent grass ploughed out one acre is re-seeded direct, the other two being cropped as necessity demands.

When pastures are already in good trim the grazing season can be extended by the judicious use of nitrogenous fertilisers. An application in February or March produces an early bite, whilst a further application in August or September will, in most years, extend the grazing season by two to three weeks.

The most satisfactory solution to the problem of a reduced acreage of meadow hay can be found by growing stock food on a proportion of the ploughed-up grassland. An example will serve to indicate how this can be done in practice.

Assuming that the maintenance ration for a cow is 20 lb. of average meadow hay per day, a herd of 20 cows would require the crop from 30 acres of meadow land (40 tons of hay) to maintain them for the eight months when winter rations are required. Feeding for an average production of two gallons of milk per head per day the cows would also require 7 lb. of concentrates daily, or a total of about 13 tons for the herd for the same period.

Now by ploughing out the 30 acres of grassland and growing, say, 15 acres oats, 7 acres of peas or beans, 4 acres of kale and 4 acres of mangolds, the oat straw plus the roots would provide a maintenance ration for the same number of cows over the same period and would entirely replace the hay, assuming, of course, that average yields of the crops were obtained. In addition some 12 tons of oats and 6 tons of peas or beans should be produced. A half-and-half mixture of oats and legume forms a good production ration when fed at the rate of 3½ lb. per gallon of milk. Thus 6 tons of beans when balanced by 6 tons of oats would replace 12 tons of purchased dairy ration for milk production and little or no feeding stuffs would have to be bought. Six tons of oats would be available for sale. This does not give the final balance sheet, of course, for the 12 tons of home-grown oats and legumes would be produced at a much lower cost than the purchase price of the corresponding 12 tons of dairy ration even if the latter were available!

On farms where roots are an uncertain crop, oat and vetch mixtures should be grown for the production of silage. Not only are such mixtures reliable under a wide range of soil and climatic conditions, but considerable economy in the labour of feeding in winter can be effected by replacing roots with silage. Moreover, as the crop is removed in July it enables a catch crop to follow, or by undersowing with ryegrass and trefoil good autumn grazing can be obtained. If, on the other hand, the land is foul with weeds the removal of the silage crop can be followed by a bastard fallow. In addition to cereal-legume silage, on all farms the meadows—whether permanent or ley—should be top-dressed with nitrogen immediately the hay crop is removed in order to produce abundant aftermath for silage. Young autumn grass or clover made into silage by the molasses method produces a first-class feed for cows, fattening cattle or sheep and can be used as part of the production ration. As a guide it is suggested that half an acre of meadow per cow in milk or calf should be top-dressed for this purpose.

UTILISATION OF STRAW

The disposal of surplus straw by ploughing it in should be more widely practised, but concrete evidence is not yet available as to the full benefits to be derived therefrom. Straw is not easily decomposed by soil organisms, and to enable the process to take place the micro-organisms are forced to draw on the available nitrogen in the soil. This may result in depressing the yield of the following crop unless additional nitrogen is supplied in the form of a nitrogenous fertiliser. The usual rate of application is 1 cwt. of sulphate of ammonia or its equivalent per ton of straw, this dressing to be over and above what would normally be given to the crop which is to be grown on the land in question. Straw ploughed in on a clover stubble decomposes more rapidly than when applied to a corn stubble, since the nitrogen content of the soil in the former case is a good deal higher. At Cockle Park, wheat straw is chaffed and spread on the root break on which sheep are folded, and here again decomposition is fairly rapid. A more recent means of disposal which is very promising is to sow mustard on the straw of a combine stubble together with sulphate of ammonia at the rate of 1 cwt. per acre. Growth is extremely rapid, and in about six to eight weeks there is likely to be a good crop of mustard which can be ploughed in with the straw.

Composting is also being developed, and on farms where the liquid manure is collected this is pumped on to straw heaps to speed up the rotting. Alternatively a rotting mixture may be used. The heap of straw is built up in 9-inch layers, adding to each ¾ cwt. sulphate of ammonia and 1 cwt. of calcium carbonate for each ton of dry straw. Each layer must be thoroughly soaked with water and the heap is built from 6 to 8 feet high. In about six weeks' time the heap may be turned, although some consider this to be unnecessary, and the compost is ready for using in four to six months' time.

Large quantities of straw are now being converted into manure by building straw-yards with bales and feeding cattle in them over the winter, the yards being well littered with straw. This method also overcomes the difficulty on so many farms that the yard accommodation for wintering fattening beasts is totally inadequate to convert the large quantity of straw available into the manure so vitally necessary to keep the land in good heart. A number of farmers have also used folds of this type for wintering sheep. Folds 30 yards by 20 yards, two bales high, appear to be satisfactory, and the sheep are fed on roots and kale with a small amount of hay and hand feed. Here again, a sprinkling of nitrogenous fertiliser assists the decomposition of the straw. One such sample of rotted straw gave an analysis of ·31 per cent. nitrogen, ·94 per cent. phosphoric acid and ·21 per cent. potash, which is rather poorer in nitrogen and potash than ordinary farmyard manure but a good deal richer in phosphoric acid. The chief point to bear in mind with all these methods of straw disposal is not so much the actual analysis of the final product as the fact that humus is returned to the land. There is still ample scope on many farms for feeding more straw and using more as litter in yards and cowsheds. Burning cannot be justified.

Cropping for Milk Production

It is on the small, heavily stocked dairy farms that the problem of cropping is likely to present the greatest difficulties. On many all-grass farms it was not uncommon, before the war, to carry 1 to 2 cows per acre, the bulk of the food being purchased in the form of maize, milling offals and oil cakes. A large percentage of these farms are situated on poor soils in the neighbourhood of large industrial centres, a combination of factors which is not conducive to good grass production and where 3 to 4 acres per cow would be a more reasonable stocking. Shortage of lime and phosphates, matted grassland of low stock-carrying capacity, contamination by industrial fumes, and a high cow population do not fit in well with any scheme of self-sufficiency. Consequently, in these areas drastic alterations are necessary in the management of the land in order to meet the needs of the times. In the national interest the milk supply must be maintained, and on these small specialised farms it is essential that the output of milk be maintained. The livelihood of the farmer depends upon it, for the acreage is too small to allow a change-over to arable farming on economic lines, and often the hilly nature of the land would not permit normal arable cultivations. Most of these farms are equipped with modernised dairies and cowsheds for the production of high quality milk and the farmer has specialised in this branch of farming. Whilst it is possible to alleviate the feeding problem in some measure by ploughing and cropping, these farms can never become entirely self-supporting, and if there is to be no reduction in the number of cows it is obvious that means must be devised whereby the surplus bulky foods from the arable districts are transported to these intensive areas. Every effort must be made, however, to attain as high a degree of self-sufficiency as possible and the following methods will help towards this end.

By ploughing out and growing forage crops for cutting and feeding green (the practice is known as soiling) a high stock-carrying capacity can be maintained. For instance, for twelve years the University of Leeds ran an experimental small-holding of 30 acres near Goole in Yorkshire, where dairy cows were maintained on the produce of arable land both summer and winter. In summer they were fed on green forage crops such as rye, vetches, buckwheat, peas and rape, and in winter they had hay made from winter oats and tares, spring oats and peas, together with roots, kale and cabbages. Under such a system it was found possible to carry one cow on just over one and a half acres of land, feeding a proportion of cake to the high-yielding cows in addition to the home-grown food.

At the present time the adoption of such a system in its entirety would be almost impracticable and a greater acreage must be allowed per cow. On average land it should be possible to produce the requirements for one cow for maintenance and two gallons of milk from 2⅔ acres once the plough has been introduced and a proper system adopted.

In planning the cropping full use must be made of such milk-producing crops as kale and roots, rye and vetches, silage, short leys and oats. For the kale and roots a small area (⅛ of an acre per cow) should be selected near the homestead. It should be generously dunged—there being an abundant supply on dairy farms—and adequately fertilised, and there is no reason why this patch should not carry the same crop for a number of years. Lime will be necessary in most cases. Cropped and manured in this way the soil quickly becomes extremely fertile and yields abundantly. The method has the advantage that cartage in winter is minimised and cleaning in summer greatly simplified, for kale is an excellent smother crop and swedes or mangolds permit inter-row cultivation. The only difficulty likely to be experienced on some soils is the incidence of "finger-

and-toe" disease, and since kale is highly resistant and mangolds immune this should not present a serious problem. Even swedes can be repeatedly grown on the same land if lime is given annually and a resistant variety grown.

At least one quarter of an acre of silage mixture or roots per cow should be grown, one half acre of oats for harvesting and grinding, and the remainder of the allocation a short-term ley for the production of grazing, hay and some high-quality silage.

The following table gives the suggested allocation for the different crops :—

Kale	$\frac{1}{8}$ acre.
Oats	$\frac{1}{2}$,,
Silage (Oat and Tare) or Roots .	$\frac{1}{4}$,,
Seeds for Hay *	$\frac{3}{4}$,,
Seeds for Grazing . . .	$\frac{3}{4}$,,

$$2\tfrac{3}{8} \text{ acres per cow.}$$

* This area should receive 1 cwt. of sulphate of ammonia per acre immediately the hay crop is removed to produce aftermath for silage making.

With cropping on these lines the following rations could be fed during the winter period :—

	Group A Cows giving up to one gallon of milk daily. Daily Rations in lb.							Group B Cows giving from one to two gallons of milk daily. Daily Rations in lb.					Group C Cows giving from two to three gallons of milk daily. Daily Rations in lb.				
	1	2	3	4	5	6	7	1	2	3	4	5	1	2	3	4	5
Hay (Medium Quality) .	14	14	10	10	—	10	14	17	17	10	20	20	14	14	14	14	14
Oat Straw . . .	7	7	10	10	20	7	7	—	—	—	—	—	—	—	—	—	—
Kale . . .	45	—	28	—	50	28	—	60	—	35	—	—	35	—	—	—	—
Roots . . .	—	55	—	40	—	—	25	—	60	—	—	—	—	50	—	—	—
Oats and Tare Silage .	—	—	—	—	—	25	25	—	—	—	—	25	—	—	25	—	—
Grass Silage . .	—	—	—	—	—	—	—	—	—	25	50	—	—	—	—	25	40
Oats . . .	—	—	3	4	5	—	—	—	1	4	—	2	3	3	3	3	3
Balanced Production Mixture	—	—	—	—	—	—	—	—	3	—	—	2	8	8	8	7	4

For a dairy cow giving 4 gallons of milk per day, the daily ration can be made up by adding 4 lb. of a balanced production mixture to any one of the rations in Group C.
A mineral lick should be provided for all stock.
Straw should not be fed to cows giving more than one gallon of milk daily.
Economy in the use of purchased foods can best be secured by feeding the lower yielding cows as far as possible on fodder and roots alone, and reserving the concentrated foods for cows producing over 2 gallons of milk daily.

On all these dairy farms there is room for a small acreage of lucerne, say $\frac{1}{10}$ acre per cow. Like the kale it should be situated conveniently for feeding and should be well treated. It is during dry spells in high summer that lucerne can be so valuable to the dairy farmer, for the crop is unrivalled as a producer of green meat at a time when pastures are burnt brown and milk yields begin to fall in spite of supplementary feeding. The crop has the additional advantage that it makes excellent hay or silage and is economical in labour and maintenance since it holds the ground for several years.

The production of better grazing on poor grass farms necessitates some immediate re-seeding, and by sowing the seeds mixture under an oat and tare silage crop, which forms an excellent cover crop for seeds, there is no loss of time or of crop. Good grazing is then obtained soon after the silage crop is removed.

Dung in plentiful supply will be available, and full use should be made of it to force the seeds ley for hay, for higher yields can be obtained from temporary leys than from permanent meadows. If provision is also made for the collection of liquid manure, this can be used as a nitrogenous dressing for the production of early spring or late autumn grass for silage making. Wherever possible it is advisable to produce some high-quality silage, for this forms an excellent substitute for purchased concentrates in the feeding of the higher-yielding cows.

CROPPING TO MEET THE LABOUR SHORTAGE

The problem of labour supply is becoming more acute each year, and whilst the extended use of machinery can do much to alleviate the trouble seed-time and harvest still cause considerable anxiety. By a wise choice of variety of cereals, silage mixtures and seeds mixtures more scope is given to these vital seasonal operations.

With the large number of cereals available to-day it is possible to extend harvest over a period of two to three weeks. Differences in time of sowing do not necessarily give the same latitude at harvest, and in all cases rainfall is a vital factor in determining when a crop is ripe, but even so, variety does count enormously.

As a guide to ripening dates some of the more popular varieties of wheat and oats are classified in order of ripening below, this order being applicable in general for localities with a rainfall up to 40 inches.

Very Early	Early	Average	Late
Wheats—			
Desprez 80.	Hybrid 40.	Yeoman.	Crown.
Bersee.	Garton's 60.	Little Joss.	Scandia.
Defiant.	Hasler's 34.	Guardsman.	Chevalier.
	Holdfast.	Victor.	Iron.
		Wilma.	Weibull's
		Juliana.	Standard.
Oats—		Wilhelmina.	
Ayr Bounty.	Marvellous.	Star.	Eagle.
Early Miller.	Onward.	Victory.	S. 84.
Monarch.	Yielder.	Resistance.	
	Royal Scot.		
	Golden Rain.		

On the poorer classes of light land a portion of the cereal acreage can be devoted to rye, which when sown in good time in autumn is the earliest cereal crop to ripen. Rye is closely followed by winter oats, the new varieties S. 147, S. 172 and Picton being well worth a trial. The inclusion of part of the oat acreage with winter varieties also eases the burden of spring work.

In the case of cereal-legume mixtures for silage it is an advantage to have part of the acreage under an autumn sown crop and part spring-sown. The former will then be fit for cutting two to three weeks before the latter in most seasons.

Again, by a wise choice of variety in compiling seeds mixtures for hay or grazing, hay harvest can be extended and the grazing animal ensured a succulent ration over a much longer period. Small fields can be sown with different mixtures or large fields subdivided, and this is surely the logical approach to the problem of producing grass over a longer period. Too often one finds that the whole of the seeds hay is ready for cutting at the same time because one mixture only has been used. There is the choice, therefore, of cutting some too early or some too late unless implements and labour are available to tackle the full acreage at the most propitious time. Now that pedigree strains of different grasses and clovers are on the market, including a wide choice of early and late species, it is possible to blend mixtures to suit most requirements, and although in some seasons abnormal weather conditions may counteract differences in plant habit this need not be a deterrent to the adoption of the practice. For hay three mixtures might be used, one largely composed of commercial ryegrass and cocksfoot for early cutting, a general-purpose mixture for the main cut and which might well cover, say, half the total acreage, and a late mixture in which timothy and late-flowering red clover predominate.

As regards cultivations many modifications are possible which help to reduce the labour requirement. When the stubble is clean a seed bed can generally be prepared by simply disc-harrowing and cutting out ploughing altogether. Where conditions are suitable roundabout ploughing in place of the more orthodox method of dividing the field into lands saves both time and labour in setting out ridges and finishing the furrows, and obviates the need for headland turning. For root crops it is usually simpler and quicker to apply the dung during the autumn and plough it in rather than adopt the practice of applying it in the rows in the spring. Trials indicate that there is little to choose between these methods as regards yield per acre.

Weed control is also a factor of great importance in regard to labour supplies. Stubble cleaning in the autumn when weather conditions are favourable cuts out the need for a good deal of work in the growing crop, and the practice of sowing all cereals with a mixture of ryegrass and trefoil has much to commend it. This mixture not only covers the ground and helps to keep weeds in suppression, but gives a useful stubble bite for cattle or sheep and some valuable green material for ploughing down.

It is always well to remember in this connection that a really full crop is by far the best weed killer we have. One has only to examine the stubble under a first-class crop of corn, or the ground beneath a full crop of kale, to realise the excellent weed suppression obtained in this way. This means, of course, sowing a crop in good time, on a good seed bed well supplied with plant food and sowing only seed of high quality. By these means one can ensure that the odds against the weeds becoming established are overwhelming.

In the years ahead there is little doubt that the introduction of multiple implements capable of performing several operations at the same time is likely to ease the labour problem very considerably. The new Lister press-combine-drill is a good example of this tendency. This outfit enables pressing, sowing, fertilising and covering in to be done while ploughing. One unit is needed for each furrow and this comprises a press wheel, a combined seed and fertiliser drill which is attached to the plough beam, and a single harrow which trails behind for covering in the seed. Briefly put, it is possible to convert either a stubble or a sward to the finished seed bed in one operation at normal ploughing speed. Doubtless there is likely to be a good deal of controversy about short-circuiting cultivations, and the outfit has limitations, for it would not be suitable for heavy land. On the medium and lighter classes of soil, however, and for land which is really clean it does good work and offers decided advantages to the small farmer with limited resources of labour and machinery.

CATCH CROPPING

Quite apart from the increased production brought about by ploughing out and cropping on the lines suggested above, the introduction of catch cropping enables every acre of arable land to give its maximum output. A catch crop is merely a quick-growing one which, when grown between two main crops in a rotation, does not interfere with it in any essential detail. In the Norfolk four-course, for instance, an interval of six months or more elapses between the harvesting of the wheat crop and the drilling of the following root crop. During this interval it is possible to obtain considerable keep from ryegrass mixtures, stubble turnips or rape, or rye and vetch mixtures.

Undersowing cereals with, say, Italian ryegrass and trefoil provides good stubble grazing, some keep during winter, and an early spring bite. This has already been referred to in connection with green manuring. Undersowing in this way is especially useful in the case of silage mixtures, for here the crop is normally removed in July, and the land need not be ploughed for the next crop until towards the end of September at the earliest.

Following early potatoes or green peas, a heavy seeding of Italian ryegrass (40 lb. per acre) ensures a bulky fodder crop for autumn. Even more productive is kale, and it is advisable for the purpose of catch cropping to have plants available in nursery beds. These can then be transplanted when weather conditions are favourable. A common and successful method is to plough them in every second furrow, the plants being laid out on the side of the furrow and the roots being covered by the next furrow turned.

Reference has been made to the versatile character of rye, which, when sown in June to July, not only provides good forage in autumn and the following spring, but also a grain crop if necessary. In districts suited to crimson clover a mixture of Italian ryegrass 10 lb. and crimson clover 4 lb. per acre can be sown on the stubble to give autumn and spring grazing, whilst on most soils a mixture of Italian ryegrass 8 lb. and rape 2 lb. per acre, or 2 lb. each of rape, kale and hardy green turnips, proves very satisfactory if drilled immediately the corn crop is removed.

In general the catch crop can be grown on the reserves of plant food left in the soil by the previous crop, but when doubt exists as to the level of fertility it is a wise precaution to apply 1 cwt. per acre nitrogenous fertiliser prior to sowing the seed.

ENSURING THE HEALTH OF CROPS

The intensification of arable cropping with the emphasis laid on certain types of crop to provide ever-increasing quantities of food for human and animal consumption undoubtedly increases the liability to pest and disease. Just as a well-filled stackyard and granary provides admirable conditions for the rapid increase of rats and mice, so our countryside, cropped to capacity with cereals, potatoes, sugar beet and other roots, lends itself at times to the ravages of both pest and disease.

Many insect pests like frit fly of oats or flea beetles are always with us, but fortunately they are to some extent seasonal, serious outbreaks only occurring when conditions are favourable to the insect and unfavourable to the crop. Enemies like the wireworm and the leatherjacket come into their own when grassland is ploughed, so that with these at least we can be forewarned and try to take suitable steps to reduce the effects of an attack. The worst kind of pest is that represented by the various species of eelworm which, once established, are so difficult to eradicate that they remain as a legacy in the land and a potential source of severe loss for many years.

Remedies on a field scale are often impossible either on account of the habits of the pest or because of the expense involved. Sound remedies, like the use of poisoned bait against leatherjacket, cut-worms and slugs, must be applied before the maximum damage is done. The future of the application of remedial measures involving the use of insecticides on a field scale would appear to depend on the development of suitable types of machinery once the efficiency of the treatment is established. It is not suggested that every farmer should equip himself with the appropriate tackle, but if there is a demand for well-tried methods then the commercial firm will find it possible to deal with both pest and disease by contract. This is already being done on a limited scale in the case of aphis infection by dusting and the spraying of potatoes against blight. It is likely to be extended to the control of carrot grub by spraying the headlands of carrot fields at the appropriate time with a poisoned bait to kill the adult flies.

The problem of prevention of pest injury must as yet lie largely in the hands of the farmer himself, and the solution, in the main, depends on following closely the rules of good husbandry, viz. a proper rotation, careful cultivation, adequate manuring and the selection of sound seed of the right variety. By so doing the crop finds a favourable environment, is given a flying start and with reasonable luck continues to grow vigorously, in which condition it is more likely to withstand attack. Overcropping the same field with, say, potatoes, sugar beet or oats must be rigorously avoided, for each of these crops is subject to attack by its own species of root eelworm. The alarming spread of potato sickness serves as a good example. No farmer should be tempted, even on land known to be free from eelworm, to grow potatoes or beet more than once in four or five years, because the pest is so easily introduced in small quantities of soil brought in bags of seed or on implements to give a small initial contamination of the soil. From such small beginnings "sickness," at first unnoticed, gradually increases until large patches of the trouble appear. These extend, if the same crop is grown, until final and complete failure results.

Nor is there a short cut to the elimination of disease amongst farm crops. As with pests, a healthy plant growing vigorously is the best protection, although in this connection weather conditions may determine the incidence of attack to a considerable degree. The 1943 season will be remembered for the extraordinary severity of mildew attack (*Erysiphe graminis*) on cereals. The mild winter and absence of killing resulted in the

R

development of thick stands of wheat in the spring. A dry spell in April and May was also conducive to its spread, and from then on the disease became very apparent in the loss of colour of the crop and the dirty white, powdery mould investing the stem bases and lower leaves. The effect of the continual drain on the plants was to prevent a good deal of the grain filling as it should, and resulted in a much higher percentage of tail corn when the crops were threshed. Much the same is true of rust, which also has been on the increase in recent years. Here, fortunately, some varieties of wheat are resistant to the disease, although the plant breeder's task is made more difficult by the fact that there are strains of rust just as there are varieties of wheat, and these strains possess varying infective capacities. In practice this means that a variety may be resistant to the disease in one district but susceptible in others, and many such cases were noted during the 1943 season.

Anticipatory action can do much to control disease, especially in districts where the trouble is of yearly occurrence. The routine dressing of seed with the organo-mercuric dusts and the pre-blight spraying of potatoes are efficient insurances against loss which amply justify the outlay on material and labour. Not less important is an insistence upon healthy, well-rogued stocks, especially of potatoes. Now that the significance of virus-free stocks is recognised there is a tendency to overlook diseases which are also carried by the tubers. Dry Rot, the source of much loss in the clamps in the spring, is present in far too great a percentage of seed tubers. As it can be detected at this stage it is an easy matter to eliminate it before planting. Collar Rot, too, can be recognised on "chitted" tubers, and thus the number of misses in the crop can be reduced. Outbreaks of Black Aphis can be forecast with reasonable certainty. This insect lays its eggs in the autumn on a shrub, the Spindle tree, and if in the winter there are no eggs on the twigs then no serious outbreak is likely, but if, on the other hand, large numbers of eggs are noted, serious infestation of beans, beet and mangolds should be expected, and measures provided for combating the pest.

There is a definite trend now towards the use of varieties which are either immune to specific diseases or pests, or which have such a measure of resistance that the yield is not likely to be seriously affected. Many instances have already been given such as the rust-resistant varieties of wheat, frit fly resistant varieties of oats, and so on. Unfortunately, these resistant properties are not always coupled with quality and heavy-yielding capacity, both of which are essential for maximum results. Plant breeders are working, however, to combine the desirable factors of resistance and immunity in varieties already established on the basis of yield and quality.

MAINTENANCE OF FERTILITY

Much concern is expressed in some quarters that the increased acreage of arable land and the more intensive system of cropping will exhaust the fertility of the soil and leave a legacy of poverty. There is a good deal of confused thinking on this point. Many, for instance, regard fertility and humus as synonymous, and so farmyard manure, the chief source of humus on most farms, becomes endowed with magical properties. Others decry the use of artificial fertilisers which, they say, rob the land of its fertility and are simply forcing agents. By long experience methods have been evolved for balancing the constructive and destructive soil processes, the system adopted being that of a sound rotation. Here restorative and exhaustive crops alternate, the plant foods are utilised equally and periodic applications of dung or green manure maintain the physical condition of the soil. Recent work in most counties has shown how modern resources of plant breeding, machinery and fertilisers can be used to establish productive leys, a most potent source of fertility, and it is evident that we can establish a balanced and safe agriculture at a much higher level of production than was possible even ten years ago.

A fertile soil contains lime, phosphates, potash and nitrogen, and minute traces of vital elements like boron and manganese. It must also be well drained and of the right texture, and a wise combination of plant food in both organic and inorganic form is necessary to obtain the maximum crops of which the soil is capable.

The maintenance of fertility, therefore, is not simply a question of adding dung. It involves all the mechanical processes necessary for tilth formation; it means making good the losses of both organic matter resulting from cultivation and of plant food following the harvesting of a crop; it may mean the protection of the surface soil from erosion as in the case of blow-away sand or on land which periodically floods. In short, it demands good husbandry, and all the evidence obtainable testifies to the fact that in the hands of a good farmer there is no need to fear a loss of fertility.

Maximum cropping demands ingenuity on the part of the farmer, combined with a thorough understanding of his soil and its capabilities. Careful planning, generous manuring, skilful cultivations and a wise selection of variety are the surest means of solving our cropping problems.

APPENDIX I

DIAGNOSIS OF PLANT PESTS

Crop	Symptoms	Pest
Wheat . .	Central shoot yellow. Crop follows bare fallow. Attack occurs before end of May .	Wheat Bulb Fly.
	Plants eaten just below ground level. Plants die in succession	Wireworm.
	Plants eaten through just below ground level, or central shoot killed, or holes in the base of highest expanded leaf blade.	Wheat Shoot Beetle.
	Yellowing of central shoot .	Frit Fly.
	Leaves eaten into shreds. Slime present . . .	Slugs.
	Plants eaten through at or slightly below ground level	Leatherjackets.
Barley . .	Yellow central shoot. Later swollen stem-twisted flags; often fails to shoot ear .	Gout Fly.
Oats . .	Yellowing of central shoot; stunting of plant; blind or deaf ears	Frit Fly.
	Plants eaten through just below ground level. Plants die in succession . . .	Wireworm.
	Stunting, swollen base, twisting of young tillers . .	Stem Eelworm.
	Patches of weak, pale, spindly plants with purplish leaf tips. Much branched roots .	Root Eelworm.
	Plants eaten through at or slightly below ground level	Leatherjackets.
Beans and Peas	Margin of leaves notched as plant comes through .	Weevils.
Kale, Cabbage, Rape	Holes in leaves; seedlings eaten away . . .	Flea Beetles.
	Larger leaves stripped or partially eaten.	Cabbage Caterpillars.

Crop	Symptoms	Pest
Beet and Man-golds	Stems of small plants severed. Cavities in larger roots.	Surface Cater-pillars.
	Young leaves eaten . .	Flea Beetles.
	Young root eaten; plant wilts	Wireworms.
	Leaves covered with small black "flies" . . .	Black Aphis.
	Leaf margins curled. Pale yellow blotches on leaves .	Blister Fly.
Beet . .	Patches of sickly plants. Beard of lateral rootlets . .	Beet Sickness.
Potatoes .	Patches of unthrifty, dwarfed plants. Few small - sized tubers	Root Eelworm.
	Small holes on tubers leading to large inner cavities .	Slugs.
	Tubers holed . . .	Wireworms.
	Leaves eaten . . .	Colorado Beetle.
Carrots . .	Foliage yellow or reddish and wilts. Maggots in surface burrows	Carrot Fly.
Turnips and Swedes	Seedlings eaten; leaves holed	Flea Beetles.
Onions . .	Foliage yellows and wilts. Maggots in larger bulbs which rot . . .	Onion Fly.

APPENDIX II

DIAGNOSIS OF PLANT DISEASES

Crop	Symptoms	Disease
Wheat . .	Empty white ears, shrivelled grains	Night-ripening.
	Yellowing of plants; roots rotting	Foot Rot.
	Straggling and scrawling of straw as distinct from lodging	Eyespot.
Barley . .	Yellowing of plants; roots rotting	Foot Rot.
	Straggling and scrawling of straw as distinct from lodging	Eyespot.
Oats . .	Rusty brown spots on leaves. Twisted shoot and withered seedlings	Leaf Spot or Stripe.
	Greyish white blotches on leaves. Stunted plants .	Grey Leaf.
	Yellowing of plants; roots rotting	Foot Rot.
Beans . .	Brown spots on leaves . .	Chocolate Spot.
Beet . .	Seedlings wilt and die. Root black and thread-like .	Black Leg.
	Central leaves wilt and die. Blackened cavities in crown	Heart Rot.
	Large yellow patches on leaves in late summer . .	Virus Yellows.
Potatoes .	Dark green blotches on leaves, these turn brown, then black	Blight.
	Cauliflower growths, dark grey or black on tubers . .	Wart.
	Small scabby patches, deep cankers	Corky Scab.
	Superficial scabs . . .	Common Scab.
	Leaves rolled, crinkled or mottled, plants dwarfed .	Virus.
Turnips or Swedes	Abnormal swellings on roots. Whitish powder on leaves .	Finger-and-Toe. Mildew.
Clover . .	Failure of plants in patches. Leaves and crowns die away	Clover Sickness.

APPENDIX III

Time and Rate of Sowing and Average Yield of Common Farm Crops

Crop	Time to Sow	Rate of Sowing per Acre		Yield per Acre	
		Drilled	Broadcast	Average	Very Good
Wheat (autumn)	Sept.-Nov.	1¼-1¾ cwt.	1½-2 cwt.	18 cwt.	33 cwt.
(spring)	Feb.-April	2¼ „	2½ „	16 „	30 „
Barley	Feb.-April	1½-2 „	—	16 „	30 „
Oats (winter)	Oct.-Nov.	1½-2 „	—	15 „	35 „
(spring)	Feb.-April	1½-2 „	—	15 „	35 „
Rye	Sept.-Oct.	1 „	—	12-16 „	30 „
	Oct.-Mar.	1½ „	—	—	—
Mixed Corn	Mar.-May	2 „	—	18-24 „	30 „
Beans (winter)	October	1½ „	—	16 „	30 „
(spring)	Feb.-Mar.	1¾ „	—	14 „	25 „
Peas	Jan.-Feb.	1½-2¼ „	—	17 „	25 „
	Mar.-April	1½-2¼ „	—	17 „	25 „
Maize	May-June	4-6 „	—	20-25 tons Green crop	35 tons
Lucerne	Mar.-April	20 lb.	25 lb.	15-20 tons	—
	July-Aug.	20 „	25 „	Green crop	—
Sainfoin	Feb.-May	56 „	—	30 cwt. hay	—
Kale	Mar.-July	94 „	6 „	20 tons Green crop	30-40 tons
Cabbage	Mar.-Aug.	4 „	—	30 tons Green crop	60 tons
Rape	March	3-4 „	10-12 lb.	10 tons Green crop	—
Vetches	September	1½ cwt.	—	12-18 cwt.	—
	Feb.-April	1½ „	—	12-18 „	—
Sugar Beet	Mar.-May	15-20 lb.	—	9 tons	20 „
Potatoes	Mar.-May	20 cwt.	—	8 „	16 „
Carrots	April-May	5-6 lb.	—	10 „	20 „
Parsnips	Feb.-Mar.	7 „	—	12 „	
Turnips	June-Aug.	3 „	4 lb.	10 „	15 „
Swedes	May-June	4 „	—	14 „	20-30 tons
Mangolds	April-May	6-10 lb.	—	20 „	30-50 „
Kohl Rabi	April	4 „	—	20 „	30 tons
Linseed	Mar.-May	91 „	117 lb.	10 cwt.	20 cwt.
Flax	Mar.-May	91 „	117 „	2 tons	3 tons
Buckwheat	April-May	100 „	150 „	10 cwt.	20 cwt.
Mustard (seed)	Feb.-April	4-8 „	—	10-12 cwt.	20 „
(forage)	Mar.-Aug.	15 „	20 „		
Lupins	April	90-120 lb.	—	12 cwt.	18 „
Onions	March	5 lb.	—	6 tons	12 tons
Crimson Clover	July-Sept.	—	20-24 lb.	—	—

APPENDIX IV

MONTHLY CALENDAR

CATCH CROPS AND FORAGE CROPS

When to Sow	What to Sow	When Ready
February	Rye and Peas . . .	June.
March .	Italian Ryegrass (10 lb. per acre) Trefoil (2 lb. per acre) } under a cereal }	Autumn to spring.
	Cabbages	Nov.-March.
	Kale	Sept.-December.
	Cereal-Legume Mixtures . .	July-August.
April .	Italian Ryegrass-Trefoil . .	Autumn to spring.
	Cabbages	Nov.-March.
	Kale	Oct.-January.
	Cereal-Legume Mixtures . .	July-August.
	Lucerne	Autumn onwards.
	Rape	6 weeks' time.
	Lupins	July onwards.
	Mustard	6 to 8 weeks' time.
May .	Turnips	September.
	Maize	August-Sept.
	Buckwheat	12 to 14 weeks' time.
	Cabbage	Early spring.
	Buckwheat, Peas and Rape .	12 weeks' time.
June .	Cabbage	Early spring.
	Maize	September.
	Mustard and Rape . . .	6 to 8 weeks' time.
	Turnips	September.
July .	Turnips	Sept.-October.
	Mustard and Rape . . .	6 weeks' time.
	Crimson Clover . . .	Sept.-June.
	Cabbage	Spring and Summer.
	Rape, Kale	Spring.
August .	Italian Ryegrass-Trefoil . .	October-Spring.
	Turnips	October.

When to Sow	What to Sow	When Ready
August .	Rape and Mustard . . .	6 to 8 weeks after sowing.
	Crimson Clover . . .	May-June.
	Cabbage	Late summer.
September	Italian Ryegrass-Trefoil . .	Spring.
	Crimson Clover . .	May-June.
	Rye	May.
	Rye and Winter Vetches . .	May.
October .	Winter Barley and Vetches .	May-June.
November	Wheat and Winter Vetches .	July.

The above table will be of assistance to dairy farmers in particular who wish to provide green forage crops for milk cows over the greater part of the year. In the months when forage crops are not available full use should be made of roots, kale and silage.

APPENDIX V

FERTILISER CONVERSION TABLE

Under the rationing scheme introduced in 1942, the allocation of fertilisers, other than nitrogen, for each farm is stated in terms of hundredweights of phosphoric acid (P_2O_5) and potash (K_2O). To enable these figures to be converted into terms of fertilisers the following table can be used:—

1 cwt. $P_2O_5 = 5\frac{1}{2}$ cwt. superphosphate ($18 \cdot 5\%$ P_2O_5)
    or   2 cwt. triple phosphate (47% P_2O_5)
    or   3 cwt. silico phosphate (33% P_2O_5)
    or   5 cwt. metaphos (20% P_2O_5)
    or $8\frac{1}{3}$ cwt. basic slag (12% P_2O_5)
    or $5\frac{1}{2}$ cwt. basic slag (18% P_2O_5)
    or   10 cwt. of a compound containing 10% P_2O_5

1 cwt. $K_2O = 1\frac{2}{3}$ cwt. muriate of potash (60% K_2O)
    or   2 cwt. sulphate of potash (48% K_2O)
    or   20 cwt. of a compound containing 5% K_2O.

The recommendations for fertilising the various crops dealt with in the preceding pages are made in the light of present supplies. In many instances the suggested rate of application for potash and phosphate can be increased with advantage when supplies are available.

APPENDIX VI

EFFECTIVENESS OF VARIOUS WEED KILLERS

CONCENTRATION OF MATERIAL PER 100 GALLONS OF SPRAY
SOLUTION PER ACRE

Weed Species	B.O.V. Acid gal.	Copper Chloride lb.	DNOC lb.	MCPA lb.	DCPA lb.
Yellow Charlock . . .	7-10*	10-15*	6-8*	1·0*	1·0*
Pennycress	7*	15*	4-6*	0·75*	(1·0)*
Treacle Mustard . . .	10*	20*	5-7*	1·5*	(1·5)*
White Charlock	13†	20-30†	8†	2·0*	2·0*
Corn Buttercup	13‡	R	8‡	2·0*	2·0*
Shepherd's Needle . . .	15‡	R	8‡	2·0*	2·0*
Corn Poppies . . .	R	R	6-8W*	2·0‡	(2·0)‡
Fat Hen	12W†	R	6-8*	2·0‡	(2·0)‡
Goosefoot or Orache . .	12W†	R	6-8*	2·0‡	(2·0)‡
Mayweeds	13W‡	R	6-8*	R	R
Chamomile	13W‡	R	6-8*	R	R
Corn Marigold . . .	13W‡	R	8W*	R	R
Cleavers	10*	20-30‡	6-8†	R	R
Knotgrass	13W*	R	8‡	R	R
Willow Weed	13W†	20-30‡	8‡	R	R
Hemp Nettle	10*	20-30†	6-8*	(2·0)†	?
Annual Nettle	10W*	(R)	6-8†	(2·0)‡	?
Spurrey	10*	20‡	6-8W†	2·0‡	?
Speedwells	10*	20†	6-8†	R	?
Bearbind	10*	20-30*	6-8†	2·0‡	2·0‡
Chickweed	13†	R	8‡	R	R
Cornflower	(13W)‡	R	(8W)†	(2·0)*	?
Parsley Piert	(13W)*	R	(5-7)*	R	?
Fumitory	R	R	6-8W*	R	(R)
Shepherd's Purse . . .	10W*	(30)†	7†	(2·0)‡	?

* = over 90 per cent. kill expected.　　† = over 80 per cent.　　‡ = over 50 per cent.
R = weed resistant.
W = wetting agent should be added to spray solution.
( ) = figures are tentative.　　　　　　　? = information is not yet available.